Digital and Analog Controls

Marvin A. Needler
Don E. Baker

Reston Publishing Company, Inc.
A Prentice-Hall Company
Reston, Virginia

Library of Congress Cataloging in Publication Data

Needler, Marvin A.
    Digital and analog controls.

    1. Electronic control.   I. Baker, Don E.   II. Title.
TK7881.2.N44   1985   629.8'95   84-13390
ISBN 0-8359-1314-7

10   9   8   7   6   5   4   3   2   1

Printed in the United States of America

Contents

8   Dynamic Response of Basic Systems   249

9   Dynamic Control   299

Preface

The purpose of this text is to present the spectrum of topics that are the subject of a college-level course in control fundamentals. The material is divided into three major parts. The first part discusses discrete control, including elementary relay control, gated logic control, and programmable control. The second part discusses continuous control systems, including dynamic system analysis and feedback control systems. The final part presents input/output devices, including transducers, solid-state linear and nonlinear amplifiers, and final control elements.

This text is primarily intended as a text for the engineering technology student as well as a resource for the continuing education of electrical sales and service persons. The student should have some experience with dc and ac electrical circuits. Due to the breadth of the material presented, even more benefit will be gained by those with backgrounds in the following:

- industrial electronics

- electric machinery

- digital circuits

- technical mathematics with elementary calculus

As nearly as possible, this text contains all the topics appropriate for a course in controls. These topics include many of the traditional areas of relay controls and analog controls as well as the newer topics of digital controls and microprocessor-based programmable logic. An effort has been made to provide the optimum mix of the traditional, the new, and the transition from the one to the other.

Since students coming to this course have a variety of backgrounds, each chapter stands alone as much as possible. Several course paths are suggested below.

1. Use of the entire text is recommended for the student wishing to cover both the digital and analog areas. To this end, the material could be used for a two-quarter or possibly two-semester course sequence, depending on the strength of the background and the use of supplementary resources.
2. The first six to seven chapters could be covered for the student wishing to cover digital controls only. Inclusion of chapter seven is left as an optional intensive treatment of the programmable controller.
3. For the student who has already had a course in digital circuits, the following ordering of material is recommended.

Chapter 1

Chapter 2

Chapter 3   Selected topics and examples

Chapter 4   Selected topics and examples

Sections 5.5 plus 5.6 and 5.7 as time permits

Sections 6.5, 6.6, 6.7

Chapter 7

Chapter 8

Chapter 9

Chapter 10, 11, 12 as time permits.

To complement the lecture material, more than a semester's worth of laboratory experiments accompanies this text under a separate cover. A list of equipment is provided at the front of each experiment that identifies the laboratory equipment requirements. Common equipment has been used for the majority of the experiments.

The authors wish to thank those who assisted and supported the writing of this text, especially the students who persevered through early editions. The support of our families is gratefully acknowledged: Priscilla, Veronica, and Elizabeth Needler; Terry, Jon, and Jacqueline Baker.

Marvin A. Needler, Ph.D., P.E.   Don E. Baker
Purdue University at Indianapolis   *Detroit Diesel Allison*

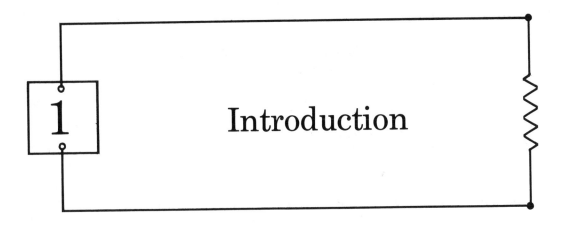

Introduction

1.0 Background

We live in an age of wonders. Modern control systems are used in our automobiles, our homes, as well as in our industrial, commercial and transportation systems.

- In the factory, complex, customized products are designed, tested, and manufactured by designers, engineers, and technicians of many disciplines using computers, CAD/CAM systems, and robots.

- In the automobile, new electronic technology is used to control the engine combustion, the heating and air conditioning, and the annunciators.

- In the home, a sewing machine can be taught a decorative stitch and repeat it on command. A microwave oven can be commanded to turn itself on at a preset time, and then defrost, cook, brown, and warm the meal.

  These descriptions sound like the beginning of a new age, something totally unprecedented in human history. What is at the heart of these innovations?

The roots of the present lifestyle revolution are reflected in control technology stretching back almost 100 years. The industrial revolution of the nineteenth century, brought about by mass production, created the need for control systems that could replace manual labor in performing tedious and repetitive tasks. Control systems were developed that could respond with greater speed, precision, and power than a human worker. In addition, these control systems could perform repetitive tasks virtually tirelessly, freeing men and women for more creative work. The introduction of electric motors to the commercial and industrial world brought another technology revolution resulting in the availability of inexpensive mechanical energy in almost every aspect of life (even providing electric toothbrushes). The growing concern for energy conservation, product quality, and low cost has added to the need for automatic control systems. This need has set the stage for the microcomputer revolution in every area of our lives. The microcomputer has allowed the creation of the complex control systems that make the marvels described above commonplace. Thus, the common thread in the majority of these modern devices and processes is improved automatic control.

What is automatic control? Automatic control of a system is the manipulation of the system output to achieve a desired result based on the system command. Most often this implies achievement without intervention once the process of control is initiated. Although subject to many interpretations, this broad definition covers the humble automatic door controller as well as the Boeing 767 autopilot.

Automatic control systems can be continuous, discrete, or a combination of the two. The discrete category is the older of the two and encompasses all systems that base control on two-value judgments, such as on or off, full or empty, closed or open. Continuous systems, on the other hand, are those in which the output can take on all values within the output's range. An example of a discrete control system is the electric door opener mentioned previously; on the other hand, the wing flap position servo controlled by the autopilot is an example of continuous control. Generally, the continuous control mechanisms have been more inherently sophisticated and costly while providing a closer degree of control than the discrete systems. However, the microprocessor, a discrete control tool, has provided the means for very fast discrete systems to emulate the control features of continuous systems.

Whether control systems employ continuous control, discrete control, or a combination of the two to achieve their ends, each physical system always contains sensing elements, control intelligence, and output manipulators, as illustrated in Figure 1-1.

1.1 The Purpose of this Text

The purpose of this text is to introduce the basic principles and implementations of industrial control and instrumentation systems. The material is divided into three parts: the first part concerns elementary discrete control systems made up of relay controls, integrated circuit logic, and programmable control systems; the second part presents continuous control; the third part covers input and output devices that are used in control systems.

FIGURE 1-1. Control system elements

1.2 Industrial Control—A Historical Approach

Part I, the discrete-control portion of this text, is organized to parallel the historical development of control system theory and applications, and in so doing, introduce the concepts of discrete control.

Relay control comprised the majority of control system applications in the early history of control technology. To this day, it is judged that more relay control systems are currently in operation than any other form of control. Chapter 2 covers this control technology as well as motor protection, ladder diagram logic, code requirements, and applications circuits.

In the 1960s, an alternative to relay came into being in the form of electronics. Digital elements were developed such as electronic logic gates for immediate control and flip-flops, registers, counters, etc., for time-dependent control schemes. The merit of this implementation emerges as applications become more complex. Time-independent logic is covered in Chapter 3, while memory-device based systems are found in Chapter 4. Chapter 5 wraps up this area with sequential and alterable logic units.

The next major landmark in the growth of control technology was the advent of the programmable controllers in the 1970s, which brought the sophistication of software technology to industry. Chapter 6 bridges the gap between hardware-dependent control technology and software-based techniques. Chapter 7 explores in depth the programmable controller, which provides a suitable design and packaging of the gate and memory devices for the industrial environment. The utility of software programmable logic is in its interactive capability, due to the microprocessor at its core.

1.3 The Development of Continuous Control

Part II of this book turns from the discrete world to the continuous one in the form of dynamic system analysis. This turn is inevitable, in that motors and devices used in processes have energy forms that are dynamic in nature and must be treated as such to provide precise control.

The continuous type of control uses analog information (e.g., voltage, current, pressure) to represent the information pertaining to environment, goals, and outputs. Some forms of this type of control are exceptionally old, but widespread industrial use began in the late 1940s when servomechanisms developed during World War II were applied to positioning problems found in industry. Chapter 9 builds the tools for this dynamic analysis. Improved electronics brought about increased equipment stability and decreased cost in the 1950s and early 1960s. A standard form of a continuous controller that featured proportional, integral, and derivative (PID) control then became widely available. Chapter 10 uses the analysis tools developed in Chapter 9 in covering dynamic controls up through PID.

All the continuous control strategies thus far are based upon the principle of feedback; but in the late 1960s, system complexities increased to the point where networks of controllers were used to implement new strategies such as feedforward, ratio, cascade, and predictor/corrector. Modern control systems are discrete microprocessor-based controllers that operate at a high speed to emulate continuous control. Thus, the division between discrete and continuous control systems is becoming more blurred, and discrete control of continuous systems is becoming commonplace.

1.4 Input and Output Devices

Part III covers sensors, amplifiers, and actuators. Measurement elements sense the environment and provide information about current system conditions upon which the control intelligence operates, regardless of whether the system is discrete or continuous. These transducers may also gather additional data about the process when coupled with recording instruments. Chapter 10 describes some basic implementations of these devices.

A principle of continuous control feedback control systems is that the information provided by the transducer must be amplified to be of sufficient power to operate the output device. An example of one type of amplifier is the control relay covered in Chapter 2. Chapter 11 describes an assortment of amplifiers that are frequently used in control systems.

Final control elements receive the signals generated by the control amplifiers and translate these signals into physical phenomena that ultimately control the output being measured. Often the final control element is a motor; other output devices are solenoids, heaters, lights, and welders. Chapter 12 describes some of the final control elements.

1.5 Summary

Although in the interest of clarity an effort has been made to divide the material into distinct parts, in practice no clear-cut division exists. Continuous control can be emulated successfully by discrete devices that convert closely spaced samples of continuous information to on or off quantities, which are used to produce closely spaced output values. For example, programmable controllers are widely used for PID control, which is a crossover between the discrete control and dynamic control. Conversely, the analog devices discussed in the later chapters are used in discrete applications such as stepper motors, analog-to-digital converters, and digital-to-analog converters. Thus, the discrete and continuous types can be mixed within a system either as independent schemes operating on a single environment, or as intercoupled systems that are exchanging information.

Although the above considerations complicate the picture, the analysis and understanding of even the most complicated control system rest on basic fundamentals, and it is these fundamentals of control that are the study of this book. Hopefully, this study will be both beneficial and fun.

2 Industrial Relay Control

2.0 Introduction

One of the most widespread applications of control systems today is in the area of industrial relay control. Industrial relay control systems are used to run machines such as lathes, grinders, broaches, presses, temperature control ovens, and automatic test equipment. These machines typically require several motors, such as drive, pump, and conveyor motors. They may also require solenoidal devices such as plungers, valves, and other devices involving rectilinear motion, or annunciator devices such as warning lights and horns. To control the motors, solenoids, and annunciators, a wide assortment of electrical switches may be used. The switches can be the manually operated type, such as push button or selector switches, the automatically operated type, such as limit switches or temperature switches, or they can be contacts on relays that are operated by the relays. To provide the desired logic operation of these actuators and switches, the interconnection of the components is made by the wiring. Thus, the wiring provides both the energy to cause the actuators to work and the logic to tell which actuator to work. Finally, the control system must be placed in an enclosure, such as a cabinet, that is appropriate for the environment.

Relay control systems are not limited to industrial applications. Wherever there is a need for automatic control of actuators (i.e., motors, electric heaters, solenoids, or annunciators), relay control is the most common control method. For example, a commercial building requires relay control for operation of the heating, ventilating, and air conditioning system, the elevator system, and the alarm system. Similarly, applications of automatic control systems that use relay control are present in residential equipment, such as furnaces, air conditioners, washers, and dryers. Mobile vehicles, such as automobiles, trucks, and aircraft, also make extensive use of relay control.

Another example of relay control is in robotics, where large numbers of relays may be used for the multifunctional capabilities of the robot manipulators.

The common element in all of these examples of controls is the following definition of the purpose of the relay control system: to direct the action to take place at the proper location and at the proper time with respect to other actions, through the use of relays. An additional feature of most relay control systems is that the relay control also protects the actuator, such as the motor, from overloading and causing damage to itself and/or to other related equipment.

This chapter is concerned with relay control systems that are used to control motors, solenoids, heaters, and other similar equipment as mentioned above. The main topics are the following:

- logic elements (i.e., the switches)
- actuators
- relays, the wiring in the form of the ladder and wiring diagrams
- analysis and design logic as expressed by the diagrams
- safety and code requirements
- a broad exposure to relay control systems.

2.1 Electrical Switching Devices

Relay control system components are divided into two categories: switches and relays. Switches are used to control the flow of power to the output device, usually the relay coil, and can be thought of as logic devices. They can also be thought of as conditional devices, since the action of the output device is conditioned by the state of the switch. A common example of such a switching device is a mechanically activated switch, such as a limit switch. A switching device has two states, which can be expressed in several ways as shown below.

- Conducting versus nonconducting
- ON versus OFF
- Closed versus open
- Logic ONE versus logic ZERO
- TRUE versus FALSE
- HIGH versus LOW.

Another reason for considering the switch to be a logic component is that it consumes zero power. When the switch is open, no current is present and the power is zero (power is the voltage-current product); when the switch is closed it is ideally a perfectly conducting path or

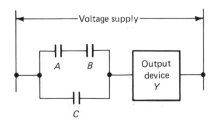

FIGURE 2-1. A simple switch circuit

short circuit, and no voltage is present across the switch. (Obviously in this closed state, another component must be in series with the closed switch that is designed to absorb the source voltage; otherwise, there will be a more serious short circuit to contend with.) Thus, in either the closed or open state, the power consumed by the switch is zero. In contrast, the second category of control components consists of nonzero-power components such as solenoids (e.g., motor starter coils and control relay coils). In these components, it is possible to have current *through* the component and voltage *across* it, simultaneously. Thus, one power component is needed in series with each combination of switch components.

In spite of the diversity of manufactured switches, their logic operation is the same. All two-position switches can be treated as two-state devices, either ON or OFF. In a Boolean algebra system, the ON state can be represented by the numeral one and the OFF state by a zero, and then the circuit condition can be expressed algebraically. For example, Figure 2-1 shows switch A in series with switch B and this combination in parallel with switch C. An ON condition can be established either with the combination A and B or by C alone, which can be written

$$Y = (A \ AND \ B) \ OR \ C$$

The above can be written in Boolean algebra as

$$Y = (A \bullet B) + C$$

(Note the "$\bullet$" symbol means AND and the "+" symbol means OR.)

2.2 Switching Devices and Their Symbols

A multitude of switches is available for a variety of applications. A partial list follows.

Disconnect	Vacuum actuated
Circuit interrupter	Liquid-level actuated
Circuit breaker	Temperature actuated
Limit	Speed
Foot operated	Selector
Pressure operated	Push button

Table 2-1 is a symbol table that shows the more common relay control symbols. There are many design variations within each of these types of switches, depending on the particular purpose and the manufacturer. Figure 2-2 shows an assortment of switches.

Toggle switches, as commonly used for residential on-off light controls, have two stable states; that is, they will remain in either the

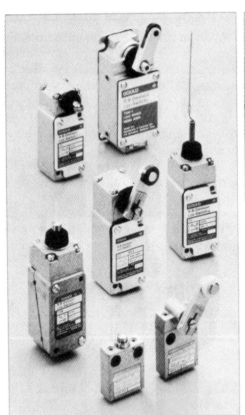

Electromechanical Limit Switches

Proximity Switches

Optic-Electronic Switches

Courtesy Gould Electronics

FIGURE 2-2. Illustration of assortment of switches

TABLE 2-1. Standard Elementary Diagram Symbols

These diagram symbols have been adopted by the Furnas Electric Company and conform where applicable to standards established by the National Electrical Manufacturers Association (NEMA).

DISCONNECT	CIRCUIT INTERRUPTER	CIRCUIT BREAKER	LIMIT SWITCH				
			SPRING RETURN				MAINTAINED
		Thermal	Normally Open	Normally Closed	Neutral Position		
					NP		
			Held Closed	Held Open			

LIQUID LEVEL		VACUUM & PRESSURE		TEMPERATURE ACTIVATED		FLOW (AIR, WATER, ETC.)	
Normally Open	Normally Closed	Normally Open	Normally Closed	Normally Open	Normally Closed	Normally Open	Normally Closed

PUSH BUTTONS					FOOT SWITCH	
Normally Open	Normally Closed	Double Circuit	Mushroom Head	Maintained	Normally Open	Normally Closed

SELECTOR SWITCH		LAMPS	TIME DELAY CONTACT			
J K L * INDICATES CONTACTS CLOSED	J – K – L J K L / A1 ×/ A2 /B1 ×/ B2 ×	PUSH TO TEST R DENOTE COLOR BY LETTER	Normally Open TC OR	Normally Open TO OR	Normally Closed TO OR	Normally Closed TC OR

GENERAL CONTACTS		CONDUCTORS		MAGNET COIL	CONTROL TRANSFORMER	METER
Normally Open	Normally Closed	Not Connected	Connected		H1 H3 H2 H4 X2 X1	VM AM

GROUND	FULL WAVE RECTIFIER	HORN, SIREN	BELL, BUZZER	MOTOR	OVERLOAD RELAY	FUSE
	AC DC DC AC			3 Phase MOTOR	Thermal	

AUTO TRANSFORMER	RESISTOR		LOCATION OF RELAY CONTACTS
	Adjustable RES	Fixed RES	ICR (2 - 3 - 4) 1 ICR 2 3 ICR 4 ICR NUMBERS IN PARENTHESIS DESIGNATE THE LOCATION OF RELAY CONTACTS. A LINE UNDERNEATH A LOCATION NUMBER SIGNIFIES A NORMALLY CLOSED CONTACT.

Courtesy Furnas Electric Co.

11

ON or OFF state with no forces applied. On the other hand, most of the switches shown in Table 2-1 have a normal position; that is, these switches will only stay in one position if they are not held in the other position. Switch construction is such that the switch may be either open or closed in its normal position. In fact, many switches have both a normally open set of contacts and a normally closed set of contacts. If the normal position is open, then the switch is said to be normally open (NO). If the normal position is closed, then the switch is said to be normally closed (NC). Switches are always drawn in their normal position unless it is specifically stated that they are illustrated in a held position—held open (HO) or held closed (HC).

Since push buttons are the interface between human control and electromagnetic operation of the circuit, they play an especially important role in control circuits. By using the NC contacts on a push button, a STOP switch is available since the actuation of the switch will deactivate the circuit. By using the NO contacts on another push button a START switch is implemented, since actuating this button will activate the circuit. The switches would be wired in series with the electromagnetic device as shown in Figure 2-3. Furthermore, the STOP button would normally be colored red and the START button colored green or black.

Push buttons may have ganged switches on one button, possibly consisting of a pair of NC switch contacts and another pair of NO switch contacts, as shown in Table 2-1 under push-button symbols. In other cases, even more switches may be ganged to a single button. It is important to note that the double-circuit, push-button switches act as "break before make" switches such that the connected power device is de-energized before another power device connected to the make switch is energized. This is an important safety consideration for equipment protection.

The switch symbol represents the nature of the NC and NO switch, e.g., a temperature switch or a pressure switch. Examples of these and other switch symbols are shown in Table 2-1.

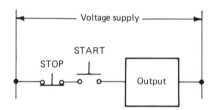

FIGURE 2-3. A START-STOP push-button control

2.3 Electromagnetic Relays

The second category consists of nonzero-power components, such as solenoids (e.g., motor starter coils and control relay coils), where it is possible to have current through the device and voltage across it simultaneously. Figure 2-4 shows a typical relay.

The principle of operation of the electromagnetic relay is that current passes through the coil (many turns of wire around an iron core), which causes the iron to become magnetized. The magnetization of the iron causes the armature (the movable part) to be forced to close the air gap in the magnetic circuit. Since the one side of each pair of contacts is attached to the armature, these contacts are similarly displaced in such a way that the contacts are brought to the closed position. This construction is shown in Figure 2-5.

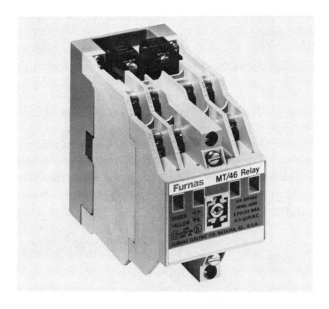

Courtesy Furnas Electric Company

FIGURE 2-4. Illustration of a relay

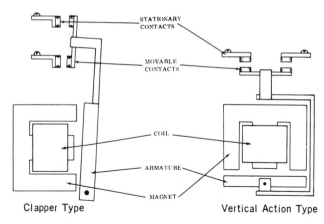

STATIONARY
CONTACTS

MOVABLE
CONTACTS

COIL

ARMATURE

MAGNET

Clapper Type   Vertical Action Type

FIGURE 2-5. Construction of an electromagnetic relay

Electromagnetic Relay Construction

The relay basically consists of a coil, a magnet, an armature, movable contacts, and stationary contacts. The magnet assembly consists of stationary laminated segments that are magnetized by the coil current. The flux causes the movable half of the magnetic circuit, the armature, to move from the normal position to the energized position. Line frequency vibration (actually 120 cycles per second for 60 Hz supply) can occur as the sine wave passes through zero. To prevent this vibration, a shading coil consisting of a single turn of conductor encircles a portion of the pole pieces. The shading coil induces a current that causes a 90-degree out-of-phase component of flux such that the total holding flux never passes through zero. This shading coil is the main difference that distinguishes the ac relay from the dc relay and explains why the dc coil, even when properly sized for the reactance component, will not work properly when used in an ac circuit.

The movable contacts are mounted to the armature so that they are self-aligning as they come in contact with the stationary contacts. This aligning assures a long life for the relay contacts.

Electromagnetic Relay Operation

The application of voltage to a relay coil causes an inrush of current (imaginatively called the *inrush current*). This inrush is due to the low inductive reactance of the coil when the air gap is large. As the air gap closes, the reactance is increased until the air gap is reduced to its minimum value. The armature is constructed so that the air gap in the middle leg never goes to zero; otherwise the residual magnetism may prevent the release when the electrically caused flux vanishes. A case in point is the residual magnetic latching relay: residual magnetism causes it to latch and it stays latched until the residual magnetism is reversed by another coil.

When the air gap is reduced to a minimum, the current then takes on its steady-state value, called the *sealed current*. The inrush current can be 6 to 10 times the sealed current, although it is of very short duration (tens of milliseconds, depending on the size of the relay).

Electromagnetic Relay Parameters

Following are some commonly used relay parameters:

Inrush current. The maximum coil current that occurs at the time voltage is applied.

Sealed current. The steady-state coil current that occurs when the inrush is over and the armature is seated.

Pickup voltage. The voltage that causes the beginning of movement of the armature.

Seal-in voltage. The voltage that is required to maintain the seating of the pole pieces of the magnet. Although this voltage varies depending on the type and size of the relay, a typical seal-in voltage is 75 percent of the operating voltage.

Drop-out voltage. The voltage at which the contacts will open. This voltage will be lower than the seal-in voltage.

Current rating. The largest steady current that is specified for the contacts. This current depends on the size and design of the contacts and connected conductors. The current rating for an inductive load is less than that for a resistive load due to the greater arcing caused by an inductive load, which increases the stress on the contacts. The de-rating factor for an inductive load is typically around 80 percent as compared to a resistive load.

Voltage rating. The largest applied voltage rating that is specified for the contacts. This voltage is determined by the ability of the contacts to open and close without arcing, flashover, or welding of the contacts.

Relay Input and Output Operation

The basic relay as explained above is used by applying the proper logic signal/information to the coil, and then using the contacts to control the signal/information that is needed at the next level of control. Figure 2-6 illustrates this principle. It is important to understand that the coil and contacts are proximate in their mechanical operation and are part of the same relay; however, in their functional

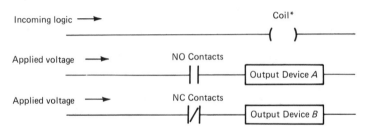

*Consistent with programmable controller symbols covered later, the parentheses will be used here for the circle coil symbol.

FIGURE 2-6. Schematic of a relay

operation they can be widely separate. For this reason, relays are useful for control at a distance, or remote control. For example, when the building thermostat calls for cooling, that information can be supplied to the relay located on the roof of the building and the coil will be energized, causing the contacts to close, which in turn will start the air conditioning system. It is also possible to cause multiple contacts to be activated when a single coil is energized. This provides a means of operating many components from one logic signal.

One more perspective on a relay is to view it as an amplifier. The contact current can be much larger than the coil current, e.g., 10.0 A versus 0.3 A. Of course even greater current gains can be established by using two relays, a small one that could respond to a very small milliampere current, and a larger one whose coil is driven by the ampere output of the smaller one and whose contacts in turn drive a tens-of-ampere output device. Naturally, this is an ON-OFF amplifier that operates in either a totally conducting or nonconducting mode, which works ideally for motor control (but does not work as well for a high-fidelity audio system).

Relay Types

Control relay describes a wide variety of devices that fit the above description of relays. The control relay may have different contact arrangements with as many as ten or twelve poles with a combination of NC and NO contacts; many times these contacts are convertible with a simple resetting operation that may be done in the field at the time of installation or modification.

Contactor typically describes a special kind of control relay for a particular application; namely, a typical contactor is large in size with contacts that are typically NO and is used to handle a power load such as a three-phase motor.

Motor starter describes a relay that is typically large (i.e., a contactor) and has the important addition of a motor-protection device that prevents overloading and damage to the equipment. The operation of the protective device is described in Section 2.4.

Time-delay relay is a relay that is used to delay the output action by causing the contacts to be delayed in their action either following the time the coil is energized, or following the time the coil is de-energized. This time-delay relay is described further in Section 2.5.

2.4 Motor Starters

By far the most commonly used motors in industrial and other kinds of control are ac induction motors. They have the advantages of simple construction, long life, and low cost. However, an important characteristic of ac induction motors is that they typically have a large inrush current when starting, generally 6 to 14 times their full load current (FLC). The starting inrush current is approximately the same as the locked rotor current (LRC) for the instant that is required to overcome the rotor inertia, since the rotor is stationary and the current is building to the LRC value. Once the rotor begins to rotate, the impedance of the motor increases and the value of current falls off to the FLC or lower, depending on the load. The significance of the large inrush current to the design of motor controllers is that the motor starter must carry the large starting current without nuisance trips or circuit shutdowns. In addition to carrying the inrush current, the motor starter must be able to sense an overload condition and provide a safe shutdown so that the overload current does not damage the motor. Figure 2-7 shows some typical motor starters.

With Melting Alloy Overload Relay   **Size 2-3½**   With Bimetal Overload Relay

Courtesy Furnas Electric Company

FIGURE 2-7. Illustration of motor starters

Ordinary fuses and circuit breakers usually are not sensitive enough to properly clear a small but significant excess in the inrush current or the running current while at the same time being able to clear the circuit of more extensive overcurrent conditions. For this reason, fuses and circuit breakers are designed and used to interrupt large currents due to short circuits. Such currents may be several times as large as inrush and operating currents. Thus, the protection provided by fuses and circuit breakers is called *overcurrent protection*.

On the other hand, steady-state currents that are only slightly larger than the full-load current need to be guarded against, since these currents can cause extensive equipment damage and can be a hazard to other equipment and persons if allowed to exist for an extended time. These excessive currents may be due to such factors as too much mechanical load for the motor or bad bearings. The protection provided in this case is called *overload protection*.

By providing protective devices like thermal melting alloy overloads (called solder pots), these overload currents can be sensed and cleared before motor damage occurs. The basis for this kind of protection is the current-time heating curve shown in Figure 2-8. The principle of this curve is that if the current-time product exceeds the safe operating curve for the motor, then the heat will be excessive and shorten the life of the motor, if not destroy it. However, if the proper overload relay is selected, then its current-time product will fall under the motor curve and cause the circuit to be cleared before any harm is done to the motor.

The operation of the overload relay depends on heaters, which are small-valued resistors that are placed in each of the three lines of

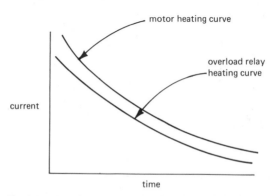

FIGURE 2-8. Current-time heating curve

the supply conductors to the motor. These heaters are located directly on the load side of the contactor contacts. The sequence of operation is as follows:

1. The motor current passes through the overload relay heaters.
2. The current causes heat to be generated in the resistors in proportion to the heat generated in the motor.
3. This heat is in turn transferred to a heat-sensitive element that causes the overload relay to interrupt the motor-starter coil current (not the motor current) when the motor current is excessive.
4. The coil is de-energized, causing the motor current to be stopped and the holding action of the coil to be disrupted so that the circuit is shut down.

Figure 2-9 shows typical motor starter heaters and overload relays.

In the case of the thermal-melting alloy overload relay, the heat-sensitive element is a solder pot that is designed so that the solder surrounding a spring-loaded shaft melts when the heat is excessive. This permits the shaft to rotate, thus causing the overload relay contacts in series with the coil to open.

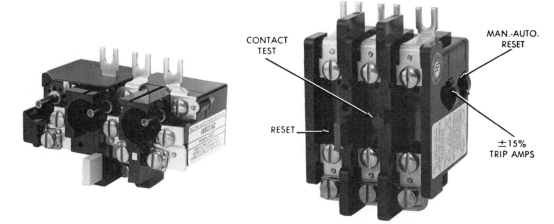

Melting Alloy Tri-Block
Overload Relay 30 & 60 Amp.

Bimetal Tri-Block Overload
Relay 30 and 60 Amps.

Courtesy Furnas Electric Company

**FIGURE 2-9. Illustration of typical motor starter heaters
and overload relays**

The operation of the bimetallic overload relay is similar to the thermal melting alloy relay, except the heat-sensitive element depends on the operation of a current-sensitive bimetallic element.

2.5 Time-Delay Relays

The operation of time-delay relays is based on one of three principles: pneumatic, thermal, or electronic.

The pneumatic time-delay relay is based on the principle of spring-loaded pneumatic bellows and an adustable orifice that controls the movement of the contacts after the coil is energized or, in the case of the off delay, after the coil is de-energized.

Thermal timers use the heat storage and mechanical distortion of bonded dissimilar metals to activate or deactivate sets of contacts.

The electronic time-delay relay is based on one of two mechanisms. One kind provides timing by comparing a standard to the rising voltage of electric charge stored in a resistor-capacitor circuit. For longer timing intervals, clock timers are used. More current technology provides integrated circuit digital timers that are replacements for pneumatic time-delay relays.

Time-delay relays provide contacts whose action is delayed from the time that the coil state is changed. In the case where the delay is set to zero time delay, the time delay provides the same operation as a control relay. (Many time-delay relays have immediate acting contacts for zero time-delay action in addition to the time-delay contacts.) In the case where the delay is not zero, the action of the contacts is delayed for the time interval of the timer setting. This time interval can vary from a few seconds up to several hours, depending on the particular relay. With the advent of electronic timers, even more flexibility in the time interval—as well as more accuracy—is possible.

The operating characteristics of a time-delay relay are illustrated in the timing diagram in Figure 2-10. The diagram shows all possible ON and OFF conditions for all contact arrangements through a complete cycle of coil operation.

In the case of the on-delay timer, the delay occurs when the coil is energized. In the case of the off-delay timer, the contacts are immediately changed from the normal to the held position, and then the timed contacts return to the normal position once the coil is energized. With this understanding, it can be seen that the on-delay time-delay relay has NOTC and NCTO contacts and the off-delay time-delay relay has NOTO and NCTC contacts. Many timers are made so that they can be modified in the field to convert from one style to the other.

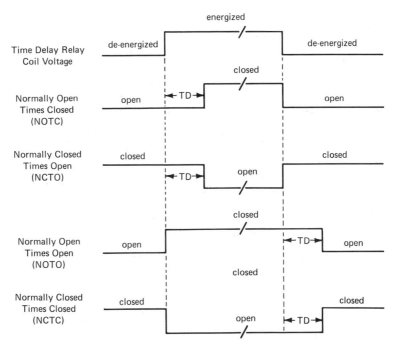

FIGURE 2-10. Diagram of NO and NC contact action for on- and off-time delays

2.6 Ladder Diagrams

Ladder diagrams provide a standard representation of circuits that is convenient for design, analysis, and troubleshooting. Wiring diagrams (also called schematic diagrams), on the other hand, provide a more convenient representation for the purpose of wiring, since these diagrams actually indicate point-to-point wiring connections. As an example of ladder diagrams versus wiring diagrams, consider multiple push-button stations where more than one START and STOP station is provided to perform these functions. A ladder diagram is shown in Figure 2-11. For comparison, a wiring diagram for the same station is shown in Figure 2-12. It can be seen that the physical relationship of the wiring to the components is more clearly laid out in the schematic diagram; however, the functional relationship of the components is greatly obscured. The ladder diagram is much more useful for seeing the functional relationship of cause and effect. Thus, the ladder diagram is the logic diagram of the circuit.

In ladder diagrams, the energy source is placed at the top of the diagram along with the fuse protection for the control circuit (not to be

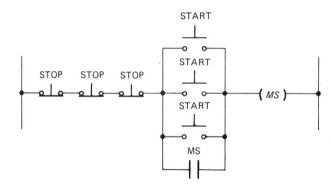

FIGURE 2-11. A ladder diagram for multiple push-button
stations

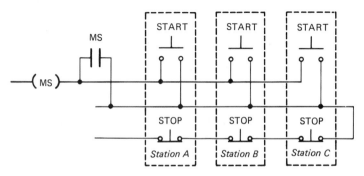

FIGURE 2-12. A schematic diagram for multiple push-
button stations

confused with the circuit interrupter or overloads for the motor circuit). Then two ladder rails are made by two vertical lines that encompass the rungs of the ladder. The various components of the circuit are placed on the rungs of the ladder, which are the horizontal lines of the diagram. (As an alternative, horizontal ladder diagrams are sometimes used, but we shall stay with more conventional vertical ladders here.)

Rules exist for the placement of the switches and/or contacts as compared to the coils of the relay logic. The switches are placed to the leftmost portion of the rung, contacts are placed in the center of the rung, and the coils are placed to the right side of the rung. An exception is that overload contacts are often placed to the far right side of the ladder, since it is convenient to wire them in this position. Figure 2-13 is an example of this placement. In this manner, the action of the coil can be traced as a consequence of the action of the switches. As an

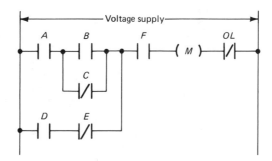

FIGURE 2-13. A relay controlled by a combination of switches

example, Figure 2-13 shows a combination of contacts that control the *M* coil. The coil can be energized if either one of the two main branches of the rung has a conducting path along with the *F* contact and the overload (OL) contacts. In words

$$M = [A \ AND \ (B \ or \ NOT \ C) \ AND \ F \ AND \ NOT \ OL] \ OR$$
$$[D \ AND \ NOT \ E \ AND \ F \ AND \ NOT \ OL]$$

In Boolean algebra

$$M = [A \bullet (B + \overline{C}) \bullet F \bullet \overline{OL}] + [D \bullet \overline{E} \bullet F \bullet \overline{OL}]$$

As an additional step, the *F* contact and OL contacts can be treated as separate conditions from the two main branches, and either by inspection of the contact placement or by Boolean algebra manipulation, the above equation can be rewritten as

$$M = \{[A \bullet (B + \overline{C})] + [D \bullet \overline{E}]\} \ \{F \bullet \overline{OL}\}$$

A requirement of shunt coils as shown in the ladder diagram is that only one coil is permitted per rung of the ladder. Since a shunt coil requires the full supply voltage to assure its proper operation, placing two shunt coils in a series arrangement such that the voltage would be divided between them would not permit their having adequate pull-in voltage. An exception is that two coils may be placed in parallel. This arrangement would provide additional contacts for duplicate operation. A corollary to the above requirement is that at least one coil must be in each rung; otherwise the closing of the switches would provide a short circuit to the source.

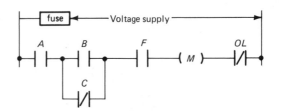

FIGURE 2-14. Diagnosing a relay control circuit

Two safety measures are incorporated. One is that the control circuit is operated at a lower voltage than the voltage used in the motor circuit. For example, the motor circuit may operate at 220 V, 440 V, or higher, but typical control circuit voltages are 24 V and 120 V. This voltage is supplied by a transformer that taps into two of the motor circuit's three phase lines between the disconnect and the contactor. A second safety measure is proper grounding. The control circuit is grounded at the node identified as the right-hand end of the ladder diagram to provide a means of clearing the circuit by spending the fuse if an additional ground is accidentally established. The reason for this feature is that an accidental contact between this circuit and a conducting element, such as the cabinet or the conduit, could cause a hazard in that someone working with this circuit could come between the accidentally energized element and an earth ground—a condition that could be "shocking." Proper fusing should clear any faults due to accidental grounding of the energized side of the line.

The ladder diagram provides a better basis for troubleshooting than the wiring diagram, although both may be needed to analyze the fault and to locate the wires. Consider the assignment of troubleshooting the circuit in Figure 2-14 where the M coil will not operate. A general method of using a ladder diagram in diagnosing circuit operation as applied to this circuit is given below:

1. Place the common or ground probe of the voltmeter to the common or ground node of the circuit as denoted by the right rail of the ladder diagram; keep it there during the diagnosis.

2. Place the other probe or the test probe to the ungrounded or energized side of the circuit as denoted by the left rail of the ladder diagram to identify the presence or absence of the proper voltage and to check for operation of the source as well as to check the operation of the voltmeter.

3. If this check confirms the presence of the supply voltage, then the probe is moved to the left side of the A contacts to check the continuity of the wire as well as the correctness of the wiring.

4. To further check the operation of this circuit branch, the A contact must be analyzed to see if it is supposed to be closed. If it is, then measurement of the voltage on the right side of the A contact should reveal the full control-circuit voltage present at that location.

5. The procedure is continued, moving across the circuit and tracing the path on the ladder diagram. If a voltage is not detected where it should be, then that is the location of the faulty part, which can be due to part failure, wiring failure, or logic fault.

6. Finally, if the voltage is present at the left side of the coil but not at the right side of the coil, then the coil should be examined for an open circuit condition or for a stuck armature condition. If the armature of the relay is stuck, then it will tend to overheat and possibly destroy itself and the control transformer that supplies it, if not properly fused.

In summary, clamping the common probe of the voltmeter to the common side of the circuit and moving the other voltmeter probe from point to point to check for proper voltage based on the ladder diagram is suggested as the most useful procedure for troubleshooting the wiring and components of the circuit.

2.7   Some Common Relay Control Circuits

In order to gain experience and practice in analyzing and later designing control circuits with the desired control characteristics, examples of commonly used control circuits are provided in this section.

Three-Wire Control with Indicators

Three-wire control designates that the START-STOP station is incorporated with a holding contact for undervoltage protection, i.e., the circuit will be disabled by a temporary loss of power to the relay coil, even for losses as short as 5 milliseconds. Indicators are included to show the ON-OFF condition of the motor, for example, red for ON and green for OFF. Figure 2-15 shows one possible arrangement. Alternate arrangements include START and STOP buttons with pilot lamps built into the plastic cap with a push-to-test facility.

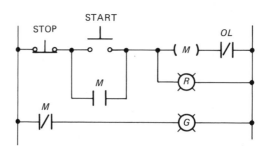

FIGURE 2-15. Three-wire control circuit with indicators

Jogging Circuits

A frequent need in relay control is a jogging circuit. A jogging circuit energizes the coil only for the time the button is manually held. In this way, the motor being operated can be more closely controlled than it could by a STOP-START station. One example of a jogging control application is a crane. The crane must be controlled so as to lift or lower the load precisely to the desired level.

Figure 2-16 shows a simple selector-switch jogging circuit, one of several jogging circuits in use. With the selector switch in position JOG, the *M* holding contact is disabled and the *M* coil is energized only as long as the START button is held (and the STOP button is not depressed). With the selector switch in position RUN, the *M* holding contacts are in operation and the circuit acts as a three-wire control circuit.

Another jogging circuit is shown in Figure 2-17. This circuit operates as a START-STOP station by use of the *S* contacts activating the *M* coil when the START button is depressed. In the case of the operation of the JOG button, no holding operation is provided by the *M* motor starter. The advantage of the push-button JOG circuit over the selector-switch JOG circuit is that each push button can be labeled for its purpose and the circuit can be operated without first determining if the selector switch is in the required position.

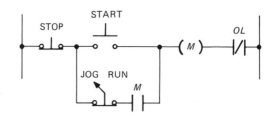

FIGURE 2-16. Selector-switch JOG circuit

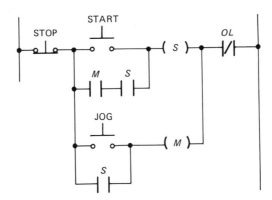

FIGURE 2-17. Push-button JOG circuit

Reversing Circuits

One of the most common relay control applications is the forward-reverse operation of a motor. A forward-reverse motor circuit is shown in Figure 2-18 and the forward-reverse control circuit is shown in Figure 2-19.

The risk involved in a forward-reverse control is that the *F* contacts and the *R* contacts may be closed at the same time, causing a line-to-line short. For this reason, the forward-reverse circuit has several safety features. The normally closed FOR and REV push-button contacts in each line release the *R* and *F* coils, respectively,

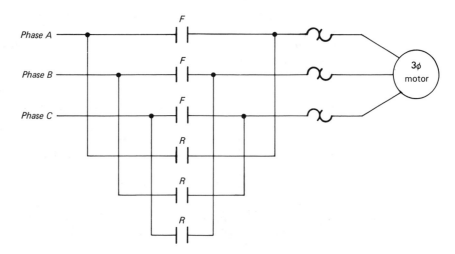

FIGURE 2-18. Forward-reverse motor circuit

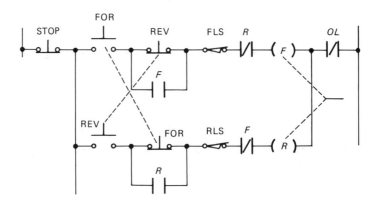

FIGURE 2-19. Forward-reverse control circuit

assuring that no accidental push-button operation will cause the *R* and *F* contacts to be energized simultaneously. Further assurance is provided by the electrical interlock, i.e., the *F* and *R* NC contacts in series with the *R* and *F* coils, respectively. A further backup is provided by using a mechanical interlock that prevents the *F* and *R* armatures from being in the held-in position simultaneously. Limit switches FLS and RLS are optional; they could be used to control the shutoff point for the *F* and *R* coils, respectively.

Multiple *STOP-FORWARD-REVERSE* stations are provided by introducing additional stop buttons in series, additional NO forward and reverse push buttons in parallel, and additional NC forward and reverse push buttons in series.

Plugging and Antiplugging Circuits

For the purpose of avoiding waiting periods while a motor and its load coasts to a halt, a plugging circuit can be implemented to "plug" the motor, i.e., to brake the motor by reversing the motor connections and developing a reverse torque. The motor circuit for the plugging circuit is shown in Figure 2-18 and the control circuit is shown in Figure 2-20. The speed switch is necessarily located on the motor or adjacent to it so that it can detect motor shaft speed. When the shaft operates at a preset or higher level of speed in the forward direction, the speed switch contacts close.

The operation of the plugging circuit is as follows. During startup, the *F* coil is energized, the motor accelerates, the speed switch closes, and the *D* coil is energized and held in by its own *D* holding contact. The *R* coil is blocked out by the NC *F* holding contacts. During shutdown, due to pushing the STOP button, the NC *F* contacts reclose, the *R* coil is energized, and reverse operation of the motor is

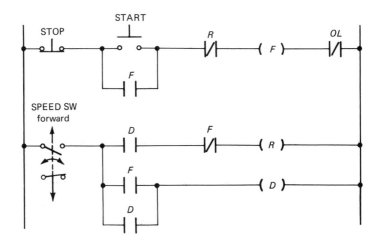

FIGURE 2-20. Plugging circuit

instituted. When the motor decelerates to the speed switch setting (e.g., 20 percent full speed), the speed switch opens and the entire circuit is deactivated.

A different need that may exist is to prevent plugging of a motor, i.e., reversing motor direction while running. A circuit to implement this need is called an antiplugging circuit, illustrated in Figure 2-21. The antiplugging circuit prevents operation in the opposite direction by causing the speed switch NC contacts to be held open when the motor is running at speed. By placing these contacts in series with the push button, the push button is disabled. Thus, the NC reverse-speed switch contact is in series with the forward push button, and the NC forward-speed switch contact is in series with the reverse push button.

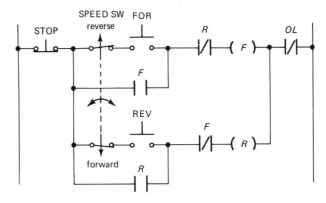

FIGURE 2-21. Anti-plugging circuit

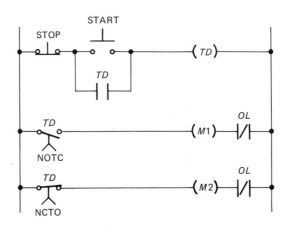

FIGURE 2-22. On-delay circuit

Timing Circuits

A simple timing circuit that produces an on-delay (delay after the coil is energized) consists of placing NOTC contacts in series with the load. When the coil is energized, the normally off load is turned on after the preset time delay. Likewise, a normally on load is turned off after the preset time delay by placing NCTO contacts in series with it. Figure 2-22 shows an on-delay circuit for a normally on load and for a normally off load. The *M2* contactor is turned off after a time delay (it is normally on), and the contactor *M1* is turned on after a time delay.

Implementation of an off-delay circuit (delay after the coil is de-energized) consists of altering the on-delay circuit so that the above NOTC and NCTO timing contacts are replaced by NCTC and NOTO contacts. The delay then occurs after the STOP button is pushed.

A one-shot timing circuit provides an active output for a preset time interval. An example is shown in Figure 2-23. The operation of the circuit is based on the opening of the *TD* NCTO contacts at the end of the preset interval. The timing will not occur again until the START button is activated; however, if the START button is held, the *M* coil will remain energized.

One more variety of timing circuits is the repeat-cycle circuit. In the one shown in Figure 2-24, *M1* and *M2* alternate between ON and OFF. The circuit starts with *M2* ON and *M1* OFF. At the end of the *TD1* timing interval, the *TD1* NOTC contacts close and *TD2* begins timing. At the end of the *TD2* timing interval, the *TD2* NCTO contacts open, but *TD1* and *TD2* are immediately reset and the cycle begins again. *M2* is on during the *TD1* timing interval, and *M1* is on during the *TD2* timing interval.

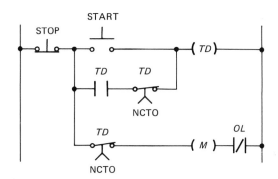

FIGURE 2-23. One-shot timing circuit

Anti-Tiedown Circuit

To provide a safe working environment, control systems for dangerous equipment such as presses and cutting machines are frequently equipped with two START buttons wired in series so that both must be activated in order to start the equipment. By locating these two push buttons at separate locations, the equipment operator cannot accidentally suffer injury during equipment operation, since both hands must be on the push buttons to start the equipment. On occasion, one of the two push buttons will be tied down such that only one hand is needed to operate the equipment. Thus, the anti-tiedown circuit is helpful for preventing such tampering. The anti-tiedown

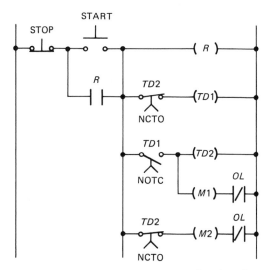

FIGURE 2-24. Repeat cycle circuit

circuit prevents the START buttons from being effective unless both are activated within a preset time interval. An anti-tiedown circuit is shown in Figure 2-25.

The principle of operation of the anti-tiedown circuit is that either START button causes the operation of the *TD* coil. If the other START button is not depressed within the preset time, the earlier pressed START button is disabled by the NCTO contacts in series with it. In the case where both buttons are depressed within the preset time interval, the *C1* and *C2* coils are energized during an overlapping time interval and the *M* coil is energized along with its holding contact to produce the desired action.

2.8 Reduced Voltage Starting

Our discussion up to this point has been limited to across-the-line starting; that is, the line is directly connected to the motor (albeit through the motor starter contacts and heaters). Thus, the full line voltage is placed across the motor at the instance of starting. However, it may not be desirable to start large, three-phase motors across the line for one of several reasons:

1. *Large inrush current.* The circuit branch conductors, the switchgear, and the motor must be sized to withstand the large inrush current that will occur when the motor is started across the line.

2. *Supply line voltage regulation.* The large inrush current will cause the line voltage to drop during motor starting. This

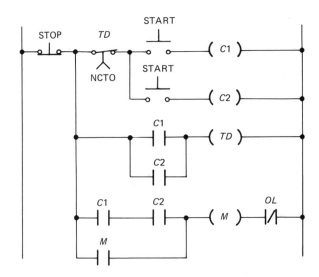

FIGURE 2-25. Anti-tiedown circuit

will affect other equipment on the same branch circuit and, to a lesser extent, equipment on the same electrical feeder. Poor voltage regulation can be a serious detriment to equipment that must perform precise jobs such as machine tool cutting or finish grinding.

3. *Torque impulse.* The large inrush current will also cause a large torque impulse or torque jerk at start-up. This impulse could be harmful to the equipment being driven by the motor shaft.

Now let us turn our attention to the case where other than across-the-line starting is used. *Reduced voltage starting* is a term used to describe one of several modes of starting wherein some provision is made to ameliorate the disadvantages of across-the-line starting.

Primary-Resistance Starting

In primary-resistance starting, the inrush current is limited by starting resistors that are in series with the motor windings during starting, and then shunted by the running contacts during running, as shown in Figure 2-26. By dropping part of the line voltage across these starting resistors, the inrush current and motor voltage are

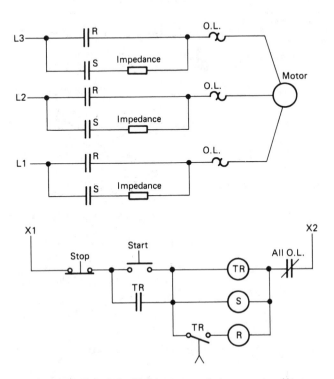

FIGURE 2-26. Primary resistance starting

reduced. As the inrush current drops due to the motor coming up to speed, the voltage drop across the series resistors is reduced, giving a smooth transition. This method of starting is called two-step starting; it is satisfactory for many applications such as controlling blowers, pumps, and compressors.

Primary-Reactance Starting

In primary-reactance starting, the inrush current is limited by reactors that are in series with the motor windings during starting, and then shunted by the running contacts during running, the same as in primary-resistance starting. The advantage of primary-reactance starting is that the phase relationship of the series reactor swings from an in-phase relationship with the motor as the motor starts and also appears as an inductive load, to an out-of-phase relationship with the motor as the motor comes up to speed. This causes the portion of the line voltage that is across the motor to vary

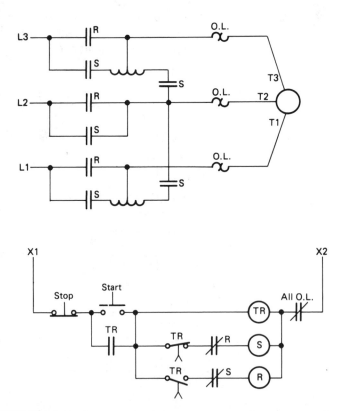

FIGURE 2-27. Open-transition autotransformer starting

from a small value when the phasor voltages add along a straight line, to a large value when the phasor voltages add at right angles.

Autotransformer Starting

In autotransformer starting, the starting voltage to the motor is reduced by the transformer action of the autotransformers in the three-phase power line to the motor. Either two or three autotransformers can be used. Two kinds of autotransformer starting are open-transition and closed-transition. In open-transition autotransformer starting, as shown in Figure 2-27, the motor is disconnected from the line during the transition period as the autotransformer is switched out of the circuit, causing a transient in the operation of the motor and the line. In closed-transition autotransformer starting, as shown in Figure 2-28, a segment of the transformer coil is connected in series with the motor where it acts as a series reactor during the transition, thus giving a smoother transition.

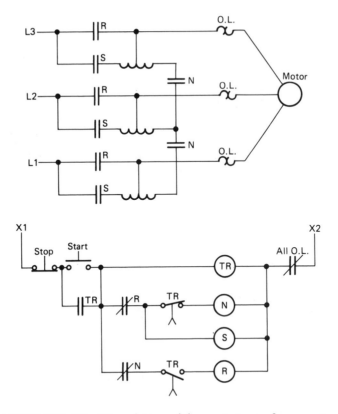

FIGURE 2-28. Closed-transition autotransformer starting

Part-Winding Starting

This kind of starting requires that two sets of stator three-phase windings be brought outside of the motor frame so that they can be accessible to individual control. The starting winding must also be rated for part-winding starting so that it can be used solely to start the motor. In part-winding starting, only the starting winding is energized initially; after an adequate time delay for the motor to accelerate to partial speed, the second winding is also energized for normal running, as shown in Figure 2-29.

Wye-Delta Starting

This kind of starting requires that both ends of the stator windings for all three phases be brought outside of the motor frame so that they can be connected in a wye configuration during starting and switched to a delta configuration during running. This reconfiguration will reduce the starting voltage across each phase by a factor of 1.732, and reduce

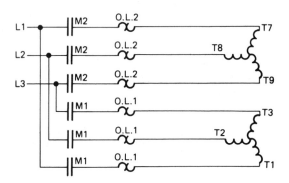

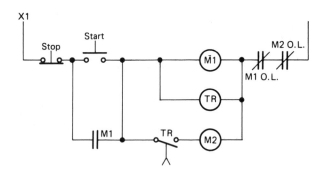

FIGURE 2-29. Part-winding starting

the starting current and torque. The control circuit for this method of starting is shown in Figure 2-30.

Reduced Voltage Starting for a Wound-Rotor Motor

So far the discussion has been confined to induction squirrel-cage motor starting where no access is available to change the internal electrical characteristics of the motor. More expensive motors, such as wound-rotor motors, provide access to the rotor windings by means of slip rings. For these motors (and dc motors), better methods of control are possible. One example is the four-step controller shown in Figure 2-31. By controlling the external resistance bank, the wound-rotor resistance as seen at the line can be changed to effect a smooth transition from 0 percent speed to full speed with only small steps in current and torque.

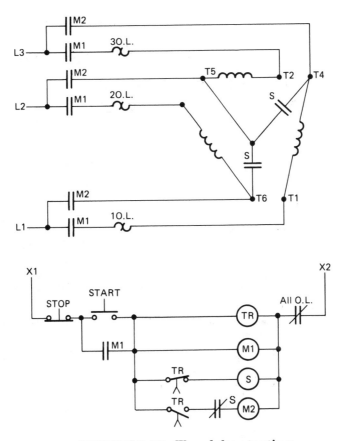

FIGURE 2-30. Wye-delta starting

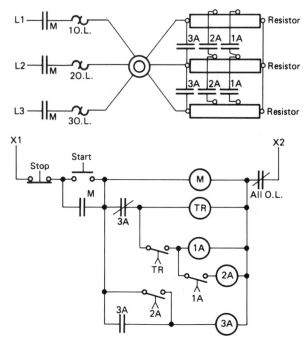

FIGURE 2-31. Reduced voltage starting for a wound rotor motor

2.9 Codes and Standards

In any design application, the prevailing codes and standards must be consulted and considered in implementing the design. The relevant code for motor control design is the National Electrical Code (NEC), especially Article 430 on motors and motor controllers and Article 500 on hazardous locations.

The U. S. Occupational Safety and Health Act as enforced by the Occupational Safety and Health Administration (OSHA) requires that employment activities be free from recognized hazards. In the electrical section of the OSHA code, the NEC is specified as the OSHA safety standard.

The National Electrical Manufacturers Association (NEMA) sets standards concerning manufacture of control equipment such as starters and relays.

The NEC requires that all installed equipment be approved for the purpose by a recognized testing laboratory. The best known laboratory that tests for the safety of products is the Underwriter's Laboratory (UL).

In addition, a wide assortment of guides, handbooks, and textbooks are available for determining standards and practices of installation, operation, and maintenance of relay controls.

Problems _____

2.1 Draw the symbols for the following devices:

a) disconnect

b) circuit interrupter

c) circuit breaker (thermal and magnetic overload)

d) limit switch (four sketches, two normal and two held)

e) foot switch (four sketches)

f) pressure and vacuum switch (four sketches)

g) liquid-level switch (four sketches)

h) temperature actuated switch (four sketches)

i) flow switch (four sketches)

j) speed switch (six sketches)

k) selector switch, three position (three sketches)

l) push button (eight sketches)

m) pilot light

n) contacts (two sketches)

o) shunt coil

p) series coil.

2.2 A JOG push-button switch is wired in series with a relay coil. The coil has an impedance of 60 ohms at the operating voltage of 120 V that is applied to the circuit. Determine the switch voltage, current, and apparent power (VA) and the coil voltage, current, and apparent power (VA) for

a) the switch open

b) the switch closed.

2.3 The inrush current to a motor starter requires 200 VA and the seal-in current requires 45 VA. The control voltage is 120 V for three identical motor starters to be supplied by the same transformer.

a) What is the minimum VA rating of the supply transformer? (*Hint:* The inrush current is of extremely short duration and is not normally high-duty cycle, e.g., not high rate of repetition.)

b) What is the minimum current rating of the supply transformer?

2.4 It is desired to design a control circuit so that if either limit switch *A* is closed or limit switch *B* is closed, the control relay coil *D* will be energized, but only if limit switch *C* is closed. Sketch such a circuit in ladder-diagram form.

2.5 It is desired to design a circuit so that the operation of either foot switch *FS* or push button *PB* will cause relay coil *R* to be energized; in turn, relay contacts *R* will cause a motor starter coil *M* to be energized; in turn, motor contacts *M* will control pilot lamp *L* such that *L* is turned off when *M* is energized. Sketch such a circuit in ladder-diagram form.

2.6 Name the basic parts of a relay and briefly explain its operation.

2.7 State the purpose of a shading coil and briefly explain its operation.

2.8 Define the following: inrush current, pickup voltage, seal-in voltage, drop-out voltage, current rating, and voltage rating.

2.9 Answer the following:

a) State the sequence of operation for an overload condition to cause the shutdown of a motor circuit and give the cause.

b) State the manual steps that must be taken to restart a motor starter in a START-STOP circuit.

2.10 Draw a multiple push-button station in a wiring diagram wherein three START-STOP stations are each separated by some distance (show this separation by putting the stations at separate locations on the worksheet). Show only three wires going into each of the three enclosures designating the START-STOP stations.

2.11 A motor-control circuit and a motor circuit are shown in Figure P2.11 to be used for START-STOP control of a blower motor.

OPERATION

• Operation of the START button causes the *B* coil to be energized along with *B* holding contact, which in turn holds the *B* motor starter on. The closure of the *B* contacts in the motor circuit also causes the motor to run. The pilot is on whenever the coil is energized.

• Operation of the STOP button causes the *B* coil to be de-energized, which in turn drops the holding contact and the motor circuit *B* contacts, which stops the motor.

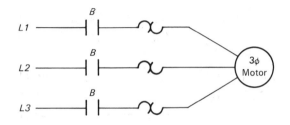

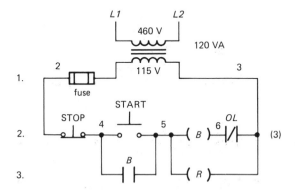

FIGURE P2.11. Blower control circuit

• Operation of the overload contacts causes the same shutdown as the operation of the STOP button. The OL contacts must be reset to their closed position before the circuit and motor can be restarted.

QUESTIONS

a) What is the purpose of the transformer?

b) What is the current capacity of the transformer?

c) (Optional) What is the current requirement of a size 2 motor starter?

d) (Optional) Is this transformer adequate for a size 2 motor starter?

e) Where should a grounding point be supplied for this circuit?

f) Assume node three is used as the grounding point. Assume a fault occurs at node 5 so that node 5 makes electrical contact with the enclosure. A maintenance person accidentally comes in contact with the enclosure as well as with earth ground. Would it be possible for this person to suffer shock? Consider the same question only for using node 2 for the grounding point. (*Hint:* First consider what happens to the fuse when the fault occurs.)

g) Due to a power interruption, the 460 V supply is disabled for one second. Will the motor continue to run? Explain.

h) If the left end of the *B* contact were accidentally moved from node 4 to node 2, how would the operation of the circuit be affected?

i) If the left end of the *B* contact were accidentally moved from node 4 to node 6, how would the operation of the circuit be affected?

j) How would the operation of the circuit be affected if the *B* holding contact would not close?

k) How would the operation of the circuit be affected if the *B* holding contact would not open?

l) What are the possible faults if the motor does not run but the pilot lamp is illuminated?

m) What are the possible faults if the motor does not run and the pilot lamp is *not* illuminated?

2.12 Three motors are to be started in sequence with three START buttons so that motor 3 cannot be started until motor 2 is started, and motor 2 cannot be started until motor 1 is started. One STOP button stops all motors. Draw the control circuit. (*Suggestion:* Use the auxillary contacts of each motor starter. *Hint:* Do not confuse the motor starters and the motors.)

2.13 A water tank is to be used as a water-storage facility so that whenever the water reaches a low level it will be filled to an upper level. As shown in Figure P2.13, the level is controlled by *LLS1* liquid-level switch at the low end and by *LLS2* liquid-level switch at the upper level. *PS1* and *PS2* are the respective pressure safety switches, such that *PS1* duplicates the action of *LLS1* and *PS2* duplicates the action of *LLS2*.

OPERATION

Manual

• The selector switch is set to the MAN position.

• Operation of the START button causes the *M* coil to be energized and held on by the holding contact in line 3.

• Operation of the STOP button causes the circuit to shut down.

Automatic

• The selector switch is set to the AUTO position.

• When the water level is at the low level, the *M* coil is energized by the *LLS1* or *PS1* switch.

• When the water level is at the upper level, the *M* coil is de-energized by either the *LLS2* or *PS2* switch.

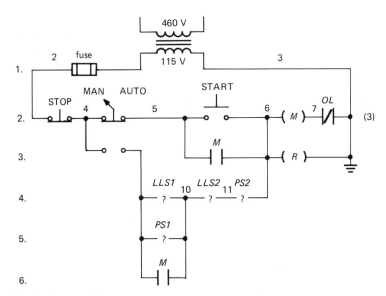

FIGURE P2.13. Water storage tank control circuit

QUESTIONS

a) What switches would be used for *LLS1, LLS2, PS1,* and *PS2:* NO or NC? (*Hint:* Consider the tank to be initially empty and work the entire cycle through the fill stage, the emptying stage, and then to the refill stage.)

b) What is the purpose of the *M* contact in line 6 and how would the circuit operate if it were removed?

c) How would the circuit operate if *LLS1* failed to close?

d) How would the circuit operate if *LLS1* failed to open?

e) How would the circuit operate if the STOP button were moved so that it was connected to node 5 (between the selector switch and the START button)?

f) How could the control circuit be modified to provide high-level control with *LLS2* and *PS2* in the manual mode?

2.14 It is desired to design a circuit so that a 460 V, three-phase electric heater is operated by a motor starter *M*, and a 460 V blower motor is operated by a motor starter *B*. When the START button is pushed, both motor starters are to be energized. When the STOP button or the electric heater OL are activated, the blower is to continue to operate for a timed interval.

  a) Design a control circuit in ladder-diagram form and also show the electric heater and blower circuit.

b) Add to the above circuit an overtemperature switch so that in the case of an overtemperature condition M will be de-energized immediately and B will be de-energized after a time delay.

3 Introduction to Semiconductor Control

3.0 Introduction

In Chapter 2, control logic was implemented in the form of relays and switches. This implementation of control logic is an important one that is widely used and worthy of study in its own right. However, control logic is independent of the use of relays. The logic operations of contacts, in series and parallel combinations, can be provided by other devices. Close examination of the logic involved in control systems reveals that a fairly small set of logic functions are the basis for control system operation. The principal logic functions are the following:

- Basic logic (equivalent to parallel and series switch combinations)
- Latching (equivalent to a control relay with holding contacts)
- Sequencing (equivalent to a drum switch)
- Time delay (equivalent to a time-delay relay)
- Counting (equivalent to a ratcheting counter)
- Selecting (equivalent to a selection switch)
- Event identification (equivalent to an annunciator panel).

These functions are not dependent upon an implementation mechanism. Hydraulics, pneumatics, fluidics, mechanics, magnetics, and electronics all serve as discrete control media. Recently, bio-logic was added to the list. Electronic systems, however, have experienced a geometric rate of growth as the implementation method most often used. Within electronics, it is the development of the integrated circuit that has enabled the widespread application of control in industry.

3.1 The Integrated Circuit

The relay approach to control is the oldest and simplest of the ON-OFF (discrete) control implementation methods. The relay gained industrial acceptance around the turn of the twentieth century, largely due to telegraphy experience, and became the standard ON-OFF control device for the next fifty years. Today it is still the most cost-effective control solution for simple, rugged systems requiring uncomplicated on-site maintenance.

As the relay made automatic industrial control a reality, the trend to larger and more complex systems increased dramatically. Technological improvements were made to improve capability and decrease size of relay control systems. System complexity continued to increase until the limits of the relay technology were reached. The limiting factors were the functional capabilities of relays. Following are some of the drawbacks that are experienced in large-scale relay systems.

- Limited system complexity
- High installation cost
- Large power requirements
- Large space requirements
- Limited mechanical life
- Slow contact operation times
- High maintenance cost.

The limitations of relays led to the search for an alternative device for control system implementation. This alternative has been sought since the introduction of the vacuum tube around the time of World War I.

The vacuum tube never achieved the widespread use that the relay enjoyed as a discrete control component. The speed and space efficiency of this early electronic alternative was offset by fragility, short operational life, and increased circuit complexity. As an extreme example, one of the first working computers, the ILLIAC, using vacuum tube technology, had such a high failure rate that it was plagued by tube failures on the average of one every twenty minutes.

It was the development of the transistor in the late 1940s that first provoked serious consideration of relay alternatives. The first commercial devices appeared at the end of the 1950s and continued on into the 1960s. In the transistor, a device had arrived that offered small size, low power consumption, high reliability, and low cost. An

FIGURE 3-1. Discrete control implementations

entire industry provides transistor-based, printed-circuit boards containing common industrial control functions. These boards are joined through plug-in connectors to input and output devices as well as other boards. This implementation can produce complex control systems that are difficult or impractical to implement in relays. Figure 3-1 illustrates the examples of discrete devices in the form of relays, vacuum tubes, transistors, and circuit boards.

The transistor followed the vacuum tube as a replacement for the relay. However, like any electronic device, the transistor does have its problems. Transistors, though touted for infinite life, may be destroyed by such things as excessive temperatures, power "spikes," and input/output transients. A transistor system requires air conditioning, high-quality power supplies and extensive support literature. Special skills are also needed to maintain transistor-based systems. These needs relegated early transistor control to large, high-speed, mass-produced, or special-purpose systems that rely on high component life, fast speeds, and compact size to produce complex control capabilities.

Even with its special considerations, solid-state control often works so well that after a satisfactory installation, breakdowns do not occur for months. However, when failures do happen, they are hard to diagnose and expensive to repair. This problem is countered by the widespread use of the plug-in assemblies that can be repaired by "factory-trained experts" at centralized repair centers.

The advent of the integrated circuit (IC) provided the reliability, simplicity, standardization, and low cost needed for universal acceptance of solid state as a discrete control methodology. Beginning in the early 1970s, "contact-closure" equivalents were assembled in standardized packages, soldered into printed circuit boards, and sold as "general-purpose" control elements, much as relays had been. The secret to industrial acceptance was the price. The cost of an integrated circuit logic system was very competitive with the increasing costs of relay systems. The new IC systems were even more compact and general purpose than the older, discrete transistor component systems. The icing on the cake was that, at mass-produced prices, on-site spare board supplies were cost-effective so that defective units could be discarded.

The integrated circuit technology did not stop with packaging single control functions. Increased density allowed an increasing number of functions to be captured in silicon. Today, entire control subsystems are packaged on single chips.

Comparison of Relay and Integrated Circuit Systems

Integrated circuit and relay control systems are supplemental in the spectrum of control applications. The proper selection of a control implementation must include consideration of the special characteristics of the problem to be solved, and the characteristic strengths and weaknesses of the potential solutions. The areas of concern in system selection include speed of operation; component life; operation energy requirements; component size; power handling capability; cost of manufacture, installation, and maintenance; supply voltages; noise immunity; temperature limits; and interconnection requirements. Each of these areas is examined below with respect to integrated circuit and relay systems.

Speed. This factor refers to the propagation time of the device. Relays require a time period on the order of milliseconds to close a set of contacts after power is applied to the relay coil. The time depends on the size of the relay. A nominal value for relay contact action is 25 milliseconds. A solid-state relay requires a nominal time period of 0.5 milliseconds for operation, while integrated circuit propagation times are in the nanosecond range.

Life. The life of the electromechanical relay is on the order of one million operations, due to contact and spring failure. The integrated circuit "switch" has a theoretically infinite life expectancy because of its nonmechanical operation mechanism.

Operation Energy. The energy necessary to operate a relay varies with the particular type of relay. Low-level switching relays consume on the order of 0.1 watt per device, whereas a midsize relay may require 25 watts. Integrated circuit switches use approximately 10 milliwatts per integrated circuit package for TTL circuits and approximately 10 microwatts for CMOS devices.

Size. Since the relay requires a coil with each group of contacts, it is limited to about 1 contact per 0.5 square inch of surface area. The integrated circuit, due to its lack of a coil, can support thousands of contact equivalents per square inch of surface area.

Power Handling. The contacts of a signal-level relay can handle tens of amperes, while integrated circuits are limited to milliamperes of load current. In addition, relays are capable of switching voltages of up to 600 volts, with the capability of handling higher voltages; the integrated circuit is generally limited to voltages under 25 volts.

Cost. Relay systems require labor-intensive assembly operations during production, while the integrated circuit counterpart is mass-produced by fully automated means costing tenths of a cent per unit.

Supply Voltage. The relay can operate from poorly regulated, electrically noisy power sources. Often the relay operates at the same voltage level as the load it controls. The integrated circuit requires a closely regulated voltage supply that is free from electrical noise.

Noise Immunity. Relay systems are usable near welding equipment, x-ray machines, and high-power switching devices, while integrated circuit controls require special shielding from both internal and external electrical noise sources.

Temperature. The relay is a physically rugged device. It can withstand wide variations in temperature as well as moderate physical abuse. The integrated circuit is more temperature-sensitive. It often fails at temperatures above 70 degrees Celsius and can be self-destructive at very low ambient temperatures, depending upon loading.

Interconnection. Although modern designs have made both relays and integrated circuits available in the same packages, the relay still requires more labor to assemble moderately complex control schemes due to its lower packing density.

Integrated Circuit Principles

The integrated circuit produces the same functions as a printed circuit board but is microminiaturized on a silicon die a few tenths of an inch square, similar to the one shown in Figure 3-2. This die, or "chip," has no serviceable parts and costs fractions of a cent per gate to manu-

FIGURE 3-2. Integrated circuit die

facture. Therefore, the details of its actual circuitry are of little importance to the control designer. Instead, the emphasis is shifted to the input, output, and processing characteristics of the device as a whole. However, there is no such thing as a "free lunch," and the microscopic chip still must interface to the real world of 16-gauge wire.

The first step in connecting the integrated circuit die to the environment is accomplished by metal "legs" called leads. The leads are spaced one-tenth of an inch from one another in two parallel rows by fastening the leads to a base material called a substrate. The integrated circuit die is bonded to the substrate and connected to the leads by microwelded, gold-alloy wires. The number of leads in a row and the spacing between the rows is determined by the complexity of the chip. A dual in-line package is shown in Figure 3-3.

Standardization of packaging has produced a cornucopia of benefits, such as

- Standardized sockets for easy insertion and replacement
- Specialized diagnostic tools fitted to standard lead spacing
- Lower equipment manufacturing costs due to automated assembly.

The price of integrated circuit miniaturization is felt in the flexibility of circuit functions and in the integrated circuit's low power-handling capabilities. The circuit functions of nonprogrammable integrated circuits are determined at the factory and are not alterable in the field, so that modifications to existing installations are labor-intensive.

The transistors used on the chip are not perfectly efficient devices; therefore, heat is generated when the circuit is in operation. The device must be capable of dissipating the heat at a rate that prevents the chip temperature from exceeding the safe operating level for the transistors it contains. The integrated circuit die is capable of

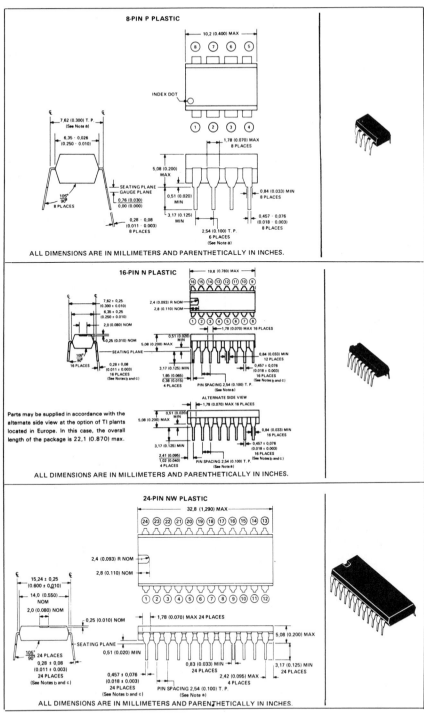

Courtesy Texas Instruments, Inc.

FIGURE 3-3. Dual in-line packaging of an integrated circuit chip

dissipating only a few watts per square inch of surface area. This limits not only the power-handling capability of each transistor, but also the number of transistors that can be integrated per chip.

Logic Families

The integrated circuit logic chip has allowed control circuitry to be treated as nearly ideal logic gates, so much so that some logic designers are trained principally in computer science and secondarily in electronics. This abstract treatment is possible only if the electrical input requirements, output drive capabilities, and processing characteristics of the integrated circuit are clearly defined. This clear definition would be a simple task if all digital integrated circuits were identical in basic nature. Not surprisingly, ICs are not alike in implementation, even though the packaging may be identical. The most significant difference is the type of semiconductor switch chosen for the building block of the integrated circuit. This choice affects all the areas below.

- Power consumption
- Speed of operation
- Power-supply voltages
- Size per gate
- Cost
- Input/output characteristics.

The ideal semiconductor switch has been pursued since before the introduction of the IC. The trade-offs occur between speed of operation, power consumption, and limits to complexity. Speed is often increased by operating the transistors in a nonsaturated mode; however, this increases the heat generated, which limits the number of devices per chip and increases the power-supply requirements. Many ICs use charge-coupled transistors to reduce power needs, but the charge-based nature of the gate slows down the switching speed. This continuing pursuit of the ideal device has produced many different semiconductor-switch technologies performing the same logic functions. Some of these types are shown in Table 3-1.

Each semiconductor switch technology has produced a family of integrated circuits that perform a variety of logic functions. These functions may be many individual gates packaged, without gate interconnection, in a single chip or a combination of gates that perform a complete function, such as a counter or adding circuit complete with display-driving circuitry. Naturally, the complexity of the chip and, therefore, its devices and area must increase as the

TABLE 3-1. Semiconductor switching families

SYMBOL	NAME	COMMENTS
TTL	Transistor-Transistor Logic	First widely used logic
STTL	Schottky-TTL	Higher speed TTL
LSTTL	Low Power STTL	Low power consumption STTL
ECL	Emitter Coupled Logic	High-speed nonsaturating transistors
PMOS	P-type Metallic Oxide Semiconductor	Dense, low power, oldest LSI
NMOS	N-type MOS	Faster than PMOS
CMOS	Complementary MOS	Most used MOS 3-18 volt supply
SOS	Silicon on Sapphire MOS	High-speed MOS

functional complexity increases. This device density factor has produced types within families that describe the scale of density of the chip. Such types include those listed in Table 3-2.

Logic Levels

When working with relay control systems, the condition of contacts is often checked by clamping one probe of a voltmeter to a common point and measuring voltage at the load side of the contacts. Based upon this fact, a voltage value can be assigned to the open and closed condition of a contact pair, and thereby to the previously defined logic ONE and logic ZERO values. The particular voltage levels vary with the implementation device selected, but once determined, they allow consistency in understanding and troubleshooting. The ONE and ZERO values for some common logic families are shown in Table 3-3.

TABLE 3-2. Scales of integrated circuit density

SSI	Small Scale Integration	<12 devices per chip
MSI	Medium Scale Integration	12–100 devices per chip
LSI	Large Scale Integration	100–1,000 devices per chip
VLSI	Very Large Scale Integration	1,000–600,000 devices per chip
ULSI	Ultra Large Scale Integration	>600,000 devices per chip
SLSI	Super Large Scale Integration	

TABLE 3-3. Logic input voltage levels for common logic families

FAMILY	LOGIC ZERO	UNDEFINED	LOGIC ONE	SUPPLY	SPEED
TTL	<0.8VDC	0.8V–2.0VDC	>2.0VDC	5.0VDC	5–50MHz
STTL	<0.8VDC	0.8V–2.0VDC	>2.0VDC	5.0VDC	30–120MHz
LSTTL	<0.8VDC	0.8V–2.0VDC	>2.0VDC	5.0VDC	5–50MHz
ECL	<−1.7VDC	−1.7V−.9VDC	>−.9VDC	−5.2VDC	>100MHz
EECL	<−0.6VDC	−0.6V–0VDC	>0VDC	−5.2VDC	>1.0GHz
PMOS	<1.0VDC	1.0V–3.2VDC	>3.2VDC	5.0VDC	<5.0MHz
NMOS	<0.6VDC	0.6V–2.2VDC	>2.2VDC	5.0VDC	<15.MHz
CMOS 5V	<1.5VDC	1.5V–3.5VDC	>3.5VDC	5.0VDC	<5MHz
CMOS 15V	<4.8VDC	4.8V–9.5VDC	>9.5VDC	15.0VDC	<5MHz

For nonprogrammable logic, the most popular families at the time of this writing are the Low Power Schottky Transistor-Transistor Logic (LSTTL) bipolar and the Complementary Metallic Oxide Semiconductor (CMOS) types.

3.2 Characteristics of CMOS and LSTTL

Since the workings of the integrated circuit are not accessible or repairable, the most important characteristics of the integrated circuit are those of the input circuit, the output circuit, and the power requirements. The characteristics of the CMOS and LSTTL families are presented in this section.

LSTTL Input Characteristics

The LSTTL family uses a surface-barrier diode between the collector and base of its switching transistors. The diode has a low forward-voltage drop of about 0.3 volt, which prevents the transistor from being driven into saturation. This allows faster switching speeds at about 20 percent of the power required for TTL. A typical gate circuit and its transfer characteristic is shown in Figure 3-4.

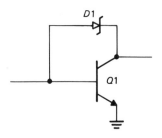

FIGURE 3-4. Schottky transistor configuration LSTTL transfer

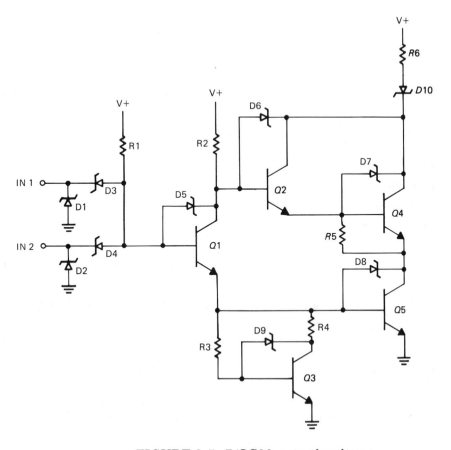

FIGURE 3-5. 74LS00 gate circuitry

A typical LSTTL gate package is illustrated in Figure 3-5, which contains four two-input NAND gates. The components of the LSTTL NAND circuit perform the following functions:

- *D1, D2* are biasing diodes that protect the input lines.
- *D3, D4* perform the NAND action.
- *Q1* is a phase splitter that provides complementary outputs.
- *Q3, Q5* is the logic ZERO output driver.
- *Q2, Q4* is the logic ONE output driver.

Not all the inputs of a gate package will be used, which leaves the problem of what to do with these uncommitted inputs. Any unconnected pin in a TTL family circuit will float at about 1.1 to 1.3 volts, which is neither a logic ONE nor a logic ZERO. This intermediate value is often interpreted by connected circuitry as a logic ONE—the

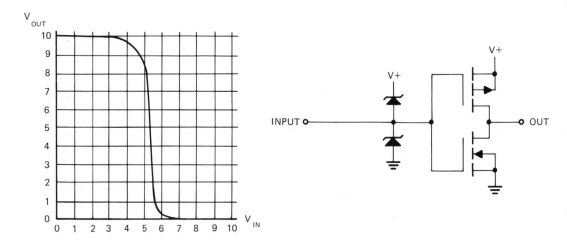

FIGURE 3-6. Input of CMOS logic gate and transfer characteristics

opposite outcome that is expected for unused relay logic contacts. In addition, the unconnected input is an antenna for stray signal pickup. Therefore, any unused input should be connected to the appropriate power supply line. In the LSTTL family, the connection to VCC should be through a 1 to 5K ohm resistor to protect the input diodes from excessive current due to power transients.

The integrated circuit has limited load-handling capabilities that must be considered when connecting an integrated circuit to an external circuit. The output driving capability of a logic gate is measured and specified in units of the number of input loads it can drive without overloading the circuit. The LSTTL input circuit constitutes one LSTTL load.

CMOS Input Characteristics

The CMOS family protects its delicate gate circuits by a combination of resistors and diodes (both junction and zener). A typical circuit is shown in Figure 3-6.

A typical CMOS gate package is illustrated in Figure 3-7. It contains four two-input NAND gates just as in the LSTTL circuit. The components of the CMOS NAND circuit perform the following functions:

- $Q1$, $Q2$ act as parallel switches that conduct when the inputs are at a logic ZERO.

- $Q3$, $Q4$ act as series switches that conduct when the inputs are at a logic ONE.

- *D1, D2, D3, D4* are input protection diodes that limit the input voltage swing to *VCC* and *GND*.

As in the LSTTL family, any uncommitted input must be terminated even when an entire gate is unused. This action not only prevents noise pickup, but also prevents inadvertent linear operation of the CMOS gate (a condition that drives up power consumption). The input circuit constitutes one CMOS load, which is used to measure the output driving capability of a CMOS gate.

LSTTL Output Characteristics

The output of an LSTTL circuit is in three forms. The first is the totem-pole output, which is the most common. The second is the open-

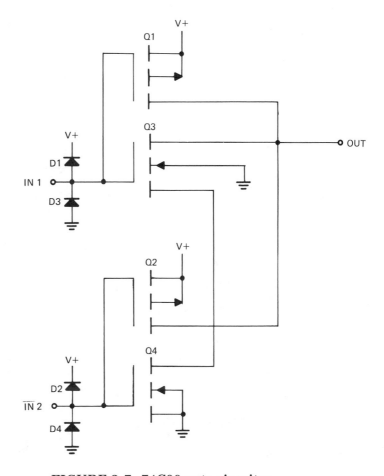

FIGURE 3-7. 74C00 gate circuitry

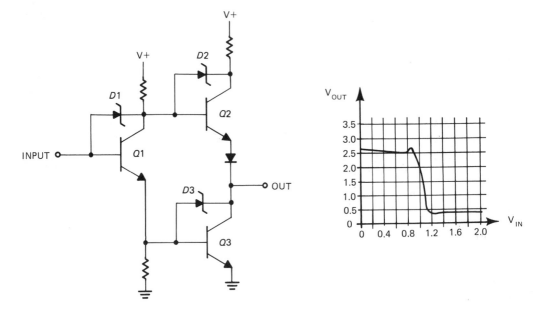

FIGURE 3-8. LSTTL output characteristics

collector output, which is most often used for interfacing with non-TTL system components. The third is the three-state output, which is used to connect to bus-based devices. The output drive capability of a device is rated in the number of similar input types it can drive. This ability is called *fan-out*.

The totem-pole output is named for its stack of output transistors that allow both supply and ground to be switched to the output connection. This connection also produces a shock to the system power-supply lines during the switching transition, since both transistors are briefly ON. This transient can cause other gates connected to the circuit to change state. The characteristic is shown in Figure 3-8. Typically, an LSTTL can drive ten inputs.

The open collector output circuit is shown in Figure 3-9. This circuit is used in output interfaces that include display drivers, logic family interfacing, and relay amplifiers. Although similar to the totem-pole circuit, it is different in that it produces a logic ZERO output only.

The three-state output circuit is shown in Figure 3-10. This circuit operates by allowing both output drivers to be turned OFF at the same time. This state is called *HI-Z* and allows multiple gates to be connected to the same circuit line. This is best used in bus-based designs such as are encountered in microprocessor applications.

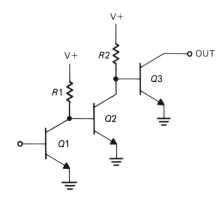

FIGURE 3-9. Open collector TTL circuit

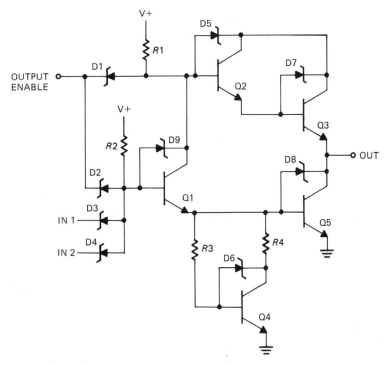

FIGURE 3-10. Three-state LSTTL output circuitry

3.3 Digital Control Analysis

The purpose of this section is to briefly review the general principles of digital logic, Boolean algebra, and integrated circuit technology. The material presented here is the framework on which rests the understanding of discrete control. These basics are applicable to microprocessor-based systems and yet are so universal that they are also applicable to switches and light bulbs.

Digital Block Diagrams

The advent of the integrated circuit shifted the way in which control systems are viewed. In relay systems, the sensing switches, control relays and, to a large extent, output contactors, all operate at the same voltages and power levels. For instance, a relay control circuit may often use line voltages for both the sensing switches and control relays. The control relay may also directly provide the contacts for the output solenoids or fractional horsepower motors.

In contrast to relay voltage levels, the integrated circuit operates at low dc voltage levels (e.g., 5 V) both for input and output, and consumes relatively small amounts of power. The die within the IC can rarely dissipate more than one-half of a watt per chip, including the control-logic power requirements. Therefore the IC itself cannot directly drive even small actuators, such as solenoids or small contactors. Methods to interface integrated circuit technology to the industrial world are required before this technology can bear fruit.

The shift to compact, prepackaged, low-power control logic caused the control system to be most often described as a system containing three subsystems. These divisions are viewed as:

- A high-voltage (e.g., 24 V dc, 120 V ac), low-power input subsystem
- A modular low-power, low-voltage logic subsystem
- A high-voltage, high-power output subsystem.

This view is shown in Figure 3-11, with the interface areas defined. Such a system representation is called a digital block diagram. The block diagram allows a complex system to be described on appropriate levels of understanding for purposes of design, maintenance, modification, or training.

FIGURE 3-11. General control system block diagram

A block diagram breaks a system down into blocks by functional areas. Each of these areas in turn can be further diagrammed until the actual circuit details are presented. Information flow is indicated in these diagrams by arrows showing the direction of the exchange. These areas most often represent actual wires or buses in the circuit, and they remain constant from diagram to diagram. This constancy allows a troubleshooter to determine the most likely defective block by its input/output signals, and then proceed to the detail diagram of the suspect block.

In this block diagram, the ICs containing the control logic are represented by the center block. This block operates at low power and low voltage levels. The input block represents the sensing switches operating at a higher voltage, but still at low power. Finally, the output block represents the high-power, high-voltage actuators that translate control decisions into action. The general flow of information in block diagrams is from left to right, as in Figure 3-11, or from top to bottom.

Logic Circuit Analysis

IC logic circuit action is analyzed by the same methods as a relay system. The analysis can proceed on an operation basis, a time-sequence basis, or on all-possible combinations of input/output conditions. In each method, the examination starts with the state of all gates known and the conditions labeled in terms of ON and OFF. Then signals are applied and each successive gate output is determined and labeled with the appropriate ON or OFF.

An example of an operation sequence analysis is the examination of a relay START-STOP station shown in Figure 3-12.

The operation sequence of the START-STOP station is based upon the following steps:

1. Determine the condition of the circuit at some starting point in time.

2. Execute the most likely set of operations in the time sequence required.

3. Execute the next most likely set of operations.

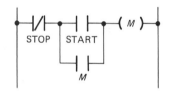

FIGURE 3-12. Relay START-STOP station for sequence analysis

For the START-STOP station, this sequence is as follows:

Normal operations

1. The motor is off; no input is applied.
2. The motor is started via the START switch.
3. The motor is stopped via the STOP switch.

Other operation conditions

1. The motor is restarted via the START switch.
2. The motor is stopped via the OVERLOAD switch.

or

1. The STOP switch is simultaneously depressed with the START switch.

The time-sequence method of analysis is most often used for machine tools or numeric control equipment diagnosis. An example of this method is illustrated by a coffee vending machine analysis. The block diagram of this machine appears in Figure 3-13. The steps in this form of analysis consist of the following:

1. Determine the at-rest condition (no money inserted, no selection in progress).
2. Determine the starting event (inserting the proper coins and initiating a selection).
3. Follow the interactions of the system without prejudgment (releasing the cup, brewing coffee, filling the cup, etc.).
4. After completing a normal sequence, introduce new or unexpected conditions and determine the effects on the cycle.

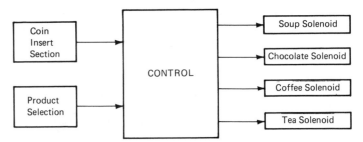

FIGURE 3-13. Coffee vending machine block diagram

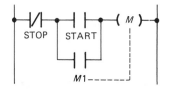

FIGURE 3-14. Relay START-STOP station for state analysis

An example of the all-possible-inputs/outputs method once again uses the relay START-STOP station shown in Figure 3-14. The steps in this method consist of the following:

1. Open all links that connect outputs to inputs (output M line in the START-STOP example) or consider the feedback lines as separate inputs.

2. Determine all possible input combinations and the resulting outputs as shown in Figure 3-15 for the START-STOP station.

3. Examine the outputs generated for each possible combination.

The pattern of inputs in Figure 3-15 is the same for all devices that have three inputs. By knowing what outputs to expect for the sequence of inputs, automated test equipment that generates this pattern of inputs can test any three-input device. The outputs generated by each type of three-input device will be unique to the device just as a signature is unique to each person. For this reason, testing by this all-possible-inputs method is called *signature analysis*.

START	STOP	$M1$	M
OFF	OFF	OFF	OFF
OFF	OFF	ON	OFF
OFF	ON	OFF	OFF
OFF	ON	ON	ON
ON	OFF	OFF	OFF
ON	OFF	ON	OFF
ON	ON	OFF	ON
ON	ON	ON	ON

FIGURE 3-15. All possible input combinations for relay START-STOP station

The all-possible-inputs/outputs method is the most complete of the methods described. It does not cover the transient conditions that occur as the inputs change, but it does describe all the possible static combinations of inputs. Each of these possible combinations is called a *state*. The table in the above example is called a *state table*. The information contained in a state table can also be represented by a special diagram called a *state diagram*. The state diagram usually does not contain all possible states, but the states which are left out are those that make no difference in the outputs of the machine under investigation. Such a diagram for the START-STOP station is illustrated in Figure 3-16. The arrows that connect the bubbles are the paths by which the machine can undergo a change of state.

Nearly all modern discrete control design is based on analysis of a control problem, resulting in an algorithmic solution. An algorithmic solution is based upon a finite number of steps. The result of these steps is the transformation of the condition of a machine from some initial state to some final state by definable intermediate states. This analysis methodology is called algorithmic finite state machine analysis and is particularly useful for microcomputer-based control solutions.

Binary Symbols

The relay ladder representation does not present the relationship of the output of a logic function with respect to the many combinations of possible input conditions. To accomplish this representation, a method must be developed to represent the input conditions of a logic circuit and the output the circuit develops. In relay logic, these inputs and outputs are the CLOSED and OPEN conditions of relay contacts. Conventionally, the numeral ONE is the symbol used to represent the CLOSED condition and the numeral ZERO is used for the OPEN

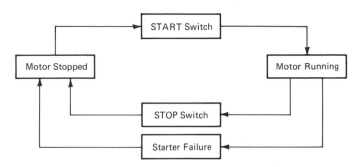

FIGURE 3-16. State diagram for a START-STOP station

condition. In a like manner, an energized coil is designated ONE, while a de-energized coil is designated ZERO. In integrated circuit systems, the designation is not so clear-cut. In some logic families, negative voltages may be considered logic ONE, resulting in confusion about the assignment of ONE and ZERO to voltage measurements of HIGH and LOW. To avoid this confusion, only the terms ONE and ZERO will be used here. They are defined as follows.

$$\text{TTL ONE} = \text{voltage} > 2.5V \qquad \text{5V CMOS ONE} = \text{voltage} > 3.5$$
$$\text{TTL ZERO} = \text{voltage} < 0.8V \qquad \text{5V CMOS ZERO} = \text{voltage} < 1.5$$

3.4 Number Systems

In relays and switches, it is seldom necessary to examine the simultaneous condition of many contacts at one time. The complexity and control capability provided by integrated circuits has produced the need for a status display method that can represent many contact states of ON and OFF simultaneously, and in a concise format. Three special numbering systems provide this capability: binary, octal, and hexadecimal. Each system is based on the radix indicated by its name. The binary system is based on the radix 2, the octal is based on the radix 8, and the hexadecimal is based on the radix 16. To illustrate these systems, consider the situation below.

Eight contacts are in the following conditions:

Contact:	1	2	3	4	5	6	7	8
Condition:	ON	OFF	ON	ON	ON	OFF	ON	OFF

Assigning ON = 1 and OFF = 0, the contact conditions look like this:

$$1 \quad 0 \quad 1 \quad 1 \quad 1 \quad 0 \quad 1 \quad 0$$

To convert this pattern of switch conditions to a binary number, powers of 2 are assigned to each of the number positions. Two to the zero power (2^0) is assigned to the rightmost position, 2^1 to the second to the right position, and so on, ending on the left with 2^7 for an 8-bit word. Evaluating this pattern of 1s and 0s as binary digits allows a compact representation of the state of the contact closures. This number can be manipulated mathematically and can be converted to other representations. For example, the decimal equivalent of this binary number is

$$1 \cdot 2^7 + 0 \cdot 2^6 + 1 \cdot 2^5 + 1 \cdot 2^4 + 1 \cdot 2^3 + 0 \cdot 2^2 + 1 \cdot 2^1 + 0 \cdot 2^1 =$$
$$128 + \quad 0 + \quad 32 + \quad 16 + \quad 8 + \quad 0 + \quad 2 + \quad 0 = 186$$

TABLE 3-4. Octal numbering system

BINARY	OCTAL	DECIMAL
0 0 0	0	0
0 0 1	1	1
0 1 0	2	2
0 1 1	3	3
1 0 0	4	4
1 0 1	5	5
1 1 0	6	6
1 1 1	7	7
1 0 0 0	10	8

This binary representation, though graphic, is difficult to manipulate and remember. By organizing the binary digits (called bits) into groups of three, starting from the right, the number appears in this easier format:

10   111   010

Three bits are capable of representing the decimal numbers in Table 3-4.

A system that uses only the symbols 0 through 7 is called an octal system and is based on powers of eight. The 10 111 010 pattern is now equal to 272 in octal, where the rightmost digit represents $2*(8^0)$ and the leftmost $2*(8^2)$. The convenience of the octal system is that the eight basic patterns for conversion to and from binary are easy to remember, and yet the octal number is also easy to manipulate. This form of representation is popular in the minicomputer world and is also used extensively in programmable controllers.

The hexadecimal system satisfies the need for a more compact form of representation. This need is prompted by the larger number of "contact" closures found in semiconductor systems. By grouping the binary notation into fours, the following arrangement results:

1011   1010

Bits, grouped in sets of four, allow the numbers to be represented as shown in Table 3-5.

The letters *A* through *F* are used to represent the numerals 10 through 15, since no single symbol exists for these numbers in decimal notation. This system is not as easy to translate as octal, but is handy in representing large combinations of contacts, or machine states, and is very popular in the microprocessor environment. The representation is based on radix 16, with the rightmost hexadecimal digit representing sixteen possible combinations of the four low-order

TABLE 3-5. Hexadecimal numbering system

BINARY	HEX	DECIMAL
0 0 0 0	0	0
0 0 0 1	1	1
0 0 1 0	2	2
0 0 1 1	3	3
0 1 0 0	4	4
0 1 0 1	5	5
0 1 1 0	6	6
0 1 1 1	7	7
1 0 0 0	8	8
1 0 0 1	9	9
1 0 1 0	A	10
1 0 1 1	B	11
1 1 0 0	C	12
1 1 0 1	D	13
1 1 1 0	E	14
1 1 1 1	F	15
1 0 0 0 0	10	16

bits, while the leftmost hexadecimal digit represents the four high-order bits of the binary status word. By this convention, the contacts in the pattern 1011 1010 can also be represented by the hexadecimal number *BA*, where *B* represents $11*(16^1)$ and *A* represents $10*(16^0)$.

A special code is used for the convenience of translation from binary to decimal. This code, called binary-coded decimal, uses four binary bits to represent the decimal numbers 0 through 9, as shown in Table 3-5. The letter codes used in the hexadecimal system are not used. This system permits four electrical lines to represent ten decimal values, and is used in programmable controllers and instrumentation systems.

Boolean Algebra

The use of mathematical symbols for logic conditions implies that a branch of that science could be specifically applied to switching logic. Such a tool could reduce complex control schemes to a minimum number of coils or contacts and perhaps allow substitutions of available NO (normally-open) or NC (normally-closed) contacts for needed unavailable ones. As expected, such a branch does exist and is called Boolean algebra.

The basic operators AND, OR, and NOT are represented in Boolean algebra as follows:

FUNCTION	SYMBOL	EXAMPLE
AND	$\bullet$	$D = A \bullet B \bullet C$
OR	$+$	$D = A + B + C$
NOT	———	$B = \overline{A}$

Operations that are permitted in Boolean statements are summarized as follows:

Commutative laws: $A + B = B + A \qquad A \bullet B = B \bullet A$

Associative laws: $A + (B + C) = (A + B) + C$

$\qquad\qquad\qquad A \bullet (B \bullet C) = (A \bullet B) \bullet C$

Distributive law: $A \bullet (B + C) = A \bullet B + A \bullet C$

Using these operations and symbols, the following identities are derived:

$$\overline{\overline{A}} = D = A$$

$$\overline{A \bullet B} = D = \overline{A} + \overline{B}$$

$$\overline{A} \bullet \overline{B} = D = \overline{A + B}$$

The DeMorgan's Transforms are used to convert logic circuits that need both AND and OR gates to circuits that may require only NAND or NOR gates.

3.5 Basic Logic

The power of switch/relay logic lies in its simplicity. The majority of discrete control functions are accomplished with little more than combinations of parallel and series switch/relay contacts. Based on this fact, symbols have been created to represent the parallel and series contact connections without specifically showing switch/relay implementation. The power of such a symbol set lies in the ability to represent complex systems in a way that concisely shows the functional intent of the circuit. The three basic logic functions are AND for series connected elements, OR for parallel elements, and NOT for inverting elements.

AND Logic Function Definition

The series contacts shown in Figure 3-17 must all be closed for the coil to be energized. This can be expressed in other words as

"If A AND B are made then coil Y will energize."

Therefore, the series connection of contacts is called an AND logic function and is given the symbol in Figure 3-18.

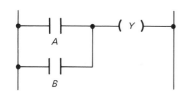

FIGURE 3-17. AND logic function relay implementation

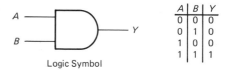

Logic Symbol

Truth Table

FIGURE 3-18. AND logic function symbol and truth table

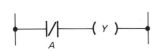

FIGURE 3-19. OR logic function relay implementation

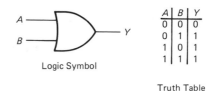

Logic Symbol

Truth Table

FIGURE 3-20. OR logic function symbol and truth table

FIGURE 3-21. NOT logic function relay implementation

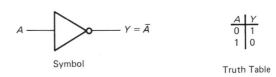

Symbol

Truth Table

FIGURE 3-22. NOT logic function symbol and truth table

OR Logic Function Definition

An example of the parallel connection of contacts is shown in Figure 3-19. If either A OR B is closed, then Y will be energized. This logic function is called OR, and is represented in Figure 3-20.

NOT Logic Function Definition

In Figure 3-21, the contacts mechanically connected to the coil of Y are made when the coil mechanically connected to contact A is NOT energized. The gate symbol for this function is shown in Figure 3-22.

The NOT function is often represented by just the "bubble," which is shown at the output of the inverting amplifier illustrated in Figure 3-22. When encountered in logic diagram analysis any bubble—whether on the output or input of a gate—can be treated as an invertor (i.e., NOT gate) that happens to be drawn very close to its associated gate, as in Figure 3-23.

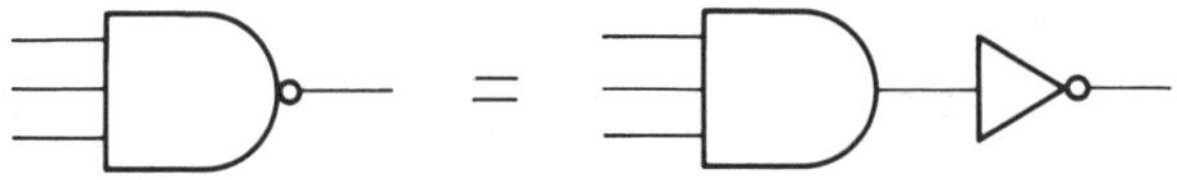

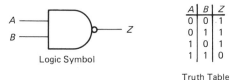

FIGURE 3-23. Functionally equivalent NOT representations

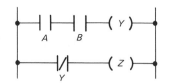

FIGURE 3-24. NAND logic function relay implementation

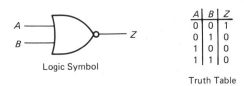

A	B	Z
0	0	1
0	1	1
1	0	1
1	1	0

Truth Table

FIGURE 3-25. NAND logic function symbol and truth table

A	B	Z
0	0	1
0	1	0
1	0	0
1	1	0

Truth Table

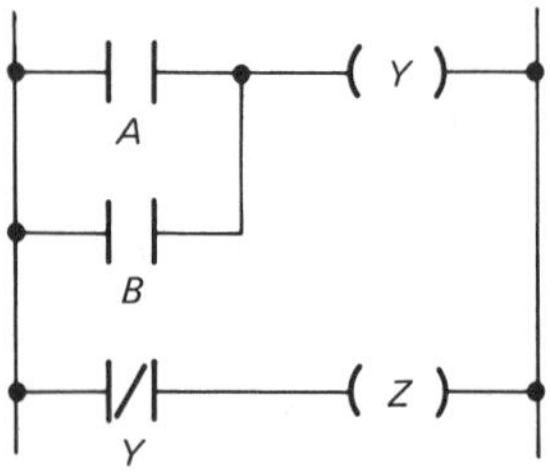

FIGURE 3-26. NOR logic function relay implementation

FIGURE 3-27. NOR logic function symbol and truth table

Gate Combinations

Even though the minimum necessary gates are defined above, some combinations of these elemental logic functions are so widely used that special symbols and definitions have been devised for them. These functions include NAND, NOR, and the Exclusive OR gate.

The NOT and AND functions are combined to produce the NAND logic function. The relay equivalent is shown in Figure 3-24 and the symbol in Figure 3-25. The NOT and OR functions are combined to produce the NOR logic function. The relay equivalent is shown in Figure 3-26 and the symbol in Figure 3-27.

A commonly used combination function is the exclusive OR. The verbal logic of the exclusive OR is

"If either input contact (but not both) is closed, then close an output contact."

The relay implementation of the exclusive OR is shown in Figure 3-28 and the symbol in Figure 3-29.

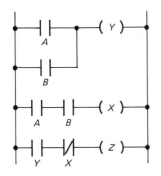

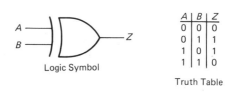

Logic Symbol

Truth Table

FIGURE 3-28. Exclusive OR logic function relay implementation

FIGURE 3-29. XOR logic function symbol and truth table

As an example of the DeMorgan's Transform introduced above, consider the circuit in Figure 3-30. This circuit requires a NOT gate, an OR gate, and an AND gate to accomplish its function. However, the standard packaging of integrated circuit gates does not provide many ICs that contain different logic functions on a single chip. This is where the DeMorgan's transform comes to the rescue. The transform works only on NAND and NOR gates; therefore, one of the gates in Figure 3-30 must be converted to a NAND or NOR while maintaining the overall logic equivalency. The resultant gate is similar to the NOT and AND gate configuration in Figure 3-30. By adding another pair of NOT gates, per the double inversion identity, the circuit becomes that shown in Figure 3-31.

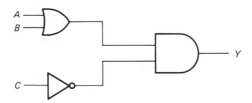

FIGURE 3-30. DeMorgan's reduction example initial circuit

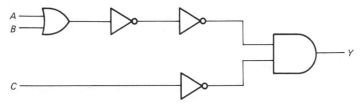

FIGURE 3-31. Gate consolidation by DeMorgan's transform—first step

FIGURE 3-32. Gate consolidation by DeMorgan's transform—final circuit

By using the DeMorgan's transform in Figure 3-31, the circuit becomes that shown in Figure 3-32. This circuit uses only two NOR gates in place of three different gate types and can be implemented in a TTL 7402 or a CMOS 4001B quad two-input NOR gate package.

Example of Gate-Based Logic

As an illustration of basic logic functions in a controls application, consider the following example.

At the end of two production lines a total must be kept of the cartons that enter the shipping dock. Individual sensors are placed at the end of each line to count the cartons as they enter the dock. If the sensors are wired as an OR input to a counter, then the simultaneous entry of two boxes will be counted as a single box. Instead, a circuit must be devised to sum the entry of boxes into the dock and send this sum to the counter.

A discrete control system reaches a higher level of applicability when it attains the power for basic arithmetic operations. But how does a controller execute $1 + 1 = 10$? The truth table for such a circuit is illustrated in Figure 3-33. The inputs are labeled A and B, the output appears as X, and the carry bit as Y. The letters A' through D' are state labels for each of the possible combinations of input conditions.

As shown in Figure 3-33, the composite truth table is broken down into two smaller tables, one for each of the outputs. When compared to the basic functions previously defined, the truth table describing the X output is the table for the Exclusive OR function, while the truth table describing the Y output is the table for the AND function. A logic circuit based on this information is shown in Figure 3-34.

IN		OUT				SUM				CARRY		
A	B	X	Y	State		A	B	X		A	B	Y
0	0	0	0	A'		0	0	0		0	0	0
0	1	1	0	B'		0	1	1		0	1	0
1	0	1	0	C'		1	0	1		1	0	0
1	1	0	1	D'		1	1	0		1	1	1

FIGURE 3-33. Truth table for two-input binary addition

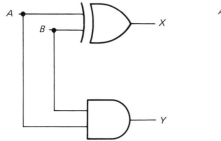 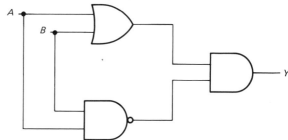

FIGURE 3-34. Implementation of a two-input addition circuit

FIGURE 3-35. Exclusive OR (XOR) equivalent circuit

In the ideal world, the solution of Figure 3-34 is sufficient. In the real world, this circuit is just the beginning. As shown, the adder requires two different types of gates: one AND and one XOR. How can this circuit be implemented in a single basic logic type?

By examining the truth table for the XOR gate, the equivalent logic circuit of Figure 3-35 is created. By DeMorgan's transformation, Figure 3-35 becomes the circuit in Figure 3-36, which uses only NOR gates.

By re-examination of the requirements for the adder circuit in Figure 3-34, the circuit in Figure 3-36 will produce the X output at the output labeled V and will produce the carry output Y at the point marked W in Figure 3-36. The TTL gate package capable of this function is the 74LS02 quad two-input NOR gate or the equivalent CMOSIC, the 4001B. An actual pin selection for such a circuit is shown in Figure 3-37. The boxed I and O symbols used in the figure represent the circuitry necessary to interface the TTL electronics to the industrial environment.

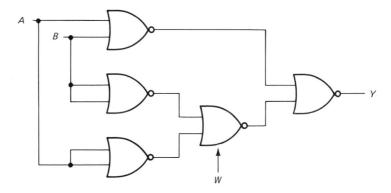

FIGURE 3-36. Exclusive OR (XOR) equivalent circuit using NOR gates

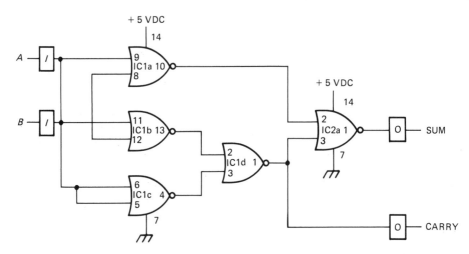

FIGURE 3-37. Adder IC implementation using TTL gates

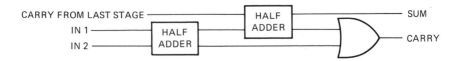

FIGURE 3-38. Full adder from half adders

In this example no provision is made for an incoming carry; for this reason, this circuit is called a *half-adder*. By adding the carry circuitry, the half-adder becomes a full-adder circuit, as shown in Figure 3-38.

3.6 Latching

Latching and holding are two methods commonly used in industrial controls to "remember" a momentary past event. The difference between these two methods is in the means by which the memory of the momentary event is maintained. "Latching" is accomplished by internal means, while "holding" is accomplished by external means. For example, the latching relay electromechanically maintains the memory of the event, while the motor starter remembers its start command through holding contacts external to the control cabinet. It is latching that is most often packaged in integrated circuit form and is the focus of this discussion. A common control problem using the latching function is the motor control START-STOP station. This function requires the "remembering" of a momentary start command, often a pushbutton, to turn on and maintain a motor contactor until a

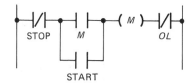

FIGURE 3-39. Relay START-STOP station

momentary STOP command is initiated. This function is illustrated in relay form in Figure 3-39. Using the conversion techniques outlined above, the relay form is transformed into the logic diagram shown in Figure 3-40.

The Boolean equation of this function is

$$M = (START + M) \cdot \overline{STOP} \cdot \overline{OL}$$

An important feature of this logic circuit is the line that connects the output M of the circuit to the input OR gate. This line feeds back the output condition to the input, thus allowing the output to "latch" the START command as a ONE condition at the M output. This latching ability is performed by ICs, magnetic bias cores, and electromechanical latching relays. Regardless of the form of the implementation, the latch exhibits the following capabilities:

- A latching input
- A releasing input
- A noninverted latched output
- An inverted latched output.

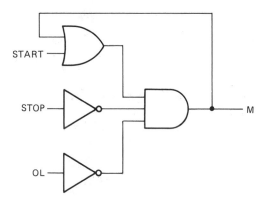

FIGURE 3-40. START-STOP station gate implementation

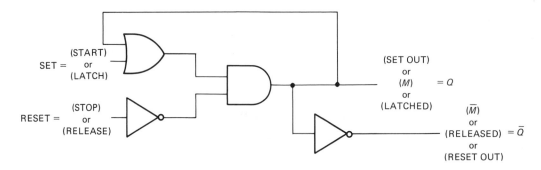

FIGURE 3-41. RS flip-flop as a START-STOP station

One way of describing latching action is to say that the device "flips" to the latched or SET condition, and "flops" to the released or RESET condition. The device that provides this latching function in the IC world is called the *flip-flop*.

Reset and Set Flip-Flop
Logic Function Definition

The flip-flop logic combination element, more than any other, has enabled the production of sophisticated control, including the microprocessor that produced the calculator, the computer, and the programmable controller.

The RESET/SET (RS) flip-flop functions can be developed from the familiar START-STOP station. For simplicity, the overload contacts are removed from the START-STOP station circuitry. The resulting gate circuit appears in Figure 3-41.

The latching input is labeled SET and the releasing input is labeled RESET. The NO output function is provided by the Q output and the NC output function is provided by the Q *NOT* output.

This form of the latch function, although fulfilling the latch requirements, has some drawbacks. The most significant of these is the need for three types of gate devices: AND, OR, and NOT. By Boolean transformation, equivalent NOR and NAND circuits for the latch in Figure 3-41 appear in Figures 3-42 and 3-43.

Although the RS flip-flop can be implemented as combinations of individual gates, it is most often used without regard to its internal elements. Therefore, the symbol and truth tables illustrated in Figure 3-44 are used to represent it. Note that in this truth table the input condition of R = ONE, S = ONE is marked X for undefined. This state is illegal and causes the outputs to go to a condition which depends upon the implementation of the flip-flop.

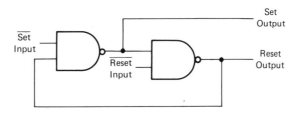

FIGURE 3-42. Latch circuit using NAND gates

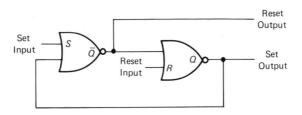

FIGURE 3-43. Latch circuit using NOR gates

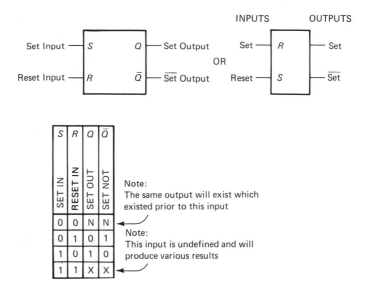

S	R	Q	$\bar{Q}$	
SET IN	RESET IN	SET OUT	SET NOT	Note: The same output will exist which existed prior to this input
0	0	N	N	←
0	1	0	1	Note: This input is undefined and will produce various results
1	0	1	0	
1	1	X	X	←

FIGURE 3-44. RS flip-flop logic symbol and truth table

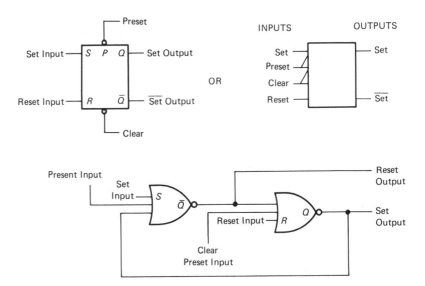

FIGURE 3-45. RS flip-flop with preset and clear logic and symbol

The initial output of this logic symbol representation can only be determined if some history is assumed. It is not always possible to determine the initial output, even when the specific implementation details are known. This fact often leads to problems in system design and start-up. One solution to the start-up problem is to provide a separate set of inputs, called PRESET and CLEAR, to force the flip-flop to a known condition. Often, these PRESET and CLEAR inputs are inverted by the flip-flop for ease in power-up circuit design. The symbol for a flip-flop with PRESET and CLEAR is shown in Figure 3-45.

In many applications of the RS flip-flop, the latching of an input is only wanted when certain other conditions are met. Two AND gates are added to the RS circuitry to enable the flip-flop to allow input under controlled conditions, as shown in Figure 3-46. This enabling input is most often used to allow input only at specific times. Therefore, this input enable is designated the *clock input*. The clock input exists in two forms: the first is the level-sensitive clock and the second is the edge-triggered clock. The level-sensitive clock allows input to the RS flip-flop only when the clock line is at a steady ONE (or a steady ZERO), while the edge-triggered clock allows input only when a transition occurs from ZERO to ONE (or ONE to ZERO). The symbol for such a device is shown in Figure 3-47.

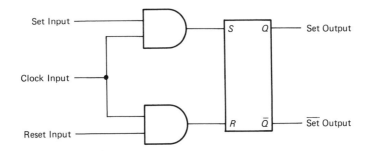

FIGURE 3-46. Clock input circuitry

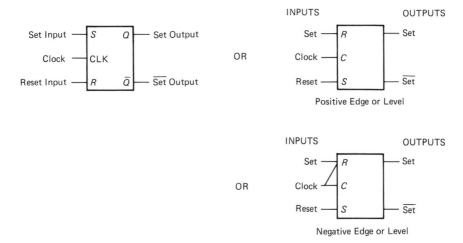

FIGURE 3-47. Clocked RS flip-flop logic and symbol

The D Flip-Flop

The flip-flop is often used for storing a condition of ONE or ZERO received from a single source. This application necessitates the D flip-flop. The D flip-flop is created from the RS in the following manner. An invertor (NOT function) is connected from the R input line of the RS flip-flop, to the S line. Thus any ONE input to the SET input is interpreted as a ZERO at the RESET input, and vice versa. The input line to this combination is labeled D (for DATA). The output of this flip-flop changes to match the input only when the clock input is triggered. The symbol for this device appears in Figure 3-48.

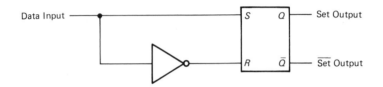

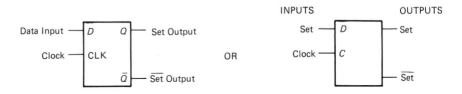

FIGURE 3-48. D-type flip-flop logic and symbol

The T Flip-Flop

One of the most common applications for clocked RS flip-flops changes the flip-flop outputs on each clock input. This application allows cascaded flip-flops to be used as a binary counter. This is accomplished by coupling the output of one flip-flop to the next flip-flop input. For industrial applications, a single input line is preferred so that a single output sensor can be used as a counting input. The T flip-flop is the variation of the RS flip-flop which is designed for this type of application. This type of flip-flop is pictured in Figure 3-49. The SET and NOT SET outputs of the T-type flip-flop alternate ONE and ZERO with each input pulse to the toggle input.

The J-K Flip-Flop

The J-K flip-flop combines the features of the flip-flops listed above and adds special features of its own. It can accept SET and RESET inputs, as does the RS type. It has a synchronizing clock input and it can toggle, as does the T type. (The toggle mode is initiated by setting both the SET and RESET inputs to ONE, simultaneously.) In addition, the J-K flip-flop is designed to be cascaded into counters and sequencers by delaying its output until the trailing edge of the clocking signal. This feature prevents a "race" condition when flip-flops are connected together. The race prevention is accomplished by a technique called *master-slave* which uses two flip-flops: one set for input latching and one for output latching. The logic diagram and symbol for this device is pictured in Figure 3-50.

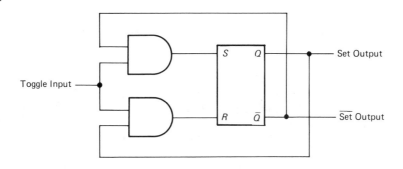

FIGURE 3-49. T-type flip-flop logic and symbol

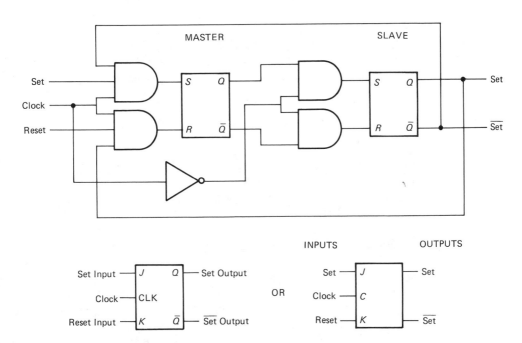

FIGURE 3-50. J-K flip-flop logic and symbol

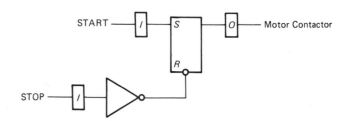

FIGURE 3-51. Flip-flop START-STOP station without shutdowns

Example of the Flip-Flop as a Control Device

As an illustration of the latching function implemented in flip-flops, consider the following example.

An automatic sump pump operates unattended. When a malfunction within the motor occurs, an indicator is illuminated on a panel board to signal the fault. The pump is automatically shut down, which may cause other indicators to illuminate, confusing the repair person as to which event caused the shutdown. All of the indications must latch to maintain the indication of problem even after the machine is shut down but, in addition, the first detected fault should indicate its special status as the first fault detected.

For the sake of simplicity, only the following three shutdown conditions are detectable:

1. Motor winding over-temperature
2. Motor bearing over-temperature
3. Motor overload.

Only the motor circuit is considered in this example, and the now-familiar START-STOP station is the first consideration. This circuit is shown, without the shutdown elements, in Figure 3-51.

The RS flip-flop START-STOP station uses the SET input for starting purposes, while the overriding CLEAR input is used for the STOP input. This design provides for stopping the motor if both START and STOP push buttons are depressed. The interfaces are represented by the *I* and *O* symbols.

The shutdown features are added to the STOP input signal in Figure 3-52. If any of the indicated conditions are present, then the motor will turn off.

Turning to the problem of annunciation, Figure 3-53 describes the basic latching annunciator circuit. This circuit illuminates a lamp for each failure-type detection, with provisions for a lamp reset that extinguishes the fault indications. In the circuit in Figure 3-54, the

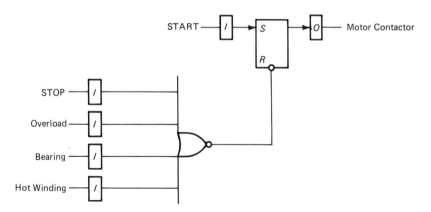

FIGURE 3-52. Flip-flop START-STOP station with shutdowns

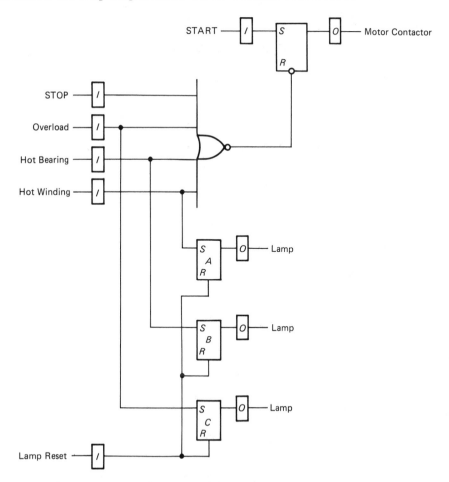

FIGURE 3-53. Motor control with basic fault annunciation

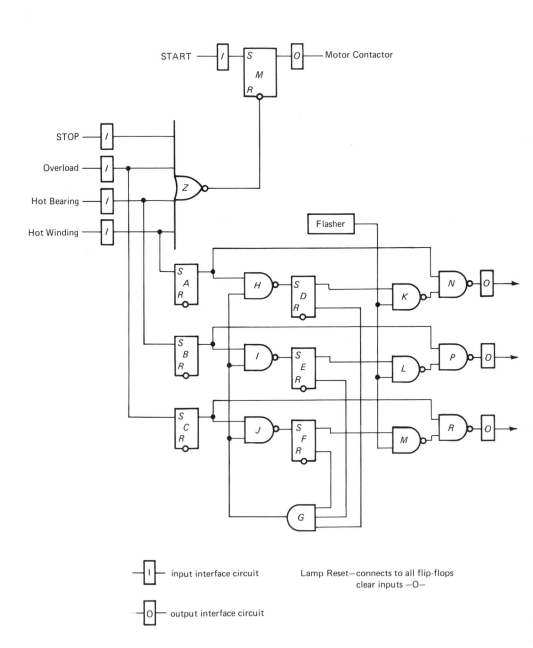

**FIGURE 3-54. Motor control with basic fault annuncia-
tion and first fail detection**

flip-flops (*A*, *B*, *C*), which latched the indication lamps in Figure 3-52, provide inputs to a second set of flip-flops (*D*, *E*, *F*), as shown in Figure 3-53.

The flip-flops *D*, *E*, *F* are the first-fail detection circuits. The *Q* NOT outputs of these flip-flops are ANDed together (gate *G*) to form an enable signal for the input AND gates (*H*, *I*, *J*). The output of the input latches (*A*, *B*, *C*), the flasher module, and the first-fail latches (*D*, *E*, *F*) are combined to produce the lamp-driver output to the output interfaces.

As an example of a shutdown sequence, assume that the motor overtemperature sensor has tripped.

1. NOR gate *Z* resets the motor control flip-flop *M*, which shuts off the motor.

2. The failure signal sets flip-flop *A*, which passes its output through AND gate *H* and sets the *D* flip-flop.

3. The NOT output of the *D* flip-flop forces the *G* AND gate output to ZERO, which disables flip-flops *E* and *F* from ever being set, leaving only the *D* flip-flop set.

4. The set output of the *D* flip-flop allows the ONEs and ZEROs of the flasher to pass through the *K* NAND gate to the *N* output AND gate.

5. The *N* output AND gate ANDs the flasher with the set output of the *A* flip-flop and flashes the lamp connected to the output interface module.

If a motor bearing overtemperature also occurs shortly after the motor winding over-temperature shutdown, the following will occur:

6. The input flip-flop *B* will set and its set output will be applied to the *P* output AND gate.

7. However, the *E* flip-flop will not set, since it is disabled by the *A* flip-flop. The output of NAND gate *L* will remain a constant ONE, allowing the lamp connected to gate *P* to be illuminated continuously.

Logic Gates in Modern Control

The small-scale integrated circuit, containing individual logic gates, is used in modern systems primarily as an interface or supplemental device. The principal logic functions are performed by specialized LSI or MSI packages that are often programmable devices.

Functions most often performed by individual gate packages are:

- Clock generation
- Input/output signal gating
- Supplemental external gates to LSI, MSI devices
- Developmental circuits for debugging
- Output drivers
- Input interfaces (de-bouncers, etc.)

The relegation of SSI to a supplemental role is, in part, due to the economics of circuit board assembly. Circuit board assembly costs are partially determined by the number of holes in the board. By using LSI integrated circuits where possible, the overall cost of the control system decreases. SSI circuit gates have the same input and output characteristics and are the logic base for the larger integrated circuit functional elements. These devices are not fully replaceable by LSI and programmable logic, and have a definite place in the spectrum of control devices.

Problems

3.1 What are the basic logic functions that are the basis for discrete logic control?

3.2 Present-day relay control systems have what three characteristics?

3.3 What are four drawbacks to relay control systems?

3.4 The vacuum tube never achieved widespread use as a control element. Why?

3.5 Discuss three of the following areas in comparing relay and solid-state control systems: speed, life, operation energy, size, power handling, cost, supply voltages, noise immunity, temperature effects, interconnection.

3.6 Original integrated circuit packages contained only individual logic gates. Discuss the present and future trends in circuit packaging.

3.7 What are the output connection problems of the integrated circuit in the industrial world?

3.8 What are the benefits of dual-in-line integrated circuit packaging?

3.9 What are three integrated circuit logic families and what areas of performance are affected by the selection of a family?

3.10 Describe the differences between SSI, MSI, and LSI integrated circuits.

3.11 What are the logic levels for logic ONE and logic ZERO for the LSTTL and CMOS logic families?

3.12 The Schottky diode in the STTL and LSTTL family improves the switching speed of these devices. Identify one such diode in Figure P3.12 and explain how the diode improves switching times.

3.13 Discuss the advantages and disadvantages of the CMOS family versus the TTL family.

3.14 The input gates of the modern B-suffix CMOS family is protected by a combination of zener and junction diodes. Identify one of these diodes in Figure P3.14.

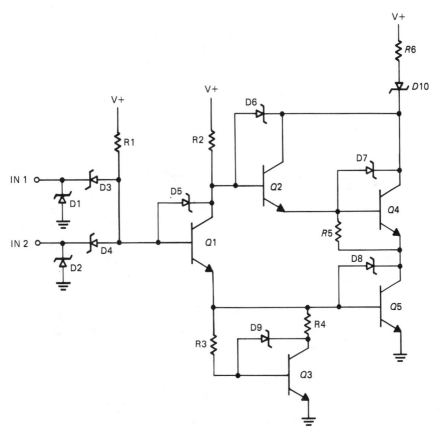

FIGURE P3.12. LSTTL 7400 gate

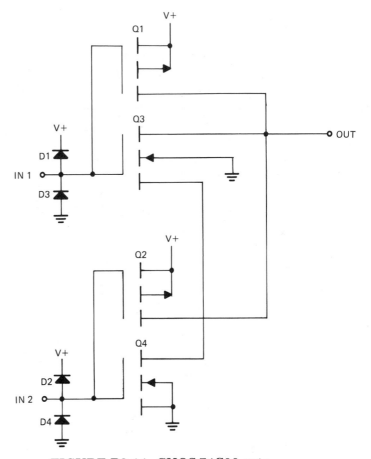

FIGURE P3.14. CMOS 74C00 gate

3.15 What is meant by the term *totem-pole output?* What are the advantages and drawbacks of this form of output switch?

3.16 What is the use of an open-collector logic gate output?

3.17 What is the purpose of the three-state logic gate output and what are its three states?

3.18 Of what use is a block diagram? What are the common elements of the schematic and block diagram?

3.19 What are the three principal sections of an integrated circuit control system?

3.20 What are three methods of integrated circuit logic analysis?

3.21 Analyze, by time sequence, an electric toaster.

3.22 What are the possible input combinations of the electric door opener diagrammed in Figure P3.22?

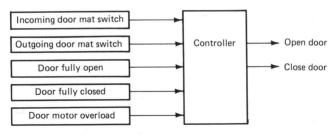

FIGURE P3.22. Electric door opener

3.23 What is meant by the term *logic signature*?

3.24 What is meant by the term *state*?

3.25 Write the algorithm for walking up a flight of stairs.

3.26 Identify states described by the algorithm of problem 25.

3.27 What is meant by the term *logic ONE*?; *logic ZERO*?

3.28 Define the number systems: binary, octal, and hexadecimal.

3.29 A group of eight switches are in the following condition, from left to right: ON, OFF, ON, OFF, ON, ON, ON, OFF. Describe this combination of switches in binary, octal, and hexadecimal notations.

3.30 What are six basic logic gates and their truth tables?

3.31 Using the basic gates, draw the relay circuit of Figure P2.13.

3.32 What is the difference between a half-adder and a full-adder?

3.33 Define the term *latching* and draw a NOR gate implementation of a latch.

3.34 What are three types of flip-flops and their differences?

3.35 Why does power-up cause problems in flip-flop-based industrial controls?

3.36 The D flip-flop is used in data communications. What special feature of this flip-flop makes it well suited to this application?

3.37 What is the purpose of PRESET and CLEAR inputs in flip-flop usage?

3.38 What is the special feature of the JK flip-flop and in what modes can it be operated?

3.39 A humidifier tank is automatically filled by a system that uses the following inputs: low-level sensor, empty-tank sensor, high-level sensor, and overflow sensor. The system controls the following outputs: water solenoid valve, empty-tank alarm, and overflow alarm. Using one or more flip-flops, draw the logic diagram for the system.

54/7400
54H/74H00
54S/74S00
54LS/74LS00

QUAD 2-INPUT NAND GATE

ORDERING CODE: See Section 9

PKGS	PIN OUT	COMMERCIAL GRADE V_{CC} = +5.0 V ±5%, T_A = 0°C to +70°C	MILITARY GRADE V_{CC} = +5.0 V ±10%, T_A = -55°C to +125°C	PKG TYPE
Plastic DIP (P)	A	7400PC, 74H00PC 74LS00PC, 74S00PC		9A
Ceramic DIP (D)	A	7400DC, 74H00DC 74LS00DC, 74S00DC	5400DM, 54H00DM 54LS00DM, 54S00DM	6A
Flatpak (F)	A	74LS00FC, 74S00FC	54LS00FM, 54S00FM	3I
	B	7400FC, 74H00FC	5400FM, 54H00FM	

PINOUT B

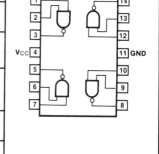

INPUT LOADING/FAN-OUT: See Section 3 for U.L. definitions

PINS	54/74 (U.L.) HIGH/LOW	54/74H (U.L.) HIGH/LOW	54/74S (U.L.) HIGH/LOW	54/74LS (U.L.) HIGH/LOW
Inputs	1.0/1.0	1.25/1.25	1.25/1.25	0.5/0.25
Outputs	20/10	12.5/12.5	25/12.5	10/5.0 (2.5)

DC AND AC CHARACTERISTICS: See Section 3*

SYMBOL	PARAMETER	54/74 Min	54/74 Max	54/74H Min	54/74H Max	54/74S Min	54/74S Max	54/74LS Min	54/74LS Max	UNITS	CONDITIONS	
I_{CCH}	Power Supply		8.0		16.8		16		1.6	mA	V_{IN} = Gnd	V_{CC} = Max
I_{CCL}	Current		22		40		36		4.4		V_{IN} = Open	
t_{PLH}	Propagation Delay		22		10	2.0	4.5		10	ns	Figs. 3-1, 3-4	
t_{PHL}			15		10	2.0	5.0		10			

*DC limits apply over operating temperature range; AC limits apply at T_A = +25°C and V_{CC} = +5.0 V.

Courtesy Fairchild Camera and Instrument Corp.

MM54HC00/MM74HC00 Quad 2-Input NAND Gate

General Description

These NAND gates utilize microCMOS Technology, 3.5 micron silicon gate P-well CMOS, to achieve operating speeds similar to LS-TTL gates with the low power consumption of standard CMOS integrated circuits. All gates have buffered outputs. All devices have high noise immunity and the ability to drive 10 LS-TTL loads. The 54HC/74HC logic family is functionally as well as pin-out compatible with the standard 54LS/74LS logic family. All inputs are protected from damage due to static discharge by internal diode clamps to V_{CC} and ground.

Features

- Typical propagation delay: 8 ns
- Wide power supply range: 2–6V
- Low quiescent current: 20 μA maximum (74HC series)
- Low input current: 1 μA maximum
- Fanout of 10 LS-TTL loads

Connection Diagram

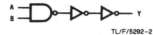

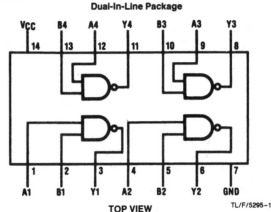

TOP VIEW

MM54HC00/MM74HC00

54HC00 (J)   74HC00 (J,N)

TL/F/5295–1.

Logic Diagram

A
B — Y

TL/F/5292–2

54/7402
54S/74S02
54LS/74LS02

QUAD 2-INPUT NOR GATE

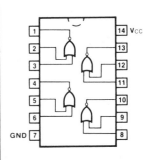

ORDERING CODE: See Section 9

PKGS	PIN OUT	COMMERCIAL GRADE $V_{CC} = +5.0$ V $\pm5\%$, $T_A = 0°$ C to $+70°$ C	MILITARY GRADE $V_{CC} = +5.0$ V $\pm10\%$, $T_A = -55°$ C to $+125°$ C	PKG TYPE
Plastic DIP (P)	A	7402PC, 74LS02PC 74S02PC		9A
Ceramic DIP (D)	A	7402DC, 74LS02DC 74S02DC	5402DM, 54LS02DM 54S02DM	6A
Flatpak (F)	A	74LS02FC, 74S02FC	54LS02FM, 54S02FM	3I
	B	7402FC	5402FM	

PINOUT B

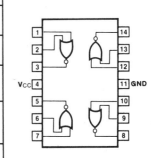

INPUT LOADING/FAN-OUT: See Section 3 for U.L. definitions

PINS	54/74 (U.L.) HIGH/LOW	54/74S (U.L.) HIGH/LOW	54/74LS (U.L.) HIGH/LOW
Inputs	1.0/1.0	1.25/1.25	0.5/0.25
Outputs	20/10	25/12.5	10/5.0 (2.5)

DC AND AC CHARACTERISTICS: See Section 3*

SYMBOL	PARAMETER	54/74 Min	54/74 Max	54/74S Min	54/74S Max	54/74LS Min	54/74LS Max	UNITS	CONDITIONS	
I_{CCH}	Power Supply Current		16		29		3.2	mA	V_{IN} = Gnd	V_{CC} = Max
I_{CCL}			27		45		5.4		V_{IN} = Open	
t_{PLH}	Propagation Delay		15	2.0	5.5		10	ns	Figs. 3-1, 3-4	
t_{PHL}			15	2.0	5.5		10			

*DC limits apply over operating temperature range; AC limits apply at T_A = +25° C and V_{CC} = +5.0 V.

Courtesy Fairchild Camera and Instrument Corp.

microCMOS

MM54HC02/MM74HC02 Quad 2-Input NOR Gate

General Description

These NOR gates utilize microCMOS Technology, 3.5 micron silicon gate P-well CMOS, to achieve operating speeds similar to LS-TTL gates with the low power consumption of standard CMOS integrated circuits. All gates have buffered outputs, providing high noise immunity and the ability to drive 10 LS-TTL loads. The 54HC/74HC logic family is functionally as well as pin-out compatible with the standard 54LS/74LS logic family. All inputs are protected from damage due to static discharge by internal diode clamps to V_{CC} and ground.

Features

- Typical propagation delay: 8 ns
- Wide power supply range: 2–6V
- Low quiescent supply current: 20 μA maximum (74HC series)
- Low input current: 1 μA maximum
- High output current: 4 mA minimum

Connection Diagram

Dual-In-Line Package

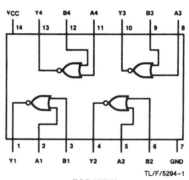

TL/F/5294–1

TOP VIEW
MM54HC02/MM74HC02

54HC02 (J)   74HC02 (J,N)

Logic Diagram

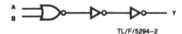

TL/F/5294–2

Courtesy National Semiconductor

94

54/7404
54H/74H04
54S/74S04
54S/74S04A
54LS/74LS04

HEX INVERTER

ORDERING CODE: See Section 9

PKGS	PIN OUT	COMMERCIAL GRADE V_{CC} = +5.0 V ±5%, T_A = 0°C to +70°C	MILITARY GRADE V_{CC} = +5.0 V ±10%, T_A = -55°C to +125°C	PKG TYPE
Plastic DIP (P)	A	7404PC, 74H04PC 74S04PC, 74S04APC 74LS04PC		9A
Ceramic DIP (D)	A	7404DC, 74H04DC 74S04DC, 74S04ADC 74LS04DC	5404DM, 54H04DM 54S04DM, 54S04ADM 54LS04DM	6A
Flatpak (F)	A	74S04FC, 74S04AFC 74LS04FC	54S04FM, 54S04AFM 54LS04FM	3I
	B	7404FC, 74H04FC	5404FM, 54H04FM	

PINOUT B

INPUT LOADING/FAN-OUT: See Section 3 for U.L. definitions

PINS	54/74 (U.L.) HIGH/LOW	54/74H (U.L.) HIGH/LOW	54/74S (U.L.) HIGH/LOW	54/74LS (U.L.) HIGH/LOW
Inputs	1.0/1.0	1.25/1.25	1.25/1.25	0.5/0.25
Outputs	20/10	12.5/12.5	25/12.5	10/5.0 (2.5)

DC AND AC CHARACTERISTICS: See Section 3*

SYMBOL	PARAMETER	54/74 Min Max	54/74H Min Max	54/74S Min Max	54/74LS Min Max	UNITS	CONDITIONS
I_{CCH}	Power Supply	12	26	24	2.4	mA	V_{IN} = Gnd V_{CC} = Max
I_{CCL}	Current	33	58	54	6.6		V_{IN} = Open
t_{PLH} t_{PHL}	Propagation Delay	22 15	10 10	2.0 4.5 2.0 5.0	10 10	ns	Fig. 3-1, 3-4
t_{PLH} t_{PHL}	Propagation Delay (54/74S04A only)			1.0 3.5 1.0 4.0		ns	Fig. 3-1, 3-4

*DC limits apply over operating temperature range; AC limits apply at T_A = +25°C and V_{CC} = +5.0 V.

Courtesy Fairchild Camera and Instrument Corp.

 **National Semiconductor**

 **microCMOS**

MM54HC04/MM74HC04 Hex Inverter

General Description

These Inverters utilize microCMOS Technology, 3.5 micron silicon gate P-well CMOS, to achieve operating speeds similar to LS-TTL gates with the low power consumption of standard CMOS integrated circuits.

The MM54HC04/MM74HC04 is a triple buffered inverter. It has high noise immunity and the ability to drive 10 LS-TTL loads. The 54HC/74HC logic family is functionally as well as pin-out compatible with the standard 54LS/74LS logic family. All inputs are protected from damage due to static discharge by internal diode clamps to V_{CC} and ground.

Features

- Typical propagation delay: 8 ns
- Fan out of 10 LS-TTL loads
- Quiescent power consumption: 10 μW maximum at room temperature
- Typical input current: 10^{-5} μA

Connection Diagram

Dual-In-Line Package

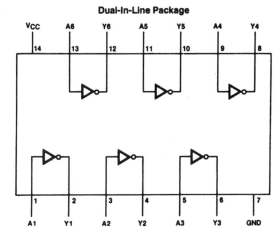

TL/F/5069-1

TOP VIEW
MM54HC04/MM74HC04

54HC04 (J)   74HC04 (J,N)

Logic Diagram

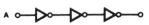

TL/F/5069-2

1 of 6 Inverters

Courtesy National Semiconductor

54/7408
54H/74H08
54S/74S08
54LS/74LS08

QUAD 2-INPUT AND GATE

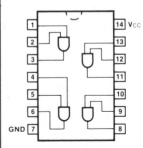

ORDERING CODE: See Section 9

PKGS	PIN OUT	COMMERCIAL GRADE $V_{CC} = +5.0$ V $\pm 5\%$, $T_A = 0°$C to $+70°$C	MILITARY GRADE $V_{CC} = +5.0$ V $\pm 10\%$, $T_A = -55°$C to $+125°$C	PKG TYPE
Plastic DIP (P)	A	7408PC, 74H08PC 74S08PC, 74LS08PC		9A
Ceramic DIP (D)	A	7408DC, 74H08DC 74S08DC, 74LS08DC	5408DM, 54H08DM 54S08DM, 54LS08DM	6A
Flatpak (F)	A	7408FC, 74S08FC 74LS08FC	5408FM, 54S08FM 54LS08FM	3I
	B	74H08FC	54H08FM	

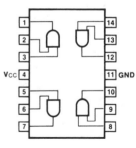

INPUT LOADING/FAN-OUT: See Section 3 for U.L. definitions

PINS	54/74 (U.L.) HIGH/LOW	54/74H (U.L.) HIGH/LOW	54/74S (U.L.) HIGH/LOW	54/74LS (U.L.) HIGH/LOW
Inputs	1.0/1.0	1.25/1.25	1.25/1.25	0.5/0.25
Outputs	20/10	12.5/12.5	25/12.5	10/5.0 (2.5)

DC AND AC CHARACTERISTICS: See Section 3*

SYMBOL	PARAMETER	54/74 Min	54/74 Max	54/74H Min	54/74H Max	54/74S Min	54/74S Max	54/74LS Min	54/74LS Max	UNITS	CONDITIONS
I_{CCH}	Power Supply		21		40		32		4.8	mA	V_{IN} = Open, V_{CC} = Max
I_{CCL}	Current		33		64		57		8.8		V_{IN} = Gnd
t_{PLH}	Propagation Delay		27		12	2.5	7.0		13	ns	Fig. 3-1, 3-5
t_{PHL}			19		12	2.5	7.5		11		

*DC limits apply over operating temperature range; AC limits apply at T_A = +25° C and V_{CC} = +5.0 V.

Courtesy Fairchild Camera and Instrument Corp.

MM54HC08/MM74HC08 Quad 2-Input AND Gate

General Description

These AND gates utilize microCMOS Technology, 3.5 micron silicon gate P-well CMOS, to achieve operating speeds similar to LS-TTL gates with the low power consumption of standard CMOS integrated circuits. The HC08 has buffered outputs, providing high noise immunity and the ability to drive 10 LS-TTL loads. The 54HC/74HC logic family is functionally as well as pin-out compatible with the standard 54LS/74LS logic family. All inputs are protected from damage due to static discharge by internal diode clamps to V_{CC} and ground.

Features

- Typical propagation delay: 7 ns (t_{PHL}), 12 ns (t_{PLH})
- Fanout of 10 LS-TTL loads
- Quiescent power consumption: 2 μA maximum at room temperature
- Typical input current: 10^{-5} μA

Connection Diagram

Dual-In-Line Package

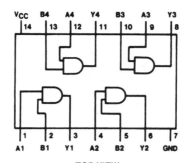

TL/F/5297–1

TOP VIEW
MM54HC08/MM74HC08

54HC08 (J)   74HC08 (J,N)

54/7432
54S/74S32
54LS/74LS32
QUAD 2-INPUT OR GATE

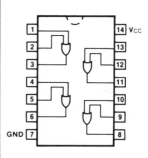

ORDERING CODE: See Section 9

PKGS	PIN OUT	COMMERCIAL GRADE V_{CC} = +5.0 V ±5%, T_A = 0°C to +70°C	MILITARY GRADE V_{CC} = +5.0 V ±10%, T_A = -55°C to +125°C	PKG TYPE
Plastic DIP (P)	A	7432PC, 74S32PC 74LS32PC		9A •
Ceramic DIP (D)	A	7432DC, 74S32DC 74LS32DC	5432DM, 54S32DM 54LS32DM	6A
Flatpak (F)	A	7432FC, 74S32FC 74LS32FC	5432FM, 54S32FM 54LS32FM	3I

INPUT LOADING/FAN-OUT: See Section 3 for U.L. definitions

PINS	54/74 (U.L.) HIGH/LOW	54/74S (U.L.) HIGH/LOW	54/74LS (U.L.) HIGH/LOW
Inputs	1.0/1.0	1.25/1.25	0.5/0.25
Outputs	20/10	25/12.5	10/5.0 (2.5)

DC AND AC CHARACTERISTICS: See Section 3 for U.L. definitions

SYMBOL	PARAMETER	54/74 Min	54/74 Max	54/74S Min	54/74S Max	54/74LS Min	54/74LS Max	UNITS	CONDITIONS
I_{CCH}	Power Supply Current		22		32		6.2	mA	V_{IN} = Open , V_{CC} = Max
I_{CCL}			38		68		9.8		V_{IN} = Gnd
t_{PLH}	Propagation Delay		15	2.0	7.0		15	ns	Figs. 3-1, 3-5
t_{PHL}			22	2.0	7.0		15		

*DC limits apply over operating temperature range; AC limits apply at T_A = +25°C and V_{CC} = +5.0 V.

Courtesy Fairchild Camera and Instrument Corp.

MM54HC32/MM74HC32 Quad 2-Input OR Gate

General Description

These OR gates utilize microCMOS Technology, 3.5 micron silicon gate P-well CMOS, to achieve operating speeds similar to LS-TTL gates with the low power consumption of standard CMOS integrated circuits. All gates have buffered outputs, providing high noise immunity and the ability to drive 10 LS-TTL loads. The 54HC/74HC logic family is functionally as well as pin-out compatible with the standard 54LS/74LS logic family. All inputs are protected from damage due to static discharge by internal diode clamps to V_{CC} and ground.

Features

- Typical propagation delay: 10 ns
- Wide power supply range: 2–6V
- Low quiescent current: 20 μA maximum (74HC series)
- Low input current: 1 μA maximum
- Fanout of 10 LS-TTL loads

Connection Diagram

Dual-In-Line Package

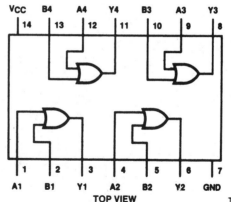

TOP VIEW

TL/F/5132–1

M54HC32/MM74HC32

54HC32 (J)   74HC32 (J,N)

Logic Diagram

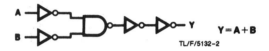

$$Y = A + B$$

TL/F/5132–2

54/7486
54S/74S86
54LS/74LS86
QUAD 2-INPUT EXCLUSIVE-OR GATE

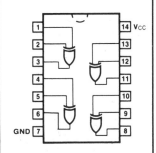

ORDERING CODE: See Section 9

PKGS	PIN OUT	COMMERCIAL GRADE V_{CC} = +5.0 V ±5%, T_A = 0°C to +70°C	MILITARY GRADE V_{CC} = +5.0 V ±10%, T_A = -55°C to +125°C	PKG TYPE
Plastic DIP (P)	A	7486PC, 74S86PC 74LS86PC		9A
Ceramic DIP (D)	A	7486DC, 74S86DC 74LS86DC	5486DM, 54S86DM 54LS86DM	6A
Flatpak (F)	A	7486FC, 74S86FC 74LS86FC	5486FM, 54S86FM 54LS86FM	3I

INPUT LOADING/FAN-OUT: See Section 3 for U.L. definitions

PINS	54/74 (U.L.) HIGH/LOW	54/74S (U.L.) HIGH/LOW	54/74LS (U.L.) HIGH/LOW
Inputs Outputs	1.0/1.0 20/10	1.25/1.25 25/12.5	1.0/0.375 10/5.0 (2.5)

DC AND AC CHARACTERISTICS: See Section 3*

SYMBOL	PARAMETER		54/74 Min	54/74 Max	54/74S Min	54/74S Max	54/74LS Min	54/74LS Max	UNITS	CONDITIONS
I_{CC}	Power Supply Current	XM		43		75		10	mA	V_{CC} = Max, V_{IN} = Gnd
		XC		50		75		10		
t_{PLH} t_{PHL}	Propagation Delay			23 17	3.5 3.0	10.5 10		12 17	ns	Other Input LOW Figs. 3-1, 3-5
t_{PLH} t_{PHL}	Propagation Delay			30 22	3.5 3.0	10.5 10		13 12	ns	Other Input HIGH Figs. 3-1, 3-4

*DC limits apply over operating temperature range; AC limits apply at T_A = +25°C and V_{CC} = +5.0 V.

4 Memories, Counting, and Sequencing

4.0 Introduction

The flip-flops covered in Chapter 3 provide a powerful tool. The control functions of memory, counting, and sequencing are possible when flip-flops are combined with logic gates. In this chapter, each of these functions is examined.

4.1 Registers

The flip-flop is rarely used as a single element in a microcomputer-based controller. Multiple flip-flops are used instead to simultaneously latch pieces of information used to compute the next action of the system under control.

In the multiple flip-flop memory, each flip-flop is termed a *cell*. The cells are coupled by connected ENABLE and CLEAR lines. Such a combination of latches is called a *register*. The block diagram of a register is illustrated in Figure 4-1. It shows the most common integrated circuit multilatch packages, based on an eight-cell configuration. The schematic representation is shown in Figure 4-2.

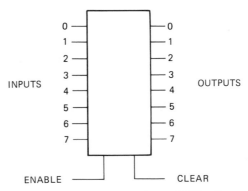

FIGURE 4-1. Block diagram of eight-cell flip-flop register

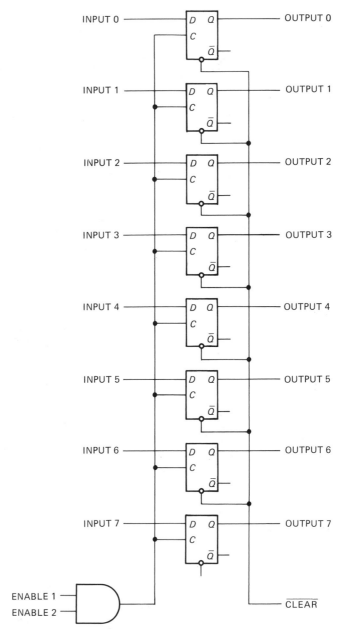

FIGURE 4-2. Eight-element register

Multiple registers that use a single set of input and output lines are called a *file*. AND gates are used to route the input and output lines to each flip-flop cell of a particular register.

A block diagram of a multiple register file is shown in Figure 4-3. The AND gates are controlled by a group of enabling inputs called *address lines*. The ONE and ZERO combination of the address inputs is decoded into separate select lines to determine which file is to be connected to the input and output lines. A typical address decoder is illustrated in Figure 4-4.

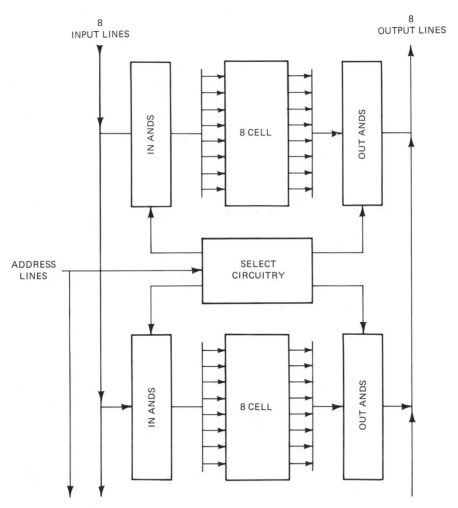

FIGURE 4-3. Block diagram of a multiple register file

ADDRESS LINE INPUTS

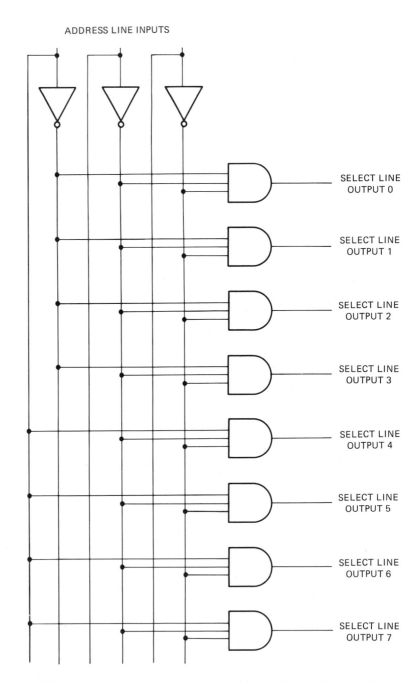

SELECT LINE
OUTPUT 0

SELECT LINE
OUTPUT 1

SELECT LINE
OUTPUT 2

SELECT LINE
OUTPUT 3

SELECT LINE
OUTPUT 4

SELECT LINE
OUTPUT 5

SELECT LINE
OUTPUT 6

SELECT LINE
OUTPUT 7

**FIGURE 4-4. Memory select circuitry (three input ad-
dress decoder)**

In addition to the address-selection inputs, memory cells also require input and output enable signals that synchronize the data with external circuitry. The synchronizing signals are named READ and WRITE. The WRITE signal is ANDed with the address-select line and the data to latch the data into the flip-flop. The READ signal is ANDed with the address select line and the output of the flip-flop to place the latched information onto the output lines of the register.

The circuitry for one cell with synchronizing signals of a multiple-register memory is illustrated in Figure 4-5.

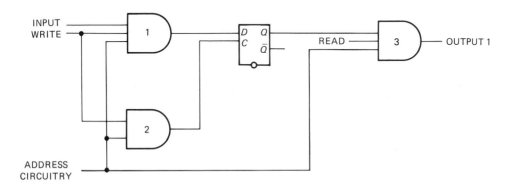

FIGURE 4-5. Single cell of a multiple file memory

4.2 Semiconductor Memory Devices

So useful is the multiple-file register that an entire family of micro-circuits, known as semiconductor memory devices, has been developed. The block diagram of a complete multiple-file memory device is pictured in Figure 4-6.

The number of electrical connections required for a memory device is minimized by utilizing one set of information lines for both input and output functions. This multiple use of the same electrical connections reduces the manufacturing cost of the IC but prevents the memory from being read and written to simultaneously. The block diagram for a memory IC that uses only one set of data lines for reading and writing is illustrated in Figure 4-7.

The READ/WRITE line permits reading the memory when the line is at a ZERO condition, and writing when it is at a logic ONE. The CHIP SELECT line acts as an additional special address enable, which is required to be at a logic ONE for the internal address decoder to operate.

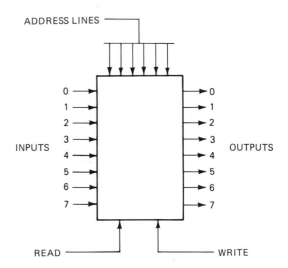

FIGURE 4-6. Block diagram of eight-cell flip-flop register

The memory IC of Figure 4-7 has three principal forms. Each form is named for the ease of reading versus the ease of writing. These forms are shown in Table 4-1.

RAM is the memory type used for temporary storage that does not require retention of its contents after power is turned off. RAM is the commonly used name for this device. The initials stand for *random access memory*, although a more accurate acronym would be R/WM for read/write memory. RAM is the fastest of the memory types, with access times typically less than 200 nanoseconds. RAM is divided into two classes: static and dynamic. Static RAM is based on a flip-flop type circuit similar to those described in Chapter 3. Dynamic RAM stores the information as a charge on a capacitor-like cell. The information in dynamic RAM must be rewritten periodically (called

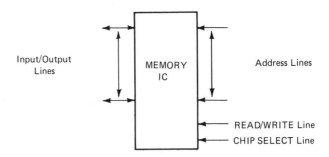

FIGURE 4-7. Block diagram of a generic memory IC

TABLE 4-1. Types of memory ICs

Name	Description	Writability	Readability	Volatility	Erasability
RAM	Random Access Memory	1	1	1	1
ROM	Read Only Memory	3	1	3	—
PROM	Programmable ROM	2	1	2	3
EAPROM	Electrically Alterable PROM	2	1	2	2

1 = Least Difficulty   3 = Most Difficulty

REFRESH) to prevent leakage loss. The static RAM is faster than the dynamic but is more expensive and uses more power. Large numbers of bytes of RAM memory can be stored in one chip. While 64K bytes has become a standard, newer chips with 256 and 1,000K bytes are becoming available.

ROM (read-only memory) is the memory type most used to store information that is known at the time of manufacture of the control system. The most common type, called *masked ROM,* is manufactured with the information in place and is not alterable. The contents of this memory type is not affected by power loss.

Alterable ROM, called PROM (programmable read-only memory), is field-programmable. Two types of PROM are used: the fuse-linked and the EPROM, or erasable PROM. The fuse-linked PROM retains its information by literally burning out connections inside the IC. This memory type can be programmed only once. The EPROM memory method is based on the storage of a charge in a high-quality, capacitor-like cell that retains the information for years but can be discharged (erased) with one of two methods. In the ultraviolet erasable EPROM, a short wavelength, ultraviolet light source shining through a transparent window in the surface of the IC package causes the memory cell surface to become partially conductive and discharges the cells. All the cells of an EPROM are erased at once, a procedure requiring only minutes to complete. In the electrically alterable PROM, or EAPROM, an electrical switch selectively discharges individually charged cells in a few hundred microseconds.

The combination of type and number of total cells is one method of naming memory ICs. The number of input/output lines and the number of address lines that access the memory cells are an alternative naming method. For example, an eight-input line memory that has eight address lines can latch 4,096 pieces of information (512 addresses by 8 cells per register). If this device is a read-only memory, then it is called a 4K ROM or a 512x8 ROM.

Example of ROM-Based Control

A large number of discrete control applications can be described in algorithmic-state machine diagrams. The ROM and flip-flop register are ideally suited as implementation devices for this form of control solution. As an example, consider a garage-door opener. The door can be in the following conditions:

- door opened
- door closed
- door intermediate (neither open or closed).

The door's condition is sensed by two switches: one switch detects when the door is fully opened and the other detects when the door is fully closed. This information determines the "state" of the door as the control system electrically views it.

The door system receives three commands: OPEN, CLOSE, and STOP. These inputs to the system are accomplished by three NO push buttons. The commands provide the goals for the control system or desired final states.

The door motor is the actual device under control. Its states are stopped, closing, and opening. These states are sensed by two auxiliary switches mounted on the motor starter. One switch senses the CLOSE contactor and the other the OPEN contactor. These conditions provide the internal state of the control system.

The possible combinations of these input, output, and motor state switches are represented in Table 4-2.

This table assumes that no unwanted combinations of conditions are possible (e.g., more than one button pushed simultaneously, motor starter failure, etc.). By assigning ONE and ZERO to each input and door state switch, a complete table is generated, as in Table 4-3.

TABLE 4-2. Table of garage door states

COMMANDS	DOOR STATE	MOTOR COMMAND
Open	Open	Stop
Open	Intermediate	Open
Open	Closed	Open
Stop	Open	Stop
Stop	Intermediate	Stop
Stop	Closed	Stop
Close	Open	Close
Close	Intermediate	Close
Close	Closed	Stop

TABLE 4-3. Memory contents for a garage door control

STATE NUMBER	STATUS							NEXT CMD		
	DOOR		MOTOR		COMMANDS			MOTOR		
	OPEN	CLOSED	OPENING	CLOSING	OPEN	CLOSE	STOP	OPENING	CLOSING	ERROR LIGHT
0	0	0	0	0	0	0	0	0	0	0
1	0	0	0	0	0	0	1	0	0	0
2	0	0	0	0	0	1	0	0	1	0
3	0	0	0	0	0	1	1	0	0	0
4	0	0	0	0	1	0	0	0	0	0
5	0	0	0	0	1	0	1	0	0	0
6	0	0	0	0	1	1	0	0	0	0
7	0	0	0	0	1	1	1	0	0	0
8	0	0	0	1	0	0	0	0	1	0
9	0	0	0	1	0	0	1	0	0	0
10	0	0	0	1	0	1	0	0	1	0
11	0	0	0	1	0	1	1	0	0	0
12	0	0	0	1	1	0	0	0	0	0
13	0	0	0	1	1	0	1	0	0	0
14	0	0	0	1	1	1	0	0	0	0
15	0	0	0	1	1	1	1	0	0	0
16	0	0	1	0	0	0	0	1	0	0
17	0	0	1	0	0	0	1	0	0	0
18	0	0	1	0	0	1	0	0	0	0
19	0	0	1	0	0	1	1	0	0	0
20	0	0	1	0	1	0	0	1	0	0
21	0	0	1	0	1	0	1	0	0	0
22	0	0	1	0	1	1	0	0	0	0
23	0	0	1	0	1	1	1	0	0	0
24	0	0	1	1	0	0	0	0	0	1
25	0	0	1	1	0	0	1	0	0	1
26	0	0	1	1	0	1	0	0	0	1
27	0	0	1	1	0	1	1	0	0	1
28	0	0	1	1	1	0	0	0	0	1
29	0	0	1	1	1	0	1	0	0	1
30	0	0	1	1	1	1	0	0	0	1
31	0	0	1	1	1	1	1	0	0	1
32	0	1	0	0	0	0	0	0	0	0
33	0	1	0	0	0	0	1	0	0	0
34	0	1	0	0	0	1	0	0	0	0
35	0	1	0	0	0	1	1	0	0	0
36	0	1	0	0	1	0	0	1	0	0
37	0	1	0	0	1	0	1	0	0	0
38	0	1	0	0	1	1	0	0	0	0
39	0	1	0	0	1	1	1	0	0	0
40	0	1	0	1	0	0	0	0	0	0
41	0	1	0	1	0	0	1	0	0	0
42	0	1	0	1	0	1	0	0	0	0
43	0	1	0	1	0	1	1	0	0	0
44	0	1	0	1	1	0	0	0	0	0
45	0	1	0	1	1	0	1	0	0	0
46	0	1	0	1	1	1	0	0	0	0
47	0	1	0	1	1	1	1	0	0	0
48	0	1	1	0	0	0	0	1	0	0
49	0	1	1	0	0	0	1	0	0	0
50	0	1	1	0	0	1	0	0	0	0
51	0	1	1	0	0	1	1	0	0	0
52	0	1	1	0	1	0	0	1	0	0
53	0	1	1	0	1	0	1	0	0	0
54	0	1	1	0	1	1	0	0	0	0
55	0	1	1	0	1	1	1	0	0	0
56	0	1	1	1	0	0	0	0	0	1
57	0	1	1	1	0	0	1	0	0	1
58	0	1	1	1	0	1	0	0	0	1
59	0	1	1	1	0	1	1	0	0	1
60	0	1	1	1	1	0	0	0	0	1
61	0	1	1	1	1	0	1	0	0	1
62	0	1	1	1	1	1	0	0	0	1
63	0	1	1	1	1	1	1	0	0	1
64	1	0	0	0	0	0	0	0	0	0
65	1	0	0	0	0	0	1	0	0	0

TABLE 4-3 (cont.)

66	1	0	0	0	0	1	0	0	1	0
67	1	0	0	0	0	1	1	0	0	0
68	1	0	0	0	1	0	0	0	0	0
69	1	0	0	0	1	0	1	0	0	0
70	1	0	0	0	1	1	0	0	0	0
71	1	0	0	0	1	1	1	0	0	0
72	1	0	0	1	0	0	0	0	1	0
73	1	0	0	1	0	0	1	0	0	0
74	1	0	0	1	0	1	0	0	1	0
75	1	0	0	1	0	1	1	0	0	0
76	1	0	0	1	1	0	0	0	0	0
77	1	0	0	1	1	0	1	0	0	0
78	1	0	0	1	1	1	0	0	0	0
79	1	0	0	1	1	1	1	0	0	0
80	1	0	1	0	0	0	0	0	0	0
81	1	0	1	0	0	0	1	0	0	0
82	1	0	1	0	0	1	0	0	1	0
83	1	0	1	0	0	1	1	0	0	0
84	1	0	1	0	1	0	0	0	0	0
85	1	0	1	0	1	0	1	0	0	0
86	1	0	1	0	1	1	0	0	0	0
87	1	0	1	0	1	1	1	0	0	0
88	1	0	1	1	0	0	0	0	0	1
89	1	0	1	1	0	0	1	0	0	1
90	1	0	1	1	0	1	0	0	0	1
91	1	0	1	1	0	1	1	0	0	1
92	1	0	1	1	1	0	0	0	0	1
93	1	0	1	1	1	0	1	0	0	1
94	1	0	1	1	1	1	0	0	0	1
95	1	0	1	1	1	1	1	0	0	1
96	1	1	0	0	0	0	0	0	0	1
97	1	1	0	0	0	0	1	0	0	1
98	1	1	0	0	0	1	0	0	0	1
99	1	1	0	0	0	1	1	0	0	1
100	1	1	0	0	1	0	0	0	0	1
101	1	1	0	0	1	0	1	0	0	1
102	1	1	0	0	1	1	0	0	0	1
103	1	1	0	0	1	1	1	0	0	1
104	1	1	0	1	0	0	0	0	0	1
105	1	1	0	1	0	0	1	0	0	1
106	1	1	0	1	0	1	0	0	0	1
107	1	1	0	1	0	1	1	0	0	1
108	1	1	0	1	1	0	0	0	0	1
109	1	1	0	1	1	0	1	0	0	1
110	1	1	0	1	1	1	0	0	0	1
111	1	1	0	1	1	1	1	0	0	1
112	1	1	1	0	0	0	0	0	0	1
113	1	1	1	0	0	0	1	0	0	1
114	1	1	1	0	0	1	0	0	0	1
115	1	1	1	0	0	1	1	0	0	1
116	1	1	1	0	1	0	0	0	0	1
117	1	1	1	0	1	0	1	0	0	1
118	1	1	1	0	1	1	0	0	0	1
119	1	1	1	0	1	1	1	0	0	1
120	1	1	1	1	0	0	0	0	0	1
121	1	1	1	1	0	0	1	0	0	1
122	1	1	1	1	0	1	0	0	0	1
123	1	1	1	1	0	1	1	0	0	1
124	1	1	1	1	1	0	0	0	0	1
125	1	1	1	1	1	0	1	0	0	1
126	1	1	1	1	1	1	0	0	0	1
127	1	1	1	1	1	1	1	0	0	1

Table 4-3 becomes the basis for control when its information is combined with a ROM and the proper interfacing circuitry. The status columns of the table, containing the state of the door, commands, and motor, become the address lines of the PROM. The data lines of the PROM then become the outputs of the controller to the contactor, through proper interfacing circuits, and to a system error light. To record the garage control information, a minimum of a 128x3 PROM is required. The cost of such a device is small and permits easy changes to the system logic by replacing the PROM chip with a new device. The basic electrical components for such a system are shown in Figure 4-8.

The OPENED DOOR switch is a limit switch attached to the door mechanism that detects the fully open position of the garage door.

The CLOSED DOOR switch is a limit switch attached to the door mechanism that detects the fully closed position of the garage door.

The OPEN CONTACTOR switch is an auxiliary switch physically connected to the motor contactor. This switch closes when the open contactor armature is fully engaged.

The CLOSE CONTACTOR switch is an auxiliary switch physically connected to the motor contactor. This switch closes when the close contactor armature is fully engaged.

The STOP, OPEN, and CLOSE push buttons are physically enclosed in a START-STOP station that is most often installed near the doorway of the garage.

The boxed *I* and boxed *O* symbols in the diagram indicate input and output interface circuits that couple the sensitive integrated circuit electronics to the input and output devices. These buffers are needed since the I/O devices may operate at different voltage levels and require more power than is available in the integrated circuit. In

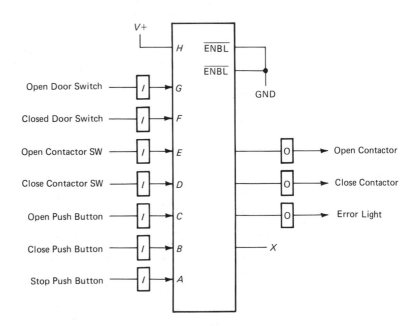

FIGURE 4-8. Garage door PROM system schematic

addition, the harsher external environment may require signal conditioning to prevent noise and nuisance actuation.

Each logic ONE in the table is "burned" into the PROM by applying each address and its data, in turn, at a controlled overcurrent. The overcurrent burns out an internal fuse that holds the data line at a ground (logic ZERO) level.

The content of the table is termed *software* and the PROM and external circuitry is termed *hardware*. The garage-door application can be accomplished by individual gates in a simpler form; however, the advantage of programmable control lies in the ability of the same hardware to be used in a variety of applications with different software for each. This powerful technique is the basis of microprocessor control methods.

4.3 Counting

In the electromechanical world, the wheel-and-ratchet switch acts as the counting, latching, and display element. Carrying from one mathematical column to the next is acomplished by mechanical linkages between switches.

In the semiconductor world, the memory cells of a RAM memory are the counting elements, acting as analogs of the ratchet switches. These solid-state counting elements have size, speed, and cost advantages over their electromechanical counterparts.

Counting comes naturally as an extension of latching. In latching, the individual memory cells are treated as independent elements. Information is simultaneously placed in the memory cells as desired. The memory content, at any time, has no necessary relation to the previous contents or the next content. The counter treats these same latches as interconnected elements. Information is placed serially into the counter through a single input called a *clock*. The number of clock pulses received is stored as a pattern of ONE and ZERO. Each pattern of ONE and ZERO is necessarily linked to the one preceding it and the one following it. The pattern sequence is accomplished by the interconnection of the latches. This interconnection corresponds to the carry function of mathematics and is implemented by linking a latch output to the next latch input via additional logic. The counting capability of a counter is determined by its possible states (patterns of ONE and ZERO) called its *modulus*.

Counters are classified by their state sequence and clocking method. The state sequence may be fixed or variable. The most common fixed state sequences are binary, octal, decimal, and Grey code. The simplified state diagrams are illustrated in Figure 4-9.

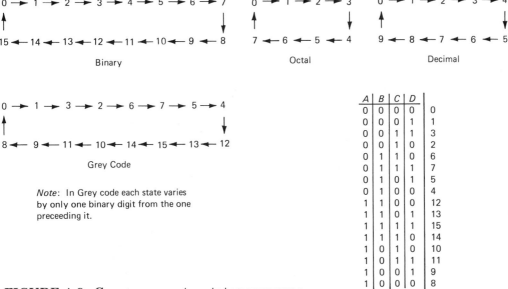

Binary

Octal

Decimal

A	B	C	D	
0	0	0	0	0
0	0	0	1	1
0	0	1	1	3
0	0	1	0	2
0	1	1	0	6
0	1	1	1	7
0	1	0	1	5
0	1	0	0	4
1	1	0	0	12
1	1	0	1	13
1	1	1	1	15
1	1	1	0	14
1	0	1	0	10
1	0	1	1	11
1	0	0	1	9
1	0	0	0	8

Grey Code

Note: In Grey code each state varies by only one binary digit from the one preceeding it.

FIGURE 4-9. Common counter state sequences

Grey Code Truth Table

The variable method of state sequencing uses an input to determine the pattern that it sequences. Information is passed from latch to latch in a chain of latches. The information may be passed to the left or right. This method of information handling is termed *shifting*. The data shifted may be provided by an external input and shifted into the register with the clock input. If a shift register output is coupled to its own input, the same pattern of ONE and ZERO may be recirculated through the register by the clock. A special application of this recirculation technique is called *ring counting*. In this method, an internal pattern containing a single ZERO or ONE is recirculated. The position of the ONE or ZERO indicates the count analogous to the armature of a selector switch. The logic of a shift register and a ring counter is illustrated in Figure 4-10.

Counter-clocking methods are classed as synchronous or asynchronous. In the asynchronous clocking method, the clocking/counting input is applied only to the first stage of the counter. Each successive stage receives its clocking pulse from the stage preceding it. The clock signal ripples from stage to stage through the counter, which gives this method its alternate name, *ripple clocking*. The ripple method of clocking has two drawbacks. The first occurs when the number of counting stages is high; the accumulated delay of each counting stage causes the last stage to be clocked long after the first. This effect may cause the second problem of glitches (unwanted

1 → 2

↑   ↓

8 ← 4

A	B	C	D	
0	0	0	1	1
0	0	1	0	2
0	1	0	0	4
1	0	0	0	8

SHIFT REGISTER

INPUT	A	B	C	D
1	0	0	0	1
0	0	0	1	0
1	0	1	0	1
1	1	0	1	1
0	0	1	1	0

Note: In a ring counter a one or a zero is passed from one bit position to the next with each clock.

Note: In a shift register a one or a zero from the input is placed in the lowest bit position with each clock while the previous bits are shifted to next bit position.

FIGURE 4-10. Shift register and ring counter logic

output) to occur for short periods of time during the ripple of the clock from stage to stage.

Both of these problems are eliminated with synchronous clocking, which changes all stages simultaneously with the input clock based on their internal state and inputs just prior to the clock. The price of this feature is that the internal logic circuits have a higher complexity than those required for asynchronous counters.

The Universal Counting Element

The most powerful form of the integrated circuit counter is the synchronous up/down counter with master reset and preset inputs. Such a device is illustrated in Figure 4-11.

PRESET ENABLE is an asynchronous control input that forces the preset inputs into the counter regardless of the state of the COUNT-UP or COUNT-DOWN inputs. This line is also termed a *jam* input, because it can also be used to disrupt the normal sequence of states of the counter.

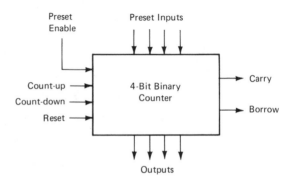

FIGURE 4-11. Universal counting element

COUNT-UP is an input that clocks the counter to its next state. COUNT-DOWN is an input that clocks the counter to its last state. Note that if the count-up and count-down inputs occur simultaneously, no change of state occurs.

RESET is an asynchronous control input that forces the counter to the first state of its modulus (usually all ZERO).

CARRY is an output that occurs when the counter is advanced from the last state of the modulus to its first state while counting up.

BORROW is an output that occurs when the counter is advanced from the first state of the modulus to its last state while counting down.

This unit can be expanded by coupling the CARRY line to the COUNT-UP input of the next stage while the BORROW line is connected to the COUNT-DOWN input. Many variations of the universal counter have been manufactured. Most of the variations result from the different methods used to select the direction of counting and the method of clocking.

Counter Applications

Counters are often used as dividers. In this application, the counter produces one pulse for every n input pulse. One convenient method uses the CARRY output of the counter to provide the output pulse. Each time the counter reaches its modulus, the counter overflows and produces a CARRY pulse. The obvious disadvantage of this method, called *modulo dividing,* is that a new counter chip must be used for each modulus needed. The universal counter eliminates this drawback by providing a programmable divider as shown in Figure 4-12.

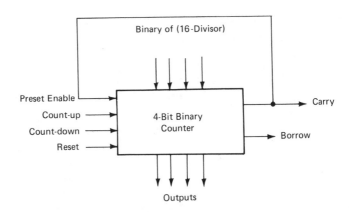

FIGURE 4-12. Programmable modulo divider

The programmable modulo divider is programmed by forcing the counter to the binary value of 16 minus the divisor desired. This is done by placing the binary value on the input lines and loading into the counter with the PRESET ENABLE line. When the counter reaches the overflow condition, the preset is enabled and the counting sequence is again forced to the state of the input lines. The counter restarts from this state and continues until overflow occurs again.

Example of the Universal Up-Down Counter

Universal counters have thousands of uses in industry. An application that shows the up-down universal counter to advantage is the following problem.

A production line uses three assembly stations to feed parts to a single, final packaging area. The assembly station's output is held in a storage bin for pickup by the packaging station. The storage bin cannot hold more than fifteen parts safely; a signal must be passed to the assembly stations if the total number of parts exceeds 15 or if the parts count falls to zero.

The logic circuit of Figure 4-13 illustrates how an up-down counter may be used to accomplish this goal. As a part arrives from

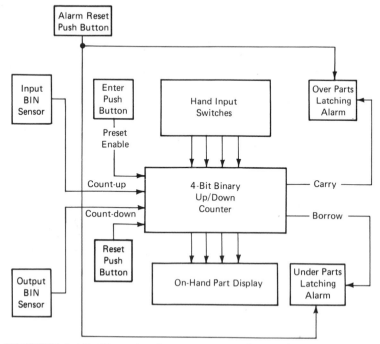

FIGURE 4-13. Over/under parts monitor with up/down counter

one of the three assembly stations, it is sensed by the input sensor, which clocks an up-count, increasing the count in the counter. If the counter exceeds 15, then the carry line sets the over-parts alarm latch. The over-parts alarm continues to signal until it is reset. In a like manner, each part that is removed by the packaging station decreases the count in the counter. If the counter drops below zero, then the under-parts alarm latch is set. The under-parts alarm will also continue to signal until it is reset. Both the over-parts and under-parts alarms are reset by the manual ENTER push button. This push button is used to correct the count in the counter once an over-parts, under-parts, or power-up condition has occurred. This is accomplished by entering on the hand switches the actual number of parts (between 0 and 15) in the bin, and then depressing the push button. This action forces the count into the counter and resets the alarm latches. A display constantly shows the number of parts in the bin by displaying the contents of the counter.

Shift Register Example

The shift register may be used to identify items in a sequence. As an example, two production lines producing small parts are feeding a single automated inspection station that has four checkpoints. Rejects detected by each station must be returned to the line that produced the defective component. A shift register is used to track the origin of the parts as they are inspected and then route the rejects back to their respective lines. The logic for such a system appears in Figure 4-14.

As a part reaches either input sensor, it is detected by its respective sensor, which triggers the advance solenoid, causing the parts within the inspection stations to advance to the next station, and generates a shift-right shift clock. If the part is from the left input line, then the shift register gates in a logic ONE with the shift clock. If the part is from the right line, then the shift register gates in a logic ZERO with the shift clock. As each part reaches an inspection station, the station equipment performs its tests. If a piece fails, then the part is rejected to the proper return line, based on the content of the shift register. Each shift register bit enables a reject solenoid routing the defective part to the correct station.

Ring Counter Example

The ring counter is the closest analog of the electromechanical counter, which has been the workhorse of the relay-based control system. As an example of control using a ring counter, consider an automated paint booth.

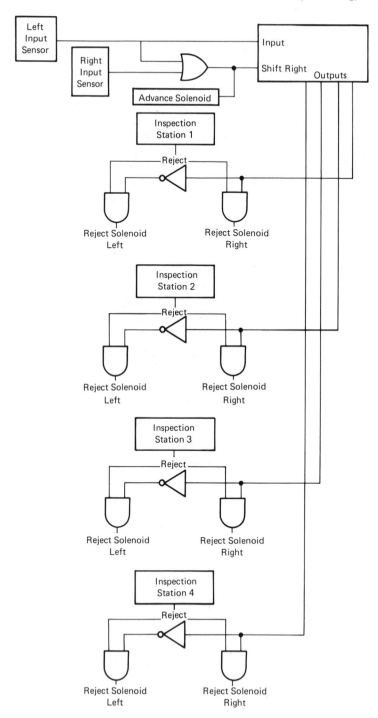

FIGURE 4-14. Inspection system using a shift register

The painting operation consists of four steps. In the first step, the part is sprayed with cleaning solution and dried. In the second step, the primer is applied and dried. In the third step, the paint is applied and dried. In the final operation, the finish is buffed. Each of these operations is handled by a separate control subsystem. The subsystems require an ENABLE signal to begin and maintain operation and will produce a FUNCTION COMPLETE signal when their operation is finished. The ring-counter logic, which provides overall control of the subsystems, is illustrated in Figure 4-15.

The ring counter is initially disabled by the master control flip-flop RESET condition. When a part is in place, in the paint station, the START push button is depressed to begin the operation. The START push button resets the ring counter to the ZERO state and sets the master control flip-flop. The output of the master control flip-flop enables the counter. The ZERO state of the flip-flop activates the cleaning operation and remains in the ZERO state until the cleaning station signals completion of its function. The FUNCTION COM-

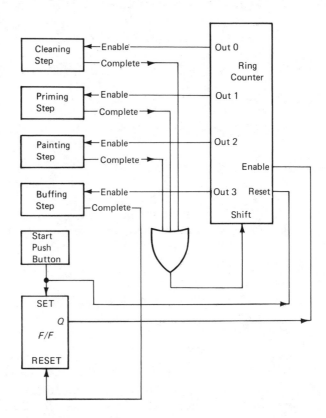

FIGURE 4-15. Automated painting operation using a ring counter

PLETE signal is gated through the OR gate and shifts the ring counter to enable the priming cycle. Similarly, the painting and buffing cycles are executed. The FUNCTION COMPLETE signal from the buffing subsystem resets the master control flip-flop, which disables the ring counter.

LSI Counter Controllers

The majority of counters in industrial control systems have the following characteristics:

Event counting requiring de-bounce circuitry

Event counting is the detection of discrete input pulses that may happen asynchronously with respect to any other event. Event counting is the opposite of frequency or time counting, in which the counting input event happens at predictable intervals.

The inputs-to-event counter are often relay or switch contacts rather than solid-state switches. These electromechanical devices have contacts that strike one another and rebound to contact many times before coming to rest. The industrial counter must detect this repeated making and breaking as a single event.

Clock speeds under 5 MHz

Unlike electronic instrumentation or computing circuitry, the industrial controller works in conjunction with mechanical devices, and therefore rarely controls events at a speed much above one megahertz.

Master reset

A master reset is a requirement for the industrial counter that must start from a known state and is not permitted the luxury of transient undefined state conditions upon start-up.

Preset capabilities

Much of the work of the industrial counter is counting from a known value to a known value. The preset feature meets this need.

Up-down capabilities

The industrial counter is used to count down from a known value to a zero. This ability is used in timer or event detecting devices. In addition, the counter may be used to totalize an unknown quantity of parts in a count-up mode.

Five to six decimal place counting capabilities

Three-decimal digit counting is adequate for many applications but, on occasion, industry requires counting of large or unknown quantities. Large counts are accomplished by cascading industrial counters or using those with the internal capacity of five to six decimal digits. Decimal counting, or decimal input and output, is required due to the human interface of the industrial counter.

Coincidence detection with settable values

Industrial control is often based upon reaching a specific event count. This count may vary and must be easy to set in decimal units.

Direct digital display of current count in decimal units

Operator actions are often based upon knowledge of the state of a machine, such as the step of a sequence or the total of parts or events. The display of this information to the operator is simplified by adding the driver circuitry directly to the counter circuitry.

Zero detection circuitry

A control action is often initiated by a system upon reaching a zero count by a count-down counter. The ZERO condition control is simplified by decoding the ZERO state in the counter as a single-output line.

So common are the above requirements that many units have been manufactured to fulfill them. Unlike many other areas, the introduction of the integrated circuit did not immediately simplify the problem. The power requirements and circuit complexities of the early TTL logic family could not produce a one-chip, cost-effective solution. The most recent CMOS logic family, however, has many one-chip complete counter systems.

Integrated Counter Controller Example

A batch-control application is well suited to the fully integrated counter circuit. A bolt-packaging machine packs 1,000 fasteners in a reinforced carton. The bolts are fed from the final inspection station past a counting station and into the carton. The carton must be shaken to settle its contents in order to fit all the bolts into it. The full carton then must be sealed and replaced with an empty one. A logic diagram of such a system using an LSI decade counter/controller is shown in Figure 4-16.

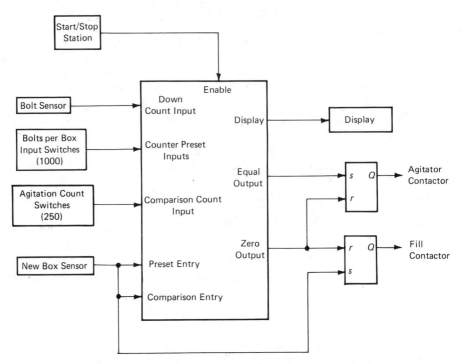

FIGURE 4-16. Carton-filling station using LSI counter controller

The station begins with both contactor flip-flops in the RESET state and the START-STOP station in the STOP state. When started, the START-STOP station provides an ENABLE to the counter chip that allows detection of a box entering the fill station. The new-box sensor loads the full-box count—1,000 bolts in this example—into the counter. This sensor also loads a comparison value—250 here—into the comparison register within the chip and sets the fill contactor flip-flop. The setting of this flip-flop engages the fill contactor, which begins loading bolts into the carton. As each bolt enters the carton, it is sensed by the bolt sensor and causes the counter to subtract one from its preset count. This count is displayed on the directly driven decimal read-out device. When the count reaches 250 (750 parts loaded), the counter equals the comparison value previously loaded and the EQUAL OUTPUT line is enabled. This EQUAL signal sets the agitator control flip-flop and closes the agitator contactor, which starts the shaker, forcing the bolts to settle in their carton. When the count reaches ZERO (1,000 bolts loaded), then the ZERO OUTPUT line is enabled and the control flip-flops are reset, causing both agitation and loading to stop. The system now awaits a new carton to begin again.

4.4 Selection

Selection in the world of discrete control implies more than its simpler English usage. It can be used to designate decoding and sequencing, as well as choosing alternatives.

   In the relay world, selection is most often implemented as a manual selector switch or as a stepping relay. Following are two common examples that are actually a small portion of the control mechanism pair, multiplexing and demultiplexing.

Multiplexing

Multiplexing encodes a large group of signal lines into a small set by selecting which lines of the larger set are connected to the smaller. Two sets of information are needed for multiplexing: one set contains the information to be multiplexed while the second contains the selection information that maps the larger set of input lines to the smaller output set. Encoding is included in multiplexing as a special case in which the lines that contain the information are the same as the lines that map the input to the output. A few examples may clarify the concept.

Multiplexing Example

   An electromechanical stepping relay is one form of a remotely controlled selector switch. A diagram for such a device is shown in Figure 4-17. The information lines of the relay are the contacts labeled "input" and "output," and the selection information is provided by the electrical impulses to the selection coil(s). Any one of the eight input lines may be transferred to the single output line. The ratchet mechanism of the stepping relay permits only sequential output access to the input lines. The line selected depends upon the number of pulses applied to the selection coil.

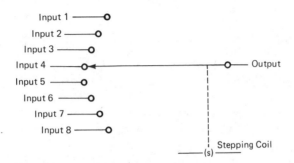

FIGURE 4-17. Electromechanical stepping switch

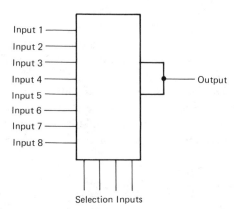

FIGURE 4-18. An eight-input multiplexer using a CMOS
selector

A solid-state replacement for the selection switch or stepping relay is the CMOS analog selector. This device uses N and P channel enhancement switches to permit analog signals to switch between input and output. The selection of the input line is determined by four digital SELECT lines. As in all solid-state devices, this device has no contacts to fail, operates at high speeds, and is small in physical size. In addition, a solid-state selector allows random access of its input lines, unlike the stepping relay; however, its transistor switches have an approximately 150-ohm resistance when switched ON compared to the milli-ohm resistance of conventional relay contacts. The switch resistance varies with temperature, signal levels, and power-supply voltages. A solid-state replacement of an electromechanical selector-switch circuit appears in Figure 4-18.

If the selection process is for digital signals only, then a number of TTL and CMOS devices are appropriate. These devices permit signal transfer in only one direction, unlike the electromechanical and CMOS analog selectors.

Encoding

Encoding is a special case of multiplexing in which the information lines are also the select lines. As an example, consider the logic circuit of Figure 4-19. In this circuit, a multiplexer is used for each of the output code lines. The SELECT lines for all the multiplexers are tied together so that lines are selected in unison. The inputs to the multiplexers do not contain variable information as they did in the selector switch example. Instead, these inputs are connected to constant logic ONE or logic ZERO potentials. As the SELECT lines are enabled, the multiplexers produce the ONE or ZERO output code

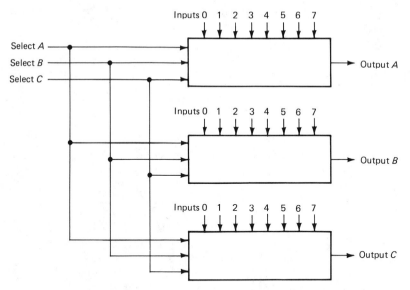

FIGURE 4-19. A three-line encoder circuit

that the SELECT lines dictate. If the multiplexer inputs are tied to programming switches, then this circuit becomes a universal code generator that can be reprogrammed to produce any required output code for any input combination.

Selector-Based Control

When the code generation circuit is united with a state machine, a very powerful tool is created. If the state-determining inputs are connected to the SELECT lines of the encoder and the control outputs are programmed by selecting ONEs and ZEROs at the multiplexer inputs, then a controller is the result—a controller that can be changed easily to fit new situations. To illustrate this concept, consider a simple washing machine.

Selector-Based Control Example

The rinse-cycle subsystem of a washing machine controls two outputs: hot-water (H) and cold-water (C) solenoids. The inputs that determine the control state consist of two encoded lines (A and B) that come from the master controller, and a level line (L) that indicates the tank is full. The encoded lines contain the information in Table 4-4.

By examining the possible combinations of the encoded input lines with the tank-full status line, the output truth table in Table 4-5. is generated.

TABLE 4-4. Input encoded states for a washing machine rinse cycle subsystem

A	B	DESCRIPTION
0	0	White
0	1	Permanent Press
1	0	Normal
1	1	Spin engaged

TABLE 4-5. Output state table for a washing machine rinse cycle subsystem

A	B	L	H	C
0	0	0	1	0
0	0	1	0	0
0	1	0	0	1
0	1	1	0	0
1	0	0	1	1
1	0	1	0	0
1	1	0	0	0
1	1	1	0	0

The logic diagram for a controller using the contents of this truth table is illustrated in Figure 4-20.

In addition to fixed ONE and ZERO logic, the input lines to the multiplexers may be tied to further logic circuits. This use of the multiplexer allows the output states to take on further values, which can depend on additional machine or input conditions.

Demultiplexing

Demultiplexing expands a smaller set of encrypted lines into a larger group of lines by selectively connecting the smaller to the larger. As in multiplexing, two sets of lines are needed: one set contains the information to be decoded and the other contains the selection information. Decoding is included in demultiplexing as a special case in which the information to be decoded and the selection information are the same.

Since demultiplexing is an extension of multiplexing, some relationship is to be expected between the hardware used for each. In the electromechanical world, switching the input and output labels of the stepping relay used for multiplexing allows it to be used for demultiplexing as well. This bidirectional ability allows the CMOS

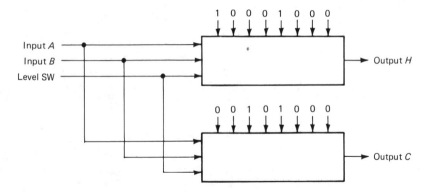

FIGURE 4-20. Rinse cycle subsystem controller using multiplexer logic

analog multiplexer to perform as a demultiplexing circuit as well. However, the digital multiplexer and demultiplexer allow information to travel in only one direction; therefore, different devices are used for digital multiplexing and demultiplexing.

Demultiplexers in Control

A common use of the demultiplexer is the generation of single-output lines from internal-coded logic. An example illustrates this concept.

Example of Demultiplexer Logic

Consider a labeling station that marks the voltage of a reference cell on the cell packaging. The gross voltage of the cell is known to the closest tenth of a volt and has been adjusted to be within $+.004/-.003$ volts of an even tenth. The purpose of this subsystem is to label the cell packaging with this difference. This is accomplished by measuring the voltage with a differential voltmeter and activating the proper label hammer when the cell is in line with the label station. Figure 4-21 contains the logic diagram for such a station.

In this circuit the differential voltmeter station determines the difference between the cell and its internal standard. The output of the voltmeter station is a binary number between 0 and 7 that acts as the selection information for a one-shot multivibrator. The one-shot is triggered by the presence of a cell package at the labeling station. The pulse output of the station is then directed by the demultiplexer to the proper labeling hammer, causing the hammer to print the cell label.

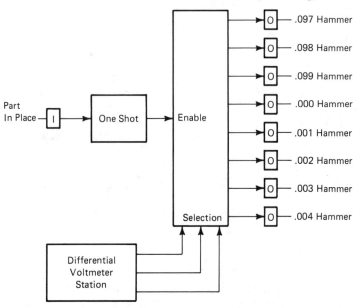

FIGURE 4-21. Reference cell labeling station using demultiplexer

Multiplexing and Demultiplexing
Paired Applications

Multiplexing and demultiplexing have been used in communications since the early days of telegraphy and are common practice in relay control systems. A combination of two stepping relays, for example, may be used to send selectively eight lines of information over three wires, as shown in Figure 4-22. The price paid for the reduction in communications lines is the loss of parallel availability of any one line.

The solid-state equivalent of the circuit in Figure 4-22 is illustrated in Figure 4-23 using TTL circuit elements. This communication scheme may use a variety of methods to determine which input/output pair is to use the communication line.

One of the most common methods is time-slice multiplexing. In this method, the select lines are driven by a time-clocked counter that selects each input/output pair in turn, whether information is present or not. This method of selection is illustrated in Figure 4-24.

A second method uses priority encoding. Under this technique, each input/output pair is assigned a priority number. If an input line has information to transmit, then a flip-flop is set indicating it is requesting time on the link. The flip-flops are scanned by a demultiplexer, the highest number flip-flop is given time on the link, and its flip-flop is reset. The flip-flops are continuously scanned and the highest priority line is serviced. This method is illustrated in Figure 4-25.

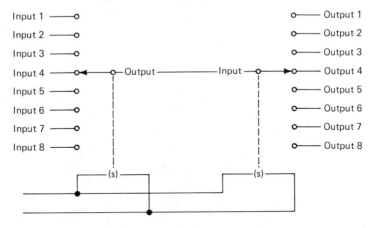

FIGURE 4-22. Eight-line transfer by multiplexing/demultiplexing

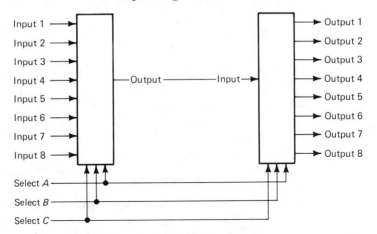

FIGURE 4-23. Eight-line communication using multiplexer/demultiplexer

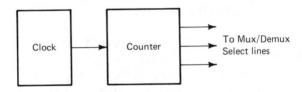

FIGURE 4-24. Multiplexer/demultiplexer selection driver

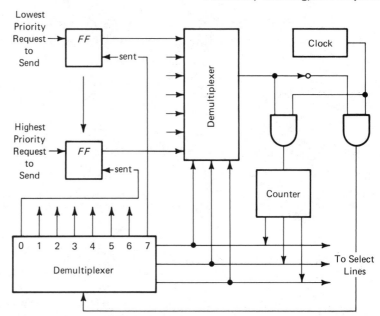

FIGURE 4-25. Priority-based multiplexing/demultiplexing selection

The multiplexing and demultiplexing examples thus far have required both a multiplexer and a demultiplexer, as the electromechanical stepper needed two stepping switches to share electrical lines. An alternative sharing scheme is based on three-state outputs. In this method, all devices are permanently tied to the shared line(s). The connection to the lines is made with a three-state output, which allows the device to be disconnected from the shared line or bus by placing the device's outputs in a high-impedance state using a single control line. This means that only one selector/decoder is required to select which device may access the line or bus. The SELECT line information to the decoder then becomes the "address" of the devices. Such a system is shown in Figure 4-26.

4.5 Memory, Counting, and Selection in Context

A large portion of both continuous and discrete control is implemented in programmable devices. At the heart of programmable control is the integrated circuit memory. Both the RAM device and the ROM are used extensively in all microcomputer-based controllers. The cost of all types of semiconductor memory is decreasing at an

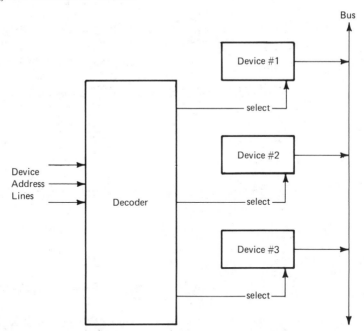

FIGURE 4-26. Three-state multiplexing using a demultiplexer/decoder

accelerated rate. In addition, larger memory parts at smaller prices per bit are appearing almost monthly. Sixteen- and 32-bit machines have increased the directly addressable memory space and further increased the demand for memory. All of these factors place integrated circuit memory at the center of concern for the foreseeable future.

Counting is the heart of batch-based control and all assembly-line applications. The stand-alone counter used both for control and data acquisition purposes has an assured place in industry. Counting, counters, and registers are essential to programmable applications where interfacing of multiple devices or systems requires hardware preservation of an accumulated total, although most counts are maintained in software registers in computer-based control systems.

When counting is combined with a time-base generator, then counting becomes sequencing. Sequencing, for the most part, has been taken over by programmable devices, but in special applications, such as small, stand-alone devices, some integrated circuit sequencers are still used.

Multiplexing, much used in communications, is also used in some industrial systems as an input-scanning mechanism. By scanning a number of input points and using a single-input interface device, the cost of an input system can be reduced with only a small loss in input capability. Very little state machine implementation is generated using multiplexing and demultiplexing sequencers, except as a development tool or in small, one-time applications.

Demultiplexing, as selection, is extensively used in support of integrated circuit memory. In this application, the selector is used as a decoder for enabling a particular memory chip from a given address. This technique is also used as an input and output strobe (ENABLE) line for microcomputer applications.

Problems

4.1   What is a memory cell and what basic logic element could be used as one.

4.2   What is a register and what devices are commonly used for register construction?

4.3   What cell functions are operated by single command lines in a register?

4.4   What is the common bit length for multiple data latches? Why?

4.5   What is the definition of the term *file* and what devices route the signals within a file?

4.6   What is meant by the term *address* and *data lines* with respect to a file?

4.7   What device routes signals from information on the address lines?

4.8   What is the purpose of READ and WRITE signals?

4.9   How are the data-line requirements minimized in semiconductor memory?

4.10 What are the principal types of semiconductor memory?

4.11 What characterizes static and dynamic memory devices?

4.12 Which memory type is used for storage determined at manufacture?

4.13 What special precautions could be needed when using ultraviolet, erasable PROMs?

4.14 The 2764 EPROM is an eight-bit-wide device. How many bytes of information can it hold?

4.15 A PROM is best used as the basis for state-based design. Convert the water storage tank control circuit of Chapter 2 to a state table, and determine the PROM size necessary to implement it.

4.16 What is the carry mechanism in the electromechanical and the electronic counter?

4.17 Latching is the basis for counting. What are the differences and similarities between these two functions?

4.18 What is a modulus and what is modulo-counting?

4.19 Counters are classified by what two characteristics? What are two common counter types?

4.20 Variable-state sequencing is provided by a counting method called what?

4.21 Ring counting is based upon what counting mechanism and feature?

4.22 Describe the two methods of counter clocking.

4.23 Describe the features and functions of a universal counting element.

4.24 Using a 74LS193, draw the circuit diagram for modulo-counting of 5, 10, 16.

4.25 Describe a code generator that uses a parallel-in, serial-out shift register.

4.26 A ring counter uses a single ONE or ZERO to indicate its count. Using a ring counter containing all ONEs and one ZERO, describe a system that disables a different one of eight induction heating coils every five minutes.

4.27 Describe the characteristics of an industrial-counter controller.

4.28 A major limitation of industrial-counter controllers is the operating speed of the device. What is the common limit and why does it exist?

4.29 Diagram a car-washing device using an industrial-counter controller as the principal device.

4.30 Selection includes what industrial functions?

4.31 Define multiplexing and list its common tasks.

4.32 What are the limitations and advantages of IC multiplexers as compared to electromechanical devices?

4.33 Encoding is a special case of multiplexing and can be used to implement a state table for a limited I/O machine. Diagram such a machine for the blower control circuit in Chapter 2.

4.34 Define demultiplexing and describe the differences between an analog and digital demultiplexer. Which type of demultiplexer best approximates the electromechanical stepping switch?

4.35 Describe three means of using multiplexer/demultiplexer pairs in communications.

4.36 What is the functional cost of using a multiplexer/demultiplexer scheme to reduce communications lines?

54/7470
JK EDGE-TRIGGERED FLIP-FLOP

CONNECTION DIAGRAMS
PINOUT A

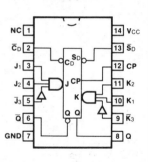

DESCRIPTION — The '70 is a gated input edge-triggered JK flip-flop offering Direct Clear and Set inputs, and complementary Q and $\bar{Q}$ outputs. Information at the J and K inputs is tranferred to the outputs on the positive edge of the clock pulse. Direct-coupled clock triggering occurs at a specified voltage level of the clock pulse. When the clock input threshold voltage has been passed, the gate inputs are locked out. These flip-flops are designed for medium to high speed applications and offer a significant saving in system power dissipation and package count where input gating is required.

PINOUT B

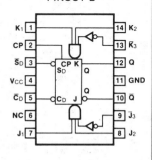

TRUTH TABLE

INPUTS		OUTPUT
@ t_n		@ t_{n+1}
J	K	Q
L	L	Q_n
L	H	L
H	L	H
H	H	$\bar{Q}_n$

Asynchronous Inputs:
LOW input to $\bar{S}_D$ sets Q to HIGH level
LOW input to $\bar{C}_D$ sets Q to LOW level
Clear or Set function can only occur when clock input is LOW
Simultaneous LOW on $\bar{C}_D$ and $\bar{S}_D$ is indeterminate

$J = J_1 \cdot J_2 \cdot \bar{J}_3$
$K = K_1 \cdot K_2 \cdot \bar{K}_3$
t_n = Bit time before clock pulse.
t_{n+1} = Bit time after clock pulse.
If inputs $\bar{J}_3$ or $\bar{K}_3$ are not used they must be grounded.
H = HIGH Voltage Level
L = LOW Voltage Level

LOGIC SYMBOL

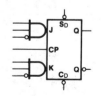

V_{CC} = Pin 14 (4)
GND = Pin 7 (11)

ORDERING CODE: See Section 9

PKGS	PIN OUT	COMMERCIAL GRADE V_{CC} = +5.0 V ±5%, T_A = 0°C to +70°C	MILITARY GRADE V_{CC} = +5.0 V ±10%, T_A = -55°C to +125°C	PKG TYPE
Plastic DIP (P)	A	7470PC		9A
Ceramic DIP (D)	A	7470DC	5470DM	6A
Flatpak (F)	B	7470FC	5470FM	3I

INPUT LOADING/FAN-OUT: See Section 3 for U.L. definitions

PIN NAMES	DESCRIPTION	54/74 (U.L.) HIGH/LOW
J_1, J_2, $\bar{J}_3$ K_1, K_2, $\bar{K}_3$	Data Inputs	1.0/1.0
CP	Clock Pulse Input (Active Rising Edge)	1.0/1.0
$\bar{C}_D$	Direct Clear Input (Active LOW)	2.0/2.0
$\bar{S}_D$	Direct Set Input (Active LOW)	2.0/2.0
Q, $\bar{Q}$	Outputs	20/10

Courtesy Fairchild Camera and Instrument Corp.

54/7474
54H/74H74
54S/74S74
54LS/74LS74

DUAL D-TYPE POSITIVE EDGE-TRIGGERED FLIP-FLOP

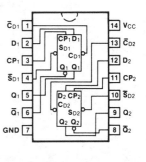

DESCRIPTION — The '74 devices are dual D-type flip-flops with Direct Clear and Set inputs and complementary (Q, $\bar{Q}$) outputs. Information at the input is transferred to the outputs on the positive edge of the clock pulse. Clock triggering occurs at a voltage level of the clock pulse and is not directly related to the transition time of the positive going pulse. After the Clock Pulse input threshold voltage has been passed, the Data input is locked out and information present will not be transferred to the outputs until the next rising edge of the Clock Pulse input.

PINOUT B

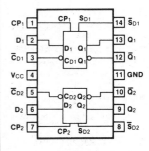

TRUTH TABLE
(Each Half)

INPUT	OUTPUTS	
@ t_n	@ t_{n+1}	
D	Q	$\bar{Q}$
L	L	H
H	H	L

Asynchronous Inputs:
  LOW input to $\bar{S}_D$ sets Q to HIGH level
  LOW input to $\bar{C}_D$ sets Q to LOW level
  Clear and Set are independent of clock
  Simultaneous LOW on $\bar{C}_D$ and $\bar{S}_D$
  makes both Q and $\bar{Q}$ HIGH

H = HIGH Voltage Level
L = LOW Voltage Level
t_n = Bit time before clock pulse.
t_{n+1} = Bit time after clock pulse.

LOGIC SYMBOL

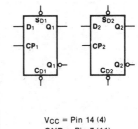

V_{CC} = Pin 14 (4)
GND = Pin 7 (11)

ORDERING CODE: See Section 9

PKGS	PIN OUT	COMMERCIAL GRADE V_{CC} = +5.0 V ±5%, T_A = 0°C to +70°C	MILITARY GRADE V_{CC} = +5.0 V ±10%, T_A = -55°C to +125°C	PKG TYPE
Plastic DIP (P)	A	7474PC, 74H74PC 74S74PC, 74LS74PC		9A
Ceramic DIP (D)	A	7474DC, 74H74DC 74S74DC, 74LS74DC	5474DM, 54H74DM 54S74DM, 54LS74DM	6A
Flatpak (F)	A	74S74FC, 74LS74FC	54S74FM, 54LS74FM	3I
	B	7474FC, 74H74FC	5474FM, 54H74FM	

Courtesy Fairchild Camera and Instrument Corp.

54S/74S138
54LS/74LS138
1-OF-8 DECODER/DEMULTIPLEXER

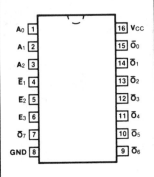

DESCRIPTION — The '138 is a high speed 1-of-8 decoder/demultiplexer. This device is ideally suited for high speed bipolar memory chip select address decoding. The multiple input enables allow parallel expansion to a 1-of-24 decoder using just three '138 devices or to a 1-of-32 decoder using four '138 devices and one inverter. The '138 is fabricated with the Schottky barrier diode process for high speed.

- **SCHOTTKY PROCESS FOR HIGH SPEED**
- **DEMULTIPLEXING CAPABILITY**
- **MULTIPLE INPUT ENABLE FOR EASY EXPANSION**
- **ACTIVE LOW MUTUALLY EXCLUSIVE OUTPUTS**

LOGIC SYMBOL

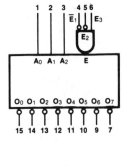

V_{CC} = Pin 16
GND = Pin 8

ORDERING CODE: See Section 9

PKGS	PIN OUT	COMMERCIAL GRADE V_{CC} = +5.0 V ±5%, T_A = 0°C to +70°C	MILITARY GRADE V_{CC} = +5.0 V ±10%, T_A = -55°C to +125°C	PKG TYPE
Plastic DIP (P)	A	74S138PC, 74LS138PC		9B
Ceramic DIP (D)	A	74S138DC, 74LS138DC	54S138DM, 54LS138DM	6B
Flatpak (F)	A	74S138FC, 74LS138FC	54S138FM, 54LS138FM	4L

INPUT LOADING/FAN-OUT: See Section 3 for U.L. definitions

PIN NAMES	DESCRIPTION	54/74S (U.L.) HIGH/LOW	54/74LS (U.L.) HIGH/LOW
$A_0 - A_2$	Address Inputs	1.25/1.25	0.5/0.25
$\overline{E}_1, \overline{E}_2$	Enable Inputs (Active LOW)	1.25/1.25	0.5/0.25
E_3	Enable Input (Active HIGH)	1.25/1.25	0.5/0.25
$\overline{O}_0 - \overline{O}_7$	Outputs (Active LOW)	25/12.5	10/5.0 (2.5)

Courtesy Fairchild Camera and Instrument Corp.

54/74151A
54S/74S151
54LS/74LS151

8-INPUT MULTIPLEXER

CONNECTION DIAGRAM
PINOUT A

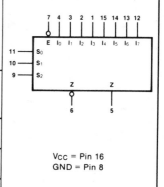

I_3 1 — 16 V_{CC}
I_2 2 — 15 I_4
I_1 3 — 14 I_5
I_0 4 — 13 I_6
Z 5 — 12 I_7
$\bar{Z}$ 6 — 11 S_0
$\bar{E}$ 7 — 10 S_1
GND 8 — 9 S_2

DESCRIPTION — The '151 is a high speed 8-input digital multiplexer. It provides in one package, the ability to select one line of data from up to eight sources. The '151 can be used as a universal function generator to generate any logic function of four variables. Both assertion and negation outputs are provided.

LOGIC SYMBOL

V_{CC} = Pin 16
GND = Pin 8

ORDERING CODE: See Section 9

PKGS	PIN OUT	COMMERCIAL GRADE V_{CC} = +5.0 V ±5%, T_A = 0°C to +70°C	MILITARY GRADE V_{CC} = +5.0 V ±10%, T_A = -55°C to +125°C	PKG TYPE
Plastic DIP (P)	A	74151APC, 74S151PC 74LS151PC		9B
Ceramic DIP (D)	A	74151ADC, 74S151DC 74LS151DC	54151ADM, 54S151DM 54LS151DM	6B
Flatpak (F)	A	74151AFC, 74S151FC 74LS151FC	54151AFM, 54S151FM 54LS151FM	4L

INPUT LOADING/FAN-OUT: See Section 3 for U.L. definitions

PIN NAMES	DESCRIPTION	54/74 (U.L.) HIGH/LOW	54/74S (U.L.) HIGH/LOW	54/74LS (U.L.) HIGH/LOW
$I_0 - I_7$	Data Inputs	1.0/1.0	1.25/1.25	0.5/0.25
$S_0 - S_2$	Select Inputs	1.0/1.0	1.25/1.25	0.5/0.25
$\bar{E}$	Enable Input (Active LOW)	1.0/1.0	1.25/1.25	0.5/0.25
Z	Data Output	20/10	25/12.5	10/5.0 (2.5)
$\bar{Z}$	Inverted Data Output	20/10	25/12.5	10/5.0 (2.5)

Courtesy Fairchild Camera and Instrument Corp.

54/74193
54LS/74LS193
UP/DOWN BINARY COUNTER
(With Separate Up/down Clocks)

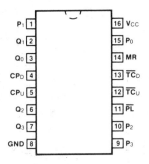

DESCRIPTION — The '193 is an up/down modulo-16 binary counter. Separate Count Up and Count Down Clocks are used and in either counting mode the circuits operate synchronously. The outputs change state synchronous with the LOW-to-HIGH transitions on the clock inputs. Separate Terminal Count Up and Terminal Count Down outputs are provided which are used as the clocks for subsequent stages without extra logic, thus simplifying multistage counter designs. Individual preset inputs allow the circuits to be used as programmable counters. Both the Parallel Load ($\overline{PL}$) and the Master Reset (MR) inputs asynchronously override the clocks. For functional description and detail specifications please refer to the '192 data sheet.

LOGIC SYMBOL

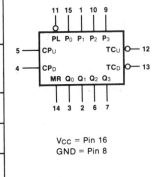

V_{CC} = Pin 16
GND = Pin 8

ORDERING CODE: See Section 9

PKGS	PIN OUT	COMMERCIAL GRADE V_{CC} = +5.0 V ±5%, T_A = 0°C to +70°C	MILITARY GRADE V_{CC} = +5.0 V ±10%, T_A = -55°C to +125°C	PKG TYPE
Plastic DIP (P)	A	74193PC, 74LS193PC		9B
Ceramic DIP (D)	A	74193DC, 74LS193DC	54193DM, 54LS193DM	6B
Flatpak (F)	A	74193FC, 74LS193FC	54193FM, 54LS193FM	4L

INPUT LOADING/FAN-OUT: See Section 3 for U.L. definitions

PIN NAMES	DESCRIPTION	54/74 (U.L.) HIGH/LOW	54/74LS (U.L.) HIGH/LOW
CP_U	Count Up Clock Input (Active Rising Edge)	1.0/1.0	0.5/0.25
CP_D	Count Down Clock Input (Active Rising Edge)	1.0/1.0	0.5/0.25
MR	Asynchronous Master Reset Input (Active HIGH)	1.0/1.0	0.5/0.25
$\overline{PL}$	Asynchronous Parallel Load Input (Active LOW)	1.0/1.0	0.5/0.25
$P_0 - P_3$	Parallel Data Inputs	1.0/1.0	0.5/0.25
$Q_0 - Q_3$	Flip-flop Outputs	20/10	10/5.0 (2.5)
$\overline{TC}_D$	Terminal Count Down (Borrow) Output (Active LOW)	20/10	10/5.0 (2.5)
$\overline{TC}_U$	Terminal Count Up (Carry) Output (Active LOW)	20/10	10/5.0 (2.5)

Courtesy Fairchild Camera and Instrument Corp.

54LS/74LS273

8-BIT REGISTER
(With Clear)

DESCRIPTION — The '273 is a high speed 8-bit register, consisting of eight D-type flip-flops with a common Clock and an asynchronous active LOW Master Reset. This device is supplied in a 20-pin package featuring 0.3 inch row spacing.

- **EDGE-TRIGGERED**
- **8-BIT HIGH SPEED REGISTER**
- **PARALLEL IN AND OUT**
- **COMMON CLOCK AND MASTER RESET**

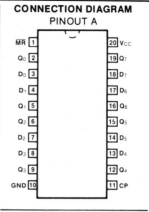

CONNECTION DIAGRAM
PINOUT A

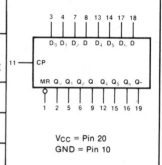

LOGIC SYMBOL

V_{CC} = Pin 20
GND = Pin 10

ORDERING CODE: See Section 9

PKGS	PIN OUT	COMMERCIAL GRADE V_{CC} = +5.0 V ±5%, T_A = 0°C to +70°C	MILITARY GRADE V_{CC} = +5.0 V ±10%, T_A = -55°C to +125°C	PKG TYPE
Plastic DIP (P)	A	74LS273PC		9Z
Ceramic DIP (D)	A	74LS273DC	54LS273DM	4E
Flatpak (F)	A	74LS273FC	54LS273FM	4F

INPUT LOADING/FAN-OUT: See Section 3 for U.L. definitions

PIN NAMES	DESCRIPTION	54/74LS (U.L.) HIGH/LOW
CP	Clock Pulse Input (Active Rising Edge)	0.5/0.25
$D_0 — D_7$	Data Inputs	0.5/0.25
$\overline{MR}$	Asynchronous Master Reset Input (Active LOW)	0.5/0.25
$Q_0 — Q_7$	Flip-flop Outputs	10/5.0 (2.5)

LOGIC DIAGRAM

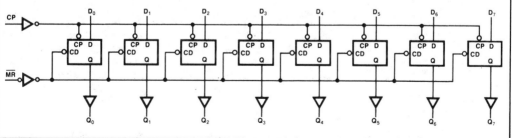

Courtesy Fairchild Camera and Instrument Corp.

141

5 | Interfacing Digital Controls

5.0 Introduction

Integrated-circuit logic is well defined and predictable in an ideal environment. The industrial environment, however, is electrically destructive and noisy. This environment would seem to preclude the use of integrated circuits in industry. For example, the voltage levels used for TTL logic levels are low and separated by only a narrow noise margin, thus making them susceptible to induced signals from heavy electrical loads. CMOS logic gates have a better noise margin, but they can be destroyed by the static charge generated by a person combing his hair. ICs per se are designed to switch small loads, typically under one watt, and have no provision for handling inductive loads. To be useful in the industrial environment of arc welders and 800 HP motor starters, the integrated-circuit control logic must be protected and its power-handling capability amplified.

Electrical signal level and power changes are not the only interface required. A host of control applications are based upon measuring and synchronizing with time as a control parameter. In this chapter, both electrical and time interfacing are considered. It is this interfacing that permits the integrated circuit to play a leading role in digital control.

5.1 Control-Circuit Timing

In today's digital world, it is time that separates control and data acquisition applications of digital electronics from general computing. The limits of industrial microcomputer use are often measured by the ability of a system to respond in "real time." Timing, when added to logic circuitry, permits the synchronization of external and internal events and processes. This permits batch control and sequencing in which time is an input parameter.

Control-action timing is not a new requirement. Timing is historically an important part of relay control, not only in sequencing circuit action, but also in delaying the execution of control action. This process of time delay is implemented in the electromechanical world as the time-delay relay. The time-delay relay, as discussed in Chapter 2, is found in the following types:

- Normally open contacts, timed close
- Normally closed contacts, timed close
- Normally open contacts, timed open
- Normally closed contacts, timed open.

These familiar relay functions are augmented by two additional needs in solid-state applications: one-shot pulse generators and clocking circuits.

In the semiconductor world, as in the electromechanical one, more than one type of timing mechanism is used. Two common IC timing methods are the RC timer and the clock counter.

The Integrated Circuit RC Timer

A series resistor and capacitor is often used in forming discrete timing circuits in all branches of electronics. All these circuits base timing action on the rising terminal voltage of a capacitor during charge, through the resistor or the falling voltage during discharge. This phenomenon has been used with a variety of discrete components, such as unijunction transistors, FETs, and op-amp comparators, to produce control circuits. The dedicated integrated-circuit version of the RC timer has incorporated the most useful features of the discrete component circuits and has become a universal element. So versatile is the timer chip that entire volumes are written on just its applications.

The RC chip timer is manufactured by a number of firms. Each timer manufacturer's timing chip has its particular advantages. Despite this variation, the principles and main features are similar. A general-purpose timer block diagram is illustrated in Figure 5-1.

Initially, the control flip-flop is in the RESET state, which causes the open collector discharge circuit to short the timing capacitor to ground. The output driver, which is fed by the SET-side output of the control flip-flop, is in the OFF state.

When the input signal line goes below one-third of the supply voltage, the lower comparator produces an output that sets the control

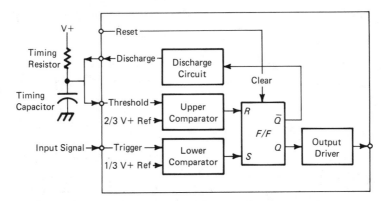

FIGURE 5-1. Integrated circuit RC timer connected as a one-shot

flip-flop. Setting the control flip-flop turns on the output stage and turns off the discharge output stage, removing the short across the timing capacitor. The timing capacitor charges through the timing resistor, increasing its terminal voltage until it reaches two-thirds of its supply voltage. At this point, the upper comparator, connected to the capacitor via the threshold line, resets the flip-flop, discharges the timing capacitor, and turns off the output. A timing diagram of this application appears in Figure 5-2.

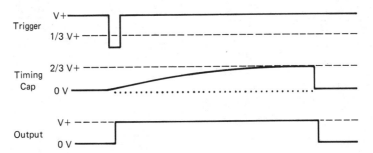

FIGURE 5-2. Timing for one-shot mode of an RC timer

One-Shot Timing Circuit

In actual operation, the one-shot circuit in Figure 5-2 is implemented as in Figure 5-3. In this circuit, the input RC network forms a differentiator which provides a negative-going pulse to trigger the one-shot. The timing RC network provides the delay, which is approximately equal to 1.1 times the resistor value in ohms times the capacitor value in farads. As shown in Figure 5-3, the output is used to

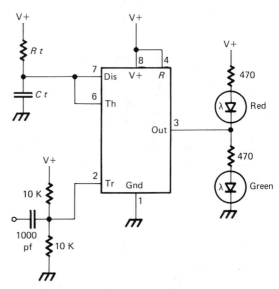

FIGURE 5-3. Integrated circuit RC timer, one-shot

turn on the green LED and simultaneously turn off the red LED during the timing cycle.

RC Timer Time-Delay Relay Replacements

The functions of the time-delay relay are required in integrated circuit control as well. A circuit that duplicates the relay functions as given above, and is often used for that purpose, is shown in Figure 5-4. Table 5-1 shows how the various delay functions are accomplished.

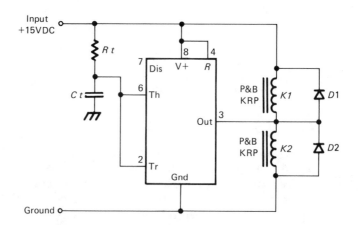

FIGURE 5-4. Normally open, timed close relay/normally open, timed open

TABLE 5-1. Functions of the time-delay relay

FUNCTION	RELAY CONTACTS
NOTO	K1 NO
NOTC	K2 NO
NCTC	K1 NC
NCTO	K2 NC

The circuit in Figure 5-4 is operated by applying power to the input line. Connection to power starts the timer by the momentary ground on the trigger input presented by the charging capacitor. The start of the timing cycle causes relay K2 to energize, closing its contacts. When the terminal voltage of the capacitor reaches two-thirds of the source voltage, the threshold input causes the output line to switch, causing relay K2 to release and relay K1 to energize. The circuit will remain in this state, since the discharge terminal is not connected, until the power is removed. Removing power at any time causes both relays to release.

Clocking Circuits

The digital circuit may operate over a wide range of speeds. This fact is both an advantage and a disadvantage to the control designer. The phenomenon of *racing* occurs when mutually exclusive conditions are initiated simultaneously. Racing may occur in relay systems, but is even more likely in integrated circuits where the devices can operate at 30–50 MHz. One partial solution to this problem is to operate all devices in synchronization. By this method, state changes are allowed only when a master clock pulse is generated. The microprocessor-based control circuit rests on this technique.

Clock circuits produce a pulse or series of pulses that coordinate circuit action. The common characteristics of a clock pulse are:

- Rapid rise time
- High-drive capability
- Rapid fall time
- Glitch- and jitter-free generation
- Repeatability.

The rapid rise and fall times are necessary to ensure activation of edge-triggered devices. The high-drive capability is necessary to avoid the need for buffering, which may insert additional propagation delays and destroy synchronization. The glitch- and jitter-free operation is necessary to prevent false triggering and inconsistent timing. Repeatability provides not only a stable clock base in time, but also a consistent duration in which the circuit function is accomplished. A long duration is desired to allow settling of circuit staging, but this must be balanced with an after-clock settling time. In addition, many systems need multiphasic clocks that produce as many as eight clock outputs differing from one another by only a phase angle.

The integrated circuit RC timer may be used in an astable mode to provide a clock source that meets many of the clock requirements. Such a circuit is shown in Figure 5-5.

This circuit begins operation with the application of power which, as before, triggers the timer by the momentary ground applied to the trigger by the charging capacitor. The output at this point goes to a logic ONE. When the capacitor terminal voltage, charging through $R1$ and the forward-biased diode, reaches the threshold point, the output is switched to logic ZERO. This switch grounds the discharge pin, discharging the capacitor through $R2$, which restarts the action. The action of this circuit, while producing a strong output, has temperature, leakage, and repeatability problems. In addition, its output duty cycle is difficult to adjust and subject to jitter.

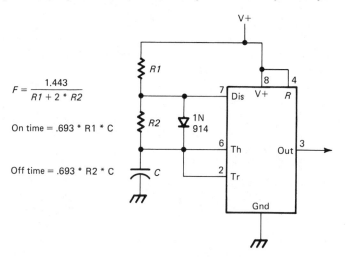

$$F = \frac{1.443}{R1 + 2 * R2}$$

On time = .693 * R1 * C

Off time = .693 * R2 * C

FIGURE 5-5. IC timer astable clock circuit

An improved clock circuit appears in Figure 5-6. This clock generator produces clock pulses at the frequency of resonance of the controlling crystal. The crystal oscillator is the heart of modern digital control circuits; it produces clean pulses with rapid rise times and does so with great precision.

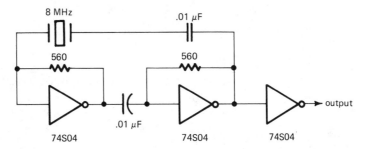

FIGURE 5-6. Crystal oscillator clock generation circuit

The crystal oscillator clock does have a drawback, however. It is adjustable over a very narrow range (by means of a crystal trimming capacitor). To provide additional frequencies, a modulo divider is used as in Figure 5-7. This circuit combines a counter to divide the master clock down to lower frequencies. As may be expected, this combination has been packaged as a single IC, called a clock generator, which incorporates the crystal amplifiers and divider circuitry.

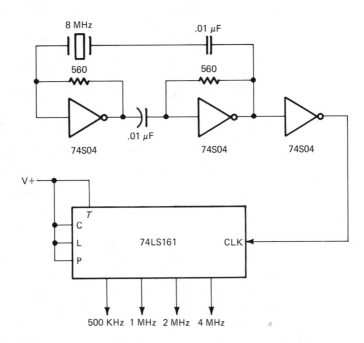

FIGURE 5-7. Crystal oscillator and divider circuit

Time Delays Using Counters

The clock/divider circuit above may also be used to produce time delays. In this method, the clock produces pulses that are counted and compared to the desired delay. When the correct number of pulses have occurred, the output of the circuit is switched. Such a circuit appears in block-diagram form in Figure 5-8.

This circuit maintains a reset to the counter when the input line is not at a logic ONE. When a logic ONE is continuously applied, the reset is removed from the counter and the clock circuit output is connected, via the AND gate, to the counter. The time delay of this device is set by the input switches to the comparator, which are continuously compared to the counter output lines. The comparator output line is switched on when the counter content is equal to or greater than the number selected by the switch settings.

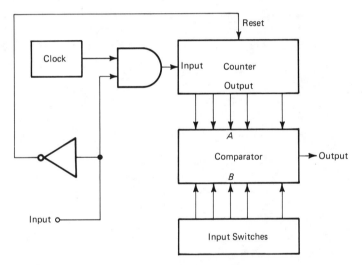

FIGURE 5-8. Counter/comparator time delay

To simplify matters, a single universal counter may be used and loaded with the complement of the desired number of pulses. In this circuit the overflow line provides the time-expired output, as shown in Figure 5-9. In this circuit the load line is constantly enabled, which loads the switch content into the counter. When the input line goes to logic ONE, the load lines are disabled and the counter counts up until overflow is reached, which disables the clock input to the counter.

As may be expected, an IC counter-based time-delay chip is available that can produce delays from milliseconds to days.

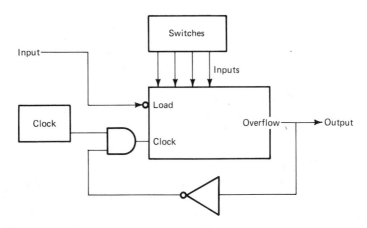

FIGURE 5-9. Time delay circuit using universal counter

Example of Time-Delay-Based Control

Time delays are often used in sequential control. This is particularly true when each step in the sequence must necessarily enable the next. Time delays are also used to prevent early operation or detection of an event by providing a conditional ignorance of an input for the specified delay. As an example of this type of system, consider a clothes dryer that has humidity-sensing in the output airstream. In this system, the dryer is started and runs for the time selected by the operator. When the time has expired, the control is switched to a temperature sensor. If the sensor has reached its threshold, indicating that no more heat is being lost in evaporating the water contained in the clothes, then the heating unit is turned off and the unit continues to run for a cool-down period before stopping. A sample timing chart appears in Figure 5-10.

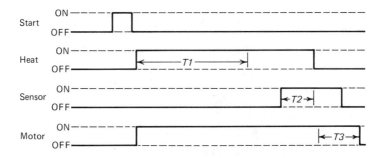

FIGURE 5-10. Timing diagram for dryer control

The times indicated by T in the diagram indicate the timers required. The $T1$ time is a heating cycle time selected by the operator. The time between the end of $T1$ and $T2$ is the time before the humidity sensor trips. The $T2$ time is the time delay before the heater is shut off, thus ensuring that the sensor trip is not a momentary contact due to vibration, etc. The $T3$ time is the cool-down period that commences at the shut-off of the heating element.

The logic diagram in Figure 5-11 illustrates one implementation of such a controller. This circuit is divided into four parts: clock generator, drying timer, humidistat timer, and cool-down timer. The clock generator uses a self-oscillator and divider to provide a one-pulse-per-minute master clock source for the dryer timer counters. The dryer timer is retained in the load condition and is not permitted by the master flip-flop to count. The count, being loaded, is the two's complement of a time set by switches on the control panel of the dryer.

When the START button is depressed, the master control flip-flop is set. This action starts the dryer motor, releases the dryer counter, and permits it to count up to its overflow value. While this count is accumulating, the heating element is engaged and the clothes are drying. When the dryer timer overflows, its output line is disabled. The dryer is then under the control of the humidistat.

When the temperature sensor switch of the humidistat reaches its threshold temperature, it closes and causes the one-shot-based timer to begin timing. When the charge on timing capacitor $C2$ reaches the threshold voltage of the timer chip, the timer output lowers and causes the heater to be turned off.

This heater output line has charged capacitor $C3$ when it was first energized. Capacitor $C3$ is the timing element of the cool-down timer. When the heater command line turns off, capacitor $C3$ discharges through its timing resistor. When the voltage on the capacitor is less than one-third the supply voltage, the timer-chip output goes to a logic ONE and causes the master flip-flop to be reset, thus ending the cycle.

5.2 Integrated Circuit Interfacing

The integrated circuit, with its low cost, high speed, and small size, has revolutionized the industrial control world—but at a price. The price paid is partially due to the fragility of the circuits. Weaknesses appear both in physical and electrical limitations, which convinced some control engineers to reject these devices out of hand. However, design improvements, careful application, and increasingly low cost have matured semiconductor-based control.

Integrated circuit physical limitations are principally heat-related. As the temperature increases, the minority carriers increase

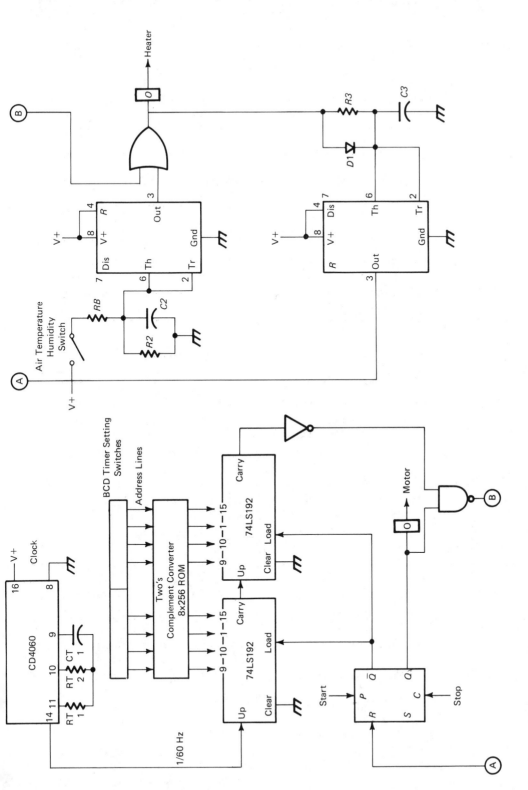

FIGURE 5-11. Electronic dryer control using timers

153

in population in the semiconductor material, thereby increasing leakage in the substrate. The increased leakage causes increased current consumption and increases the power dissipated by the chip. The increased power raises the chip temperature, and the cycle continues. If the temperature increases above approximately 40 degrees Celsius, the cycle of heat and leakage eventually destroys the device. This phenomenon, known as *thermal runaway*, limits the power that an integrated circuit can control to a value that will not cause more than about one-half a watt dissipation in the circuit die. This limit requires buffering of high current loads by interfacing circuitry, as well as making it necessary to maintain a cool environment (25 degrees Celsius preferred).

The integrated circuit has high speed to its credit. It is the one-to-forty MHz switching speeds that permit inexpensive supervisory control, programmable controllers, and self-tuning analog controllers. This high speed also permits inadvertent circuit operation caused by power supply transients, motor starter closures, bouncing switch contacts, and even static discharge from nylon rain suits. Fast IC response alone does not create this problem. The problem is aggravated by the low voltage levels that are used as logic signals in integrated circuit controls. These low levels permit induced voltages to be interpreted as logic signals. In the case of CMOS, inputs are even more susceptible to electrical noise due to the high-input impedance of CMOS gates. Input isolation circuits, power supply filtering, protection circuits, and careful grounding are required to assure predictable control.

The problems of noise and heat can be addressed and successfully beaten in almost every industrial environment. Power conditioning, input interfacing, and output interfacing requirements have all stimulated the creation of products and techniques that expand the limits of integrated circuit technology. The secret of reliable integrated-circuit operation is summarized in the word "isolation"— low signal-level control logic operates most predictably when it has no direct electrical connection with any input or output device and when it is earth-shielded from induced signals. How is it possible to operate an electronic control device that has no direct connection with even its own power source? The methods of accomplishing this are described in three sections: power, input, and output isolation techniques.

5.3 Power Supply Protection

One of the most difficult problems to troubleshoot in digital technology is that of noise pick-up through power supply lines. In most digital control applications, the logic circuit power is supplied by a dc

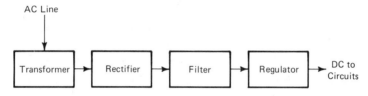

FIGURE 5-12. Block diagram of a dc power supply

supply powered by a single-phase, 120-volt ac line. Although many voltages may be produced by a dc supply, the most heavily used potential is 5 volt dc, which is the common digital integrated circuit supply voltage. Such a supply is diagrammed in block form in Figure 5-12.

The transformer performs the conversion from line voltage to a lower ac voltage (often 8–10 volts ac) and isolates the dc circuitry from direct connection to the ac main. Radio frequency interference may be generated by SCRs, contactors, or universal motors and coupled through transformer winding intercapacitance, as well as by inductive coupling into the enclosure that houses the digital circuitry. Once inside the enclosure, radio frequencies can be coupled through the air to the sensitive digital-switching circuits. One of the first noise-prevention methods is to supply the digital equipment from a separate ac line from the load center. As the second measure to prevent the influx of electrical noise, a protective circuit such as the one in Figure 5-13 is used on the incoming ac feed where the power line enters the enclosure.

The devices labeled MOV are metallic oxide varistors. The purpose of the MOVs is to absorb voltage spikes that occur on the ac line. The MOVs are voltage-dependent resistors designed to respond quickly to voltage transients over their threshold rating. When such a

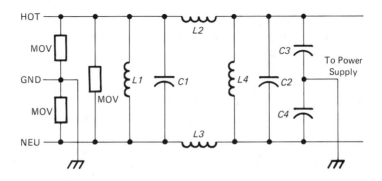

FIGURE 5-13. ac line filter with transient suppression

spike occurs, the MOV resistance drops and the energy of the spike is dissipated as heat. Since many of the equipment-damaging spikes are less then 200 microseconds in duration, the total energy can well be handled by a device about the size of a quarter. Three MOVs are used to provide phase-to-neutral, phase-to-ground, and neutral-to-ground protection.

The LC filter that follows the MOV protection circuits provides a low-pass filter that will attenuate frequencies above 1 kHz. This frequency is well below the 10 kHz to 10 MHz range that most often causes problems in digital-switching circuits. The problem of radio frequency absorption is so common that the filter network pictured in Figure 5-13 is manufactured by many firms as a complete assembly.

All external interference solutions rely on a good earth ground. Even equipment designed with industrial environments in mind must have a separate earth ground to allow the faraday shielding of the enclosure to be fully effective. A power-line ground or structural-steel ground is often subject to general use, such as a welding ground. The circulating currents in such a grounding scheme may cause more problems in the digital controls shielded by the same grounding system than no earth connection at all.

5.4 Internal De-Noising Techniques

The precautions just described reduce electrical interference entering the digital control system from the power line. Once the dc power is produced, new problems arise that are internal to the control cabinet.

Many integrated circuit systems use 5 volts as the principal power source. The current requirement may be in the 10 to 20 ampere range, even for moderate-size power supplies. This load may also vary widely with the logic state of the controller. One method of decoupling the effect of these load changes is to provide individual voltage regulators on each printed circuit board. In addition, high-current load devices, principally display and output devices, may have separate power supplies and be additionally filtered.

Printed circuit boards are the most common method of construction for integrated circuit controls. These boards allow low assembly cost and easy replacement. But they also act as antennae for transmission and reception of high-frequency noise. TTL integrated circuit gates themselves act as transmitters along power supply lines. This effect occurs as a result of the totem-pole outputs used in this logic family, shown in Figure 5-14. As a TTL gate switches, both the transistor that couples the output line to the supply voltage and the transistor that couples the output line to ground, are ON. This short circuit from supply to ground lasts only nanoseconds, but causes

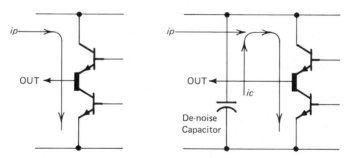

FIGURE 5-14. Totem pole output

noise to be generated along the power supply lines to surrounding integrated circuits. To prevent this noise from switching nearby gates, capacitors are coupled between the power and ground pins of the integrated circuits. The capacitance value is approximately 0.05 to 0.1 microfarads and is applied across about every fourth integrated circuit package. Using a single large capacitor between the power and ground buses does not have the same effect as the distributed capacitance.

Many manufacturers of digital control equipment add an additional layer of fiberglass and foil to their printed circuit boards. These layers (called *ground planes*) are located at either power supply or earth potential as an additional shield to reduce transmission and reception of noise. In some boards the ground planes are the center layers, while on others they may be the outermost layers, or, in military applications, both.

5.5 Input/Output Interfacing

One of the best ways to prevent noise problems is to keep the voltages used for logic separate from input and output circuits. Instead of internal voltages, a dedicated power supply should be provided. This supply is most often at higher potential than the 5-volt internal source (typically 24–48 volts dc). Again, the ac feed to the external supply needs the transient and radio frequency (RF) filter conditioning described above. In addition to ac feed noise, this dc supply is exposed to the abuse of the industrial world. The circuit in Figure 5-15 describes an output protection network that protects against common abuses.

The input *PI* filter, consisting of *C1, L1,* and *C2,* reduces the potential for RF coupling from external sources back into the control cabinetry. The MOV absorbs transients generated by external sources. The zener network protects the power supply and other

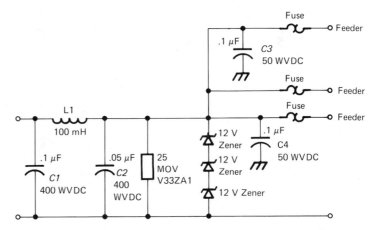

FIGURE 5-15. Input/output external power supply protection network

devices connected to it from overvoltage forced in from the outside. The most likely occurrence is the connection of 120 volts ac to the power supply lines. The zener network causes an effective short circuit to occur if the voltage applied rises above 36 volts. This potential is much above the MOV voltage of 25 volts, and 12 volts above the normal supply line. If a higher voltage is forced into the supply, the zener network short will blow the fuse in the offending line.

Input Isolation

The purpose of input interfacing circuitry is threefold. Its first purpose is to provide a wide noise margin between logic ONE and logic ZERO inputs. The second function is to filter the input signal to the input circuit from the micro- to nanosecond response times to the 20-millisecond responses normally found in industry. This filtered response helps prevent false triggering and eliminates contact bounce. The final function is to isolate the internal circuitry from direct electrical connection with the outside environment.

For the purposes of the following examples, consider the field inputs to be a 24-volt supply system as described above, while the control circuitry is operating at 5 volts with the logic levels of the TTL logic family.

Input interfacing functions are commonly provided by optical isolation, transformer isolation, and relay isolation. Relay isolation is the oldest of the input isolation types. This type of circuit is based on a small reed relay whose coil operates at the higher voltage of the field supply and whose contacts are switching the lower logic-level

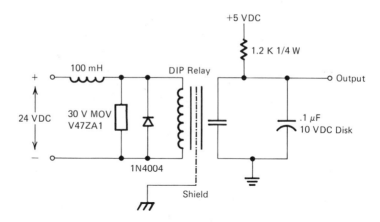

FIGURE 5-16. Relay input isolation circuit

voltages. A typical relay for this purpose is one packaged in a dual-in-line case of the same type as those used for integrated circuits. This packaging technique allows easy assembly and replacement. A complete interface is described in Figure 5-16.

The choke, MOV, and reverse-bias diode protect the DIP relay coil from overvoltage and transients. The shield lead connects a foil shield, which wraps the reed switch to earth ground. This reduces inductive coupling of noise and electrostatic charge transfer. The pull-up resistor on the output line keeps the output at a logic ONE until the relay is energized. Energizing the relay pulls the output line to a logic ZERO by connecting the line to 5-volt common. The one-tenth microfarad capacitor reduces the effect of contact bounce characteristically produced by contact closure. Note the logic inversion of this circuit. This characteristic must be remembered when incorporating such an interface.

Contact Debouncing

Contact closure bounce, such as occurs in the relay interface, is a problem in the interface of operator controls, relays, and limit switches. Contact bounce describes the rapid making and breaking of switch contacts that occurs as the result of the rebound of contacts after they initially strike each other. The RC network illustrated in Figure 5-16 gives some protection by its first-order filter action, but this is inadequate for rapidly changing signals and must be designed for the specific frequency range of input closures expected.

A general-purpose debouncing circuit is illustrated in Figure 5-17. In this circuit the single-pole, double throw switch provides a ground connection to one or the other inputs to the RS flip-flop. The flip-flop will not change state until the ground connection is made.

Contact bounce is not severe enough to cause the swinger of the switch to bounce from contact to contact. The obvious drawback of this circuit is that a double throw switch is required, with the attendant increase in wiring.

An alternate method uses a time-delay circuit as shown in Figure 5-18. The delay circuit activates the output 5 milliseconds after the contacts close. The contacts must be maintained closed for the time of the delay before the timer will time out.

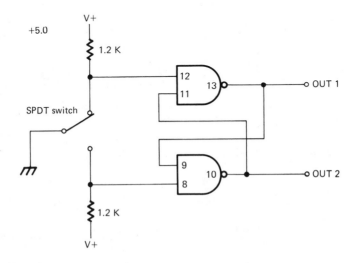

FIGURE 5-17. Switch debounce circuit

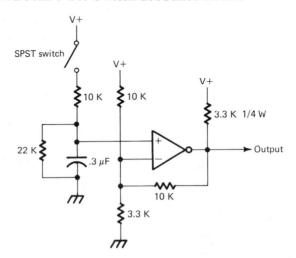

FIGURE 5-18. Debounce circuit with comparator using hysteresis

In this circuit, the timing action is performed by the 10K, 22K and 0.5 microfarad capacitor network at the input. The comparator circuit uses a voltage divider, consisting of the 10K and 3.3K resistors, as a reference. This reference divider also includes the 10K feedback resistor connected to the pull-up output resistor and the open-collector output of the comparator. The effect of the feedback coupling is to increase the reference level when the input level is below the threshold, and decrease the reference level when the input is above the original threshold. The direction-sensitive action may also be performed by a Schmitt-trigger.

Transformer Interfacing

The second oldest method of input interfacing is the transformer-driven circuit. In this method, the input signal is inductively coupled by either a pulse or small signal transformer. Two such circuits are illustrated in Figure 5-19 for the dc signal pulse transformer and Figure 5-20 for the ac signal transformer.

In the circuit shown in Figure 5-19, the dc input signal is applied to the pulse transformer primary. The amplitude of this input is limited by the series resistor Rs, which also reduces the sensitivity of the input to noise, and the MOV, which absorbs signal spikes above the 24-volt design value. When the input signal current flows in the primary, a pulse occurs in the secondary. This pulse is limited by the action of the 4.7-volt zener and its associated series resistor to a logic ONE value. When the dc input signal is removed, the magnetic field of the primary collapses. The primary sees a short circuit in the 1N4004 diodes and expends its energy through the diode. On the secondary side, the zener diode acts as a short to the coupled pulse and prevents additional triggering. This circuit is not widely used. It is most commonly used as a counting circuit input when a switch contact is the counting mechanism.

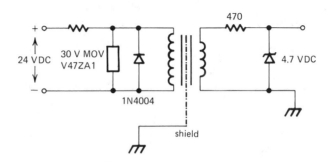

FIGURE 5-19. Pulse transformer coupling

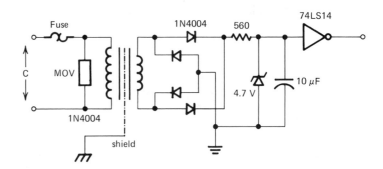

FIGURE 5-20. Transformer coupled ac input interface

The first stage of the circuit in Figure 5-20 consists of the input fuse, the MOV, and the primary of the input transformer. The selected rating of these devices depends on the intended application voltage. The fuse and MOV are rated typically 10 to 20 percent above the nominal peak-to-peak voltage and current expected, and the transformer is selected to produce approximately 6 to 12 volts at the secondary. The second stage consists of a full-wave rectifier (often packaged as a single four-lead device), a voltage regulator, and a first-order filter. This combination produces a low-power dc power supply which is driven by the ac input signal and produces logic-compatible output.

Optical Isolation

Optical isolation is the most common of all input isolation techniques, and the most recent. This input method is based on an LED and optical transistor pair called an *opto-isolator*. This device operates by biasing the optical transistor base with the photons produced by the LED. As the LED increases in illumination, the transistor conduction increases. The ratio of transistor conduction and LED input current is called its *transconductance* characteristic. The breakdown voltage of the insulation between the LED circuit and the phototransistor is called the *isolation voltage*. In general, the greater the tranconductance or the greater the isolation, the higher the cost.

The opto-isolator may be used for both ac and dc input interfacing using a single circuit such as the one illustrated in Figure 5-21. The field side of this circuit consists of the input capacitor, series resistor *Rs*, an MOV, a power rectifier, and the LED of the opto-isolator. The input capacitor absorbs high-frequency noise below the voltage level of the MOV. The MOV absorbs high-voltage transients above its threshold. The power rectifier provides half-wave rectification of the input signal, thereby allowing both ac and dc signals to

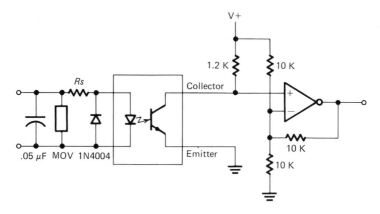

FIGURE 5-21. Universal opto-isolator input interface

power the circuit. The resistor *Rs* limits the current in the opto-isolator LED, determining the output voltage of the isolator. For discrete logic purposes, a conservative LED current is 15 mA. This level of current flow permits inexpensive opto-isolators to be used by assuring that the output transistor goes into saturation. More expensive devices may work on inputs as low as 5 mA of signal current; however, this sensitivity allows greater susceptibility to noise signals. The value of the resistor *Rs* is calculated using the following equation:

$$Rs = \frac{Input\ Voltage\ -\ 1.2\ V}{.0015}$$

1.2 volts is the drop across the isolator LED.

The output elements of this circuit consist of the opto-isolator phototransistor and a Schmitt-trigger comparator, which switches at the one-third and two-thirds voltage levels.

So enormously popular is the opto-isolator and so great is the need for a universal input device for 5-volt logic circuits, that the input opto-isolation circuit has been packaged in standardized modules. These modules are interchangeably produced by a large number of manufacturers. Just as the octal base became a standard for the early relay system, these modules are the standard for integrated circuit control interfacing. The modules are nonrepairable encapsulated units that plug into a heavy-duty printed circuit board that contains fusing, indicators, and screw terminations for field wiring. The 5-volt dc outputs are brought out to an edge connector for connection via ribbon cable to the integrated circuit logic.

Modules are often color-coded by voltage level and type, ac and dc. The common types are as follows:

- dc input 5 volt—White case
- dc input 15 volt—White case
- dc input 24 volt—White case
- dc input 60 volt—White case
- ac input 120 volt—Yellow case
- ac input 240 volt—Yellow case

A back-plane printed circuit board for the input modules holds up to 16 such units.

5.6 Output Interfacing

The low-power dissipation capability of an integrated circuit die necessitates a buffer device for an industrial load. This interface amplifies the power of the control and output and protects the logic circuitry from electrical noise. Interfacing is not limited to heavy-duty outputs; even local operator displays require interfacing circuits to drive them. These displays commonly consist of single annunciators, alphanumeric displays, and bar graphs.

The electrical power used in industrial control circuits falls into two main areas: 24 to 48 volts dc and 120 volts to 480 volts ac. The ac potentials may be one to three phase, but the interface circuitry is essentially the same per phase. Therefore, only single-phase control will be considered here. The interconnection techniques presented in this chapter form a base for further use of integrated circuit control.

Display Interfacing

The simplest annunciator consists of a single lamp that illuminates for a particular condition. In the majority of cases, this function is provided by the light-emitting diode (LED). The most common driver circuit for such an annunciator is shown in Figure 5-22 and is also available in an advanced form in an integrated circuit package.

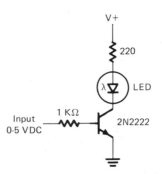

FIGURE 5-22. LED driver interface

The single LED does not easily convey numeric or alphanumeric data. Seven LEDs provide this capability in a single package, called the *seven-segment display*. This device is most often used in industry in .6- to 1-inch high characters and is most commonly available in the colors red, green, and yellow. The problem now lies in providing a conversion device that can convert binary information to high-current signals required for the seven segments. A complete decoder driver circuit appears in Figure 5-23.

The apparent usefulness of the circuit in Figure 5-23 predicts that a further integrated circuit exists to perform this function, and indeed a four-bit data latch, a decoder, and the LED driver is often packaged in the same package as the LEDs.

Bar Graph Interface

An original device for displaying analog data on a control console is the *pneumatic gauge*. Based on the data observed on the gauge, the operator changes switches and relay controls to provide any control action required. The gauge provides a means of displaying the value of the variable being measured and also gives an indication of the time value of the variable by the trend of the indicating pointer. The digital display described above, when coupled to analog-to-digital conversion circuits, provides the value of the measurement as does the

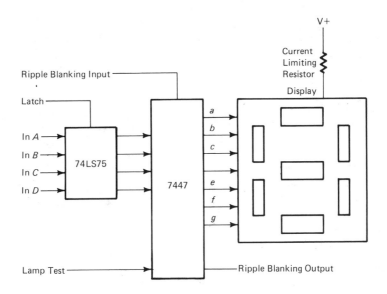

FIGURE 5-23. Decimal decoder driver latch circuit

gauge, but the indication of the time variation of the variable is missing. The LED bar graph provides this time-variation indication. The bar graph display typically consists of 100 small LEDs packaged in a line. An integrated circuit comparator is connected to each one of the LEDs. The chip is tied to an analog input voltage and a reference. The comparators display the percent value of the analog input with respect to the reference by turning on their individual LEDs if the input voltage is equal to or above each successive one-hundredth of the reference. Both value and trend information are available from this display, even at a distance.

dc Output Interfacing

Direct current output interfacing is used mainly for small machine controls and analog-process control connections. The voltages are generally 24, 36, or 48 volts, stemming from battery voltage standards of older dc-supplied systems. The techniques are similar for both potentials; therefore, only the 24-volt dc techniques will be considered.

An elementary method of interface is to substitute a small reed relay for the LED in the display-driving circuit. This circuit is illustrated in Figure 5-24. This method requires a reverse-biased diode across the relay coil to prevent damage to the driver transistor when the magnetic field collapses after the relay is turned off. An RC network across the contacts provides an electrical noise filter by "snubbing" the peak transients, and is therefore termed a *snubber*.

The reed-relay interface has to its credit isolation, simplicity, and both ac and dc switching capabilities, but its drawbacks are limited current-handling ability (usually limited to one ampere), limited cycle life, and noise generation.

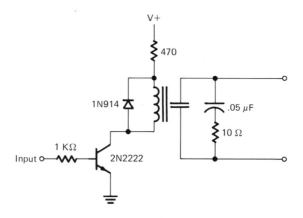

FIGURE 5-24. Reed relay output interface

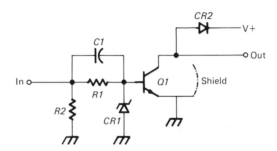

FIGURE 5-25. Practical transistor discrete driver circuit

A second method affords no isolation but does provide higher output voltage and current capability than the simple LED driver while retaining the advantages of long life and low noise generation.

Transistors, in comparison with relays, have the advantages of spark-free operation, immeasurable cycle life, compact size, low cost, and high speed. However, transistors also have drawbacks. Some problems include high temperature sensitivity, output-voltage limitations, and high "on-resistance" between emitter and collector. To guard against these problems, additional components are added to the circuit of Figure 5-24 as shown in Figure 5-25.

The zener diode *(CR1)*, resistor *(R2)*, and diode *(CR2)* are added to prevent reverse polarity or over-voltages from damaging the input base circuit. The capacitor *(C1)* is added to speed up the time necessary to saturate the transistor, thereby reducing power dissipated by the device. Power dissipation is further helped by adding a heat-sink to the transistor package. The output diode *(CR2)* is added to the collector lead to prevent destruction of the transistor by reverse polarity voltages, such as those generated when an inductive load is switched off by the transistor.

A second method uses an open collector, multistage transistor amplifier as the interface device, as shown in Figure 5-26. This circuit, as with many other commonly needed circuits, is packaged in integrated circuit form as a peripheral device driver. The peripheral device driver is often used to interface small solenoids or relays to a digital controller. Such applications include printer hammers, relay contactors, pilot valves, and interposer coils. The driver-integrated circuit handles currents up to 300 milliamperes and voltages to 36 volts. An inductive interface circuit, such as is used for pilot-valve interface, is illustrated in Figure 5-27.

In the pilot-valve driver circuit, the valve solenoid draws between 75 and 250 milliamperes at a voltage of between 12 and 30 volts. The output driver has a dissipation capability of 800 milliwatts,

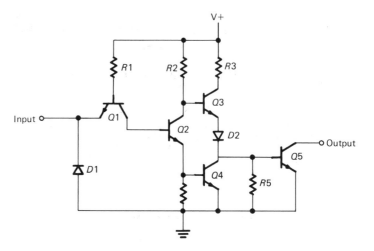

FIGURE 5-26. Peripheral device driver

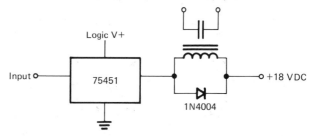

FIGURE 5-27. Pilot valve driver using 75451

which can be enhanced with the addition of an external heat sink. The reverse-biased diode provides protection for the turn-off spike generated by the solenoid coil.

Silicon-Controlled Rectifiers

The need for a compact, high-power switch prompted the development of the class of semiconductor devices called *thyristors*. Power devices of this class include the silicon-controlled rectifier (SCR) and the triac. The SCR came into widespread use during the 1960s, introducing semiconductor devices into industrial environments such as those of welding, induction furnace control, and motor drives. Improvements in manufacturing and understanding have led to a wide variety of devices, from microscopic integrated circuit thyristors to liquid-cooled giants controlling thousands of amperes.

The SCR is ideally suited for discrete application in its similarity to the latching relay. The power gain of the SCR can be very large, which has obvious advantages but also introduces problems with noise and false triggering. In addition the switching action of an SCR generates radio frequency interference, which can cause false triggering of other control circuits. Figure 5-28 illustrates an SCR circuit that contains some solutions to SCR circuit problems. Note that a normally closed switch is in series with the SCR to turn off the device once it has been triggered.

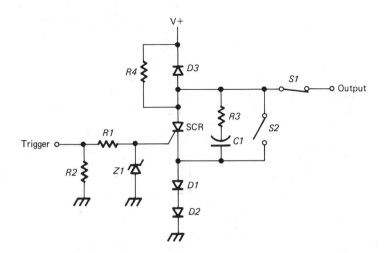

FIGURE 5-28. Practical SCR latching driver

Rectifiers *D1* and *D2*, in series with the cathode of the SCR, raise the gate potential required for firing the device, while the zener diode *Z1* protects the gate circuit from reverse polarity or excessive gate voltages. Resistor *R1* limits gate current, while resistor *R2* in parallel with the input circuit prevents false triggering by loading the input signal. Switching transients are "snubbed" (removed) by the RC network *R3* and *C1*. Reverse polarity protection is provided by rectifier *D4*. An SCR may gate itself ON if noise spikes are received at its anode. This effect is called the *dv/dt effect* and is caused by the coupling of the spike via the inter-electrode capacitance between the anode and gate. A loading resistor, *R4*, is provided to dampen these noise spikes. Note that a normally closed switch, *S1*, is in series with the SCR to turn off the device once it has been triggered. An alternate turn-off switch, *S2*, is shown by dashed lines in parallel with the SCR. However, this method forces the load ON while it turns the SCR OFF.

TRIAC

Full-wave ac control can be accomplished with two SCRs, but this circuit requires two power devices, the need for matching of device characteristics, and gating circuit complications. The triac combines the switching capabilities of the SCR elements in a single package while eliminating the drawbacks of the SCR method.

The triac is the single-most popular semiconductor device for replacing output relays and small contactors in ac control schemes. So common is this application that the gating and noise suppression circuitry is packaged with the triac in an encapsulated assembly with an intrinsic heat-sink.

Triacs and SCRs are treated further in chapter 11.

Optical Isolation

The most commonly used output interfacing techniques incorporate an optical isolator. Output circuits using this device parallel the input isolation techniques described earlier. Isolators are named for the type of elements that comprise them. For instance, an LED/phototransistor coupler uses an LED as the input device and a phototransistor as the output. A variety of isolators are used in industrial control. Although many types of input devices are possible, the LED dominates. Six types of output devices are commonly used with the LED. These are:

- Photoresistor
- Photodiode
- Phototransistor
- PhotoDarlington
- Optical SCR
- Optical triac

The photoresistor and photodiode types are the oldest devices and, due to low gain and slow response, are the least used. The phototransistor and the photoDarlington have higher gain and are the principal dc power-circuit isolation devices. The optical SCR and optical triac are used extensively for control of ac circuits and special motor control applications. The photoDarlington and the optical triac are the most common of the six isolators in present dc and ac control circuits. They are further examined in the following material.

Example of a 24-Volt dc Optically Isolated Output Interface

The purpose of the dc output interface is to provide power amplification for the control output signal, electrical isolation of the control circuitry, electrical noise reduction, and protection of the output circuit. A typical 24-volt dc output interface is illustrated in Figure 5-29.

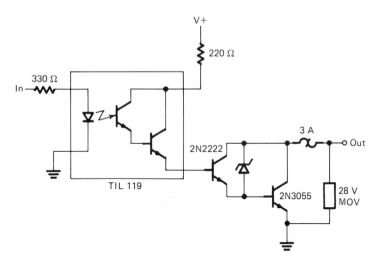

FIGURE 5-29. Three-amp 24 V dc output interface

The circuit in Figure 5-29 consists of an opto-isolator and a Darlington pair power amplifier. The LED of the isolator provides the photon bias current necessary to saturate the Darlington pair of the isolator. The current through the isolator, limited by the collector resistor, provides the base current for the final Darlington pair. The Darlington configuration is used due to its low input current requirement and its low power-device dissipation during both cut-off and saturation conditions. The zener diode protects the final output transistor from inductive feedback during cut-off and overvoltages generated by external misapplication. The MOV reduces the effect of output transients above its 28-volt threshold. The output fuse does not protect the transistor pair, but instead clears the circuit in the event the output current exceeds the fuse value. This overcurrent condition may occur if the output transistor short circuits, as in the case of transient or thermal damage. The power transistor requires a heat-sink to prevent overtemperature damage.

A Line-Voltage Interface

A large percentage of the outputs of discrete control systems use a transformer-isolated 120-volt line as the control voltage. A minimum interface for integrated circuit interface is shown in Figure 5-30.

The circuit in Figure 5-30 uses an optical triac as the interface device. In this circuit, the triac is gated ON by the photon of the LED and continues in condition until a ZERO crossing occurs. If the LED is OFF, then ac conduction ceases. If the LED is still ON, then ac con-

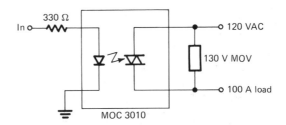

FIGURE 5-30. 100 mA 120 V ac interface

duction begins for the opposite half-cycle. The MOV in this circuit provides protection for the triac and, in addition, provides a radio frequency noise suppressor for the noise generated by the turn-on of the
triac. This noise suppression is necessary due to the fact that the triac
switch is not synchronized to the zero crossings of the current and
voltage waveforms of the load. Such synchronization is not essential
at the low-load levels of this circuit, but it is necessary at higher loads.

A higher power-line voltage interface appears in Figure 5-31.
This circuit also uses the optical triac as the isolation device, but in
this implementation the output device is a 6 ampere triac. The MOV in
this circuit also absorbs transients and damps some radio frequency
noise. The MOV damps noise above 130-volt peaks, but to handle
lower amplitudes an RC network is used in shunt with the output
triac.

The RC network is tuned to the particular application of the
triac. This circuit is critical to the interface, not only due to the
reduction of radio frequency noise, but also due to a particular
characteristic of four-layer devices called the *dv/dt effect*. This effect
causes a thyristor to turn on if the rate of change of the voltage across
the *MT1* and *MT2* terminals exceeds a given value. This effect occurs

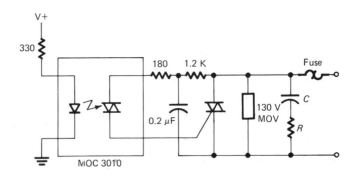

FIGURE 5-31. Six ampere 120 V ac interface

both in SCRs and triacs. When coupled with the tendency of semi-conductor power devices to short, the dv/dt effect has prevented many machine tool applications from using SCR and triac output interfaces. The dv/dt effect can be countered by an RC network as illustrated in Figure 5-31.

The RC values are calculated as follows:

Given:

        The critical dv/dt for the particular thyristor, dv/dt

        The resistive value of the load, r

        The inductive value of the load, l

        The line voltage, E

$R = (.8 \cdot (dv/dt) \cdot l)/E$

$C = 4 \cdot l/r$

The RC network slows the rise time of voltage across the thyristor and reduces the potential for false triggering.

To reduce the noise generation and inrush current problems associated with asynchronous switching, a ZERO-crossing network is added to the circuit in Figure 5-31. This device detects when voltage crosses ZERO and produces a gating pulse that permits the logic input to gate the thyristor. Such a device is shown in the interface circuit in Figure 5-32.

The ZERO-crossing network reduces the need of the RC network for dv/dt protection, but it is included as an external noise filter. This circuit permits the triac interface to be used with heavy loads as well as in inductive applications, with minimum impact on surrounding circuitry and minimum concern for false triggering.

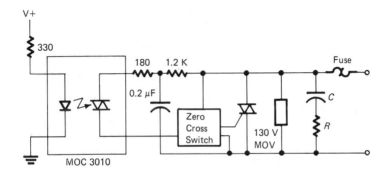

FIGURE 5-32. Six ampere 120 V ac interface with zero switching

Solid-State Relays

The popularity of the line-voltage triac interface has caused it to be packaged as a module. Such a device is termed a *solid-state relay* (SSR). In addition to the advantages of longer life and smaller space, the SSR is immune to vibration, produces no contact bounce, and switches only at ZERO crossing in comparison to the electro-mechanical relay.

Output Modules

The use of the microcomputer has produced a need for a standardized output package that would permit rack mounting and easy change of output interfaces. As in the input realm, this need is answered by the universal output interface modules. These modules are the same size and configuration as the input modules previously described and are produced by many manufacturers.

The dc output module is color-coded with a red case, indicating its function. It is limited to 3 amperes, both by its small size and in the printed circuit board foil requirements necessary for any larger load. Optical isolation techniques are used within the module while fusing and indication is provided on the mounting PC board. The connection to the control logic is provided by an edge-card connector. Although screw termination is available, the trend to microprocessor-based control has strengthened the mass termination edge–connector with shielded ribbon cable as the standard method for bringing control signals to interfacing circuitry.

The ac output module uses ZERO crossing, internal snubbing, and opto-isolation to achieve its interface to low-voltage circuitry. Its case color-code is black. Like the dc module, the ac module is limited to 3 amperes and uses the same mounting hardware.

5.7 The Role of Interface Circuitry

The interface between low power, sensitive-control logic, and the industrial environment has been the area of greatest turmoil as the microprocessor-based control has come of age. This is in part due to the independent development of control devices and computing without close ties between power and digital branches of engineering. A solution has evolved as an *ipso facto* standard in the marketplace in the universal I/O module interface described in this chapter. Not only are these devices being interchangeably produced by a number of manufacturers, but now analog interface devices also are available in the same physical packages. The success or failure of a discrete control scheme in the modern setting depends heavily upon the reliability and predictability of its input and output interfaces and the degree of understanding of the characteristics by both design and maintenance personnel.

Problems

5.1 What is the principal difference between the application of the computer to general computing and to data acquisition and control?

5.2 What are three of the problems faced by industrial-control electronics that are not required by consumer electronic applications?

5.3 What functions does timing permit when added to discrete control circuits?

5.4 The time-delay relay is manufactured in what four types?

5.5 What are two common integrated-timing circuits?

5.6 What components determine the time delay of the circuit in Figure P5.6?

5.7 Using normally open and normally closed contacts from relay *K1* and *K2* of Figure P5.6, construct a timing diagram for the possible time-delay actions of this circuit.

5.8 Synchronization of integrated circuit state changes is possible through the use of a master clock circuit. What problem is avoided by synchronizing control circuit activity?

5.9 What are three desirable characteristics of a clock pulse?

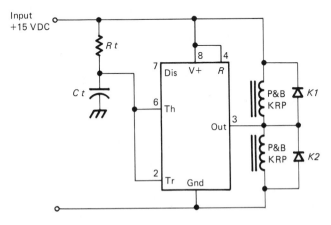

FIGURE P5.6. Normally open, timed close relay/normally open, timed open

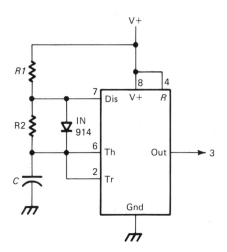

FIGURE P5.10. IC timer astable clock circuit

5.10 Determine the values for *R1, R2,* and *C* for the circuit of Figure P5.10 to produce a 50 percent duty cycle 100 KHz clock generator.

5.11 What are the advantages and disadvantages of crystal-controlled clock generation over RC timer networks?

5.12 Describe the sequence of events in the operation of the time-delay circuit in Figure P5.12.

5.13 The dryer control of Figure P5.13 fails to turn off the heater during cool down. What is the most probable cause of the failure?

5.14. The cool-down period of the dryer circuit in Figure P5.13 is to be extended. What components or settings must be altered to accomplish this?

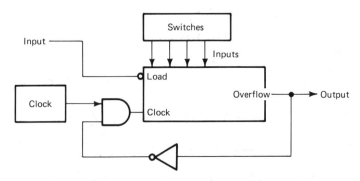

FIGURE P5.12. Time delay circuit using universal counter

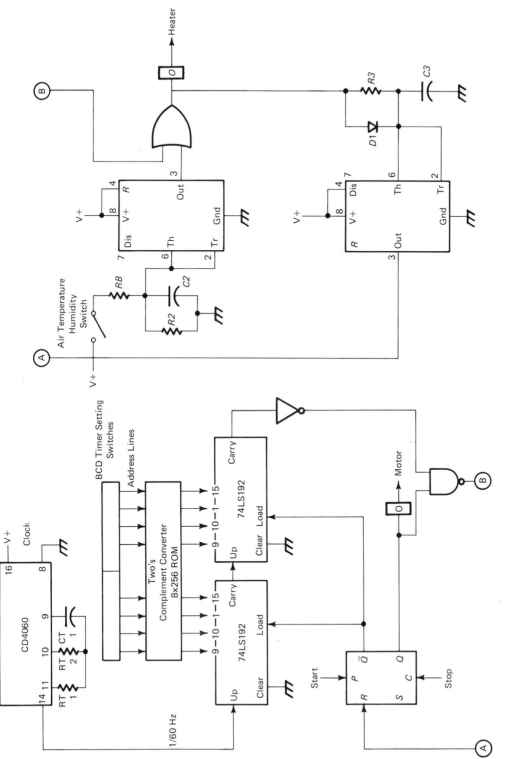

FIGURE P5.13. Electronic dryer control using timers

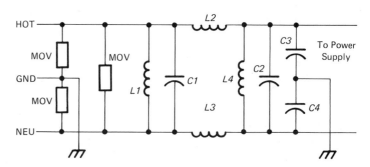

FIGURE P5.18. AC line filter with transient suppression

5.15 What is the largest single cause of integrated circuit failure?

5.16 What characteristics of integrated circuits hinder their application to industrial controls?

5.17 Power, input, and output isolation techniques are used to protect integrated-circuit control circuits. What are three methods of isolation?

5.18 What are the purposes of the MOVs found in Figure P5.18?

5.19 What problems are generated by the use of totem-pole output transistor configurations and what is a common solution?

5.20 What are the advantages and disadvantages of relay-based input isolation?

5.21 In Figure P5.21, what is the purpose of the 0.1 microfarad capacitor?

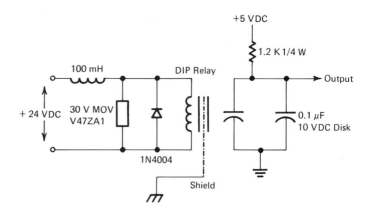

FIGURE P5.21. Relay input isolation circuit

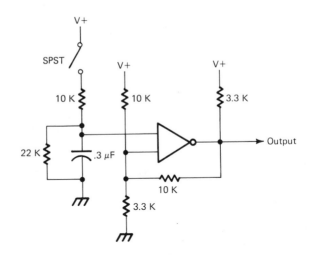

FIGURE P5.22. Debounce circuit with comparator using hysteresis

5.22 What is the purpose of the circuit in Figure P5.22 and how is its circuit action adjusted?

5.23 What are the advantages of optical isolation over relay and transformer methods?

5.24 Identify the purposes of each component in Figure P5.24.

5.25 The circuit in Figure P5.24 is to interface to a 24-volt ac input signal. Calculate the component values necessary.

5.26 What are the advantages and disadvantages of modular input and output interfacing techniques?

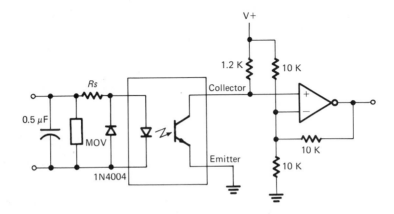

FIGURE P5.24. Universal opto-isolator input interface

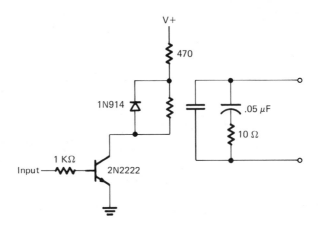

FIGURE P5.27. Reed relay output interface

5.27 What is the purpose of the .05-microfarad and 10-ohm resistor in the output interface circuit of Figure P5.27?

5.28 A peripheral device driver is often used for small inductive loads. Why?

5.29 The output circuit in Figure P5.29 is designed for 3-ampere service. What components would need to be altered to change this circuit to 20-ampere use?

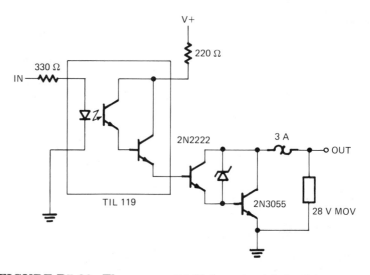

FIGURE P5.29. Three amp 24 V dc output interface

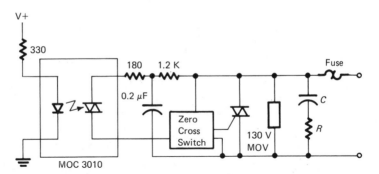

FIGURE P5.30. Six ampere 120 V ac interface with zero switching

5.30 The circuit in Figure P5.30 is designed for minimum RF inter-ference. What components address this problem?

5.31 What are the advantages of the solid-state relay over the conventional power relay?

5.32 What are the advantages and disadvantages of the SSR over individual component-based output interface designs?

54/7416

HEX INVERTER BUFFER/DRIVER
(With Open-Collector High-Voltage Output)

CONNECTION DIAGRAM
PINOUT A

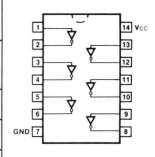

ORDERING CODE: See Section 9

PKGS	PIN OUT	COMMERCIAL GRADE $V_{CC} = +5.0$ V ±5%, $T_A = 0°$ C to $+70°$ C	MILITARY GRADE $V_{CC} = +5.0$ V ±10%, $T_A = -55°$ C to $+125°$ C	PKG TYPE
Plastic DIP (P)	A	7416PC		9A
Ceramic DIP (D)	A	7416DC	5416DM	6A
Flatpak (F)	A	7416FC	5416FM	3I

INPUT LOADING/FAN-OUT: See Section 3 for U.L. definitions

PINS	54/74 (U.L.) HIGH/LOW
Inputs	1.0/1.0
Outputs	OC**/10

DC AND AC CHARACTERISTICS: See Section 3*

SYMBOL	PARAMETER		54/74 Min	54/74 Max	UNITS	CONDITIONS	
V_{OL}	Output LOW Voltage	XC		0.7	V	$I_{OL} = 40$ mA	$V_{CC} = $ Min
		XM		0.7		$I_{OL} = 30$ mA	$V_{IN} = V_{IH}$
		XC, XM		0.4		$I_{OL} = 16$ mA	
I_{OH}	Output HIGH Current			0.25	mA	$V_{OH} = 15$ V, $V_{CC} = $ Min $V_{IN} = V_{IL}$	
I_{CCH}	Power Supply Current			48	mA	$V_{IN} = $ Gnd	$V_{CC} = $ Max
I_{CCL}				51		$V_{IN} = $ Open	
t_{PLH}	Propagation Delay			15	ns	Figs. 3-2, 3-4	
t_{PHL}				23			

*DC limits apply over operating temperature range; AC limits apply at $T_A = +25°$ C and $V_{CC} = +5.0$ V.

**OC — Open Collector

Courtesy Fairchild Camera and Instrument Corp.

54/7446A • 54/7447A
54LS/74LS47
BCD TO 7-SEGMENT DECODER/DRIVER

CONNECTION DIAGRAM
PINOUT A

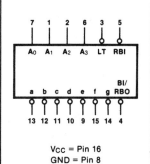

DESCRIPTION — The '46A, '47A and 'LS47 accept four lines of BCD (8421) input data, generate their complements internally and decode the data with seven AND/OR gates having open-collector outputs to drive indicator segments directly. Each segment output is guaranteed to sink 40 mA (24 mA for the 'LS47) in the ON (LOW) state and withstand 15 V (30 V for the '46A) in the OFF (HIGH) state with a maximum leakage current of 250 µA. Auxiliary inputs provide blanking, lamp test and cascadable zero-suppression fuctions. Also see the 'LS247 data sheet.

- **OPEN-COLLECTOR OUTPUTS**
- **DRIVE INDICATOR SEGMENTS DIRECTLY**
- **CASCADABLE ZERO-SUPPRESSION CAPABILITY**
- **LAMP TEST INPUT**

LOGIC SYMBOL

V_{CC} = Pin 16
GND = Pin 8

ORDERING CODE: See Section 9

PKGS	PIN OUT	COMMERCIAL GRADE V_{CC} = +5.0 V ±5%, T_A = 0°C to +70°C	MILITARY GRADE V_{CC} = +5.0 V ±10%, T_A = -55°C to +125°C	PKG TYPE
Plastic DIP (P)	A	7446APC, 7447APC 74LS47PC		9B
Ceramic DIP)D)	A	7446ADC, 7447ADC 74LS47DC	5446ADM, 5447ADM 54LS47DM	7B
Flatpak (F)	A	7446AFC, 7447AFC 74LS47FC	5446AFM, 5447AFM 54LS47FM	4L

INPUT LOADING/FAN-OUT: See Section 3 for U.L. definitions

PIN NAMES	DESCRIPTION	54/74 (U.L.) HIGH/LOW	54/74LS (U.L.) HIGH/LOW
$A_0 — A_3$	BCD Inputs	1.0/1.0	0.5/0.25
$\overline{RBI}$	Ripple Blanking Input (Active LOW)	1.0/1.0	0.5/0.25
$\overline{LT}$	Lamp Test Input (Active LOW)	1.0/1.0	0.5/0.25
$\overline{BI/RBO}$	Blanking Input (Active LOW) or	-/2.5	-/0.75
	Ripple Blanking Output (Active LOW)	5.0/5.0	1.25/2.0 (1.0)
$\overline{a} — \overline{g}$	Segment Outputs (Active LOW)	OC*/25	OC*/15 (7.5)

*OC — Open Collector

Courtesy Fairchild Camera and Instrument Corp.

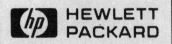

HEWLETT PACKARD

LED LIGHT BARS

HIGH EFFICIENCY RED HLMP-2300/-2600 SERIES
YELLOW HLMP-2400/-2700 SERIES
HIGH PERFORMANCE GREEN HLMP-2500/-2800 SERIES

TECHNICAL DATA   JANUARY 1984

Features

- **LARGE, BRIGHT, UNIFORM LIGHT EMITTING AREAS**
  Approximately Lambertian Radiation Pattern
- **CHOICE OF THREE COLORS**
- **CATEGORIZED FOR LIGHT OUTPUT**
- **YELLOW AND GREEN CATEGORIZED FOR DOMINANT WAVELENGTH**
- **EXCELLENT ON-OFF CONTRAST**
- **EASILY MOUNTED ON P.C. BOARDS OR INDUSTRY STANDARD SIP/DIP SOCKETS**
- **MECHANICALLY RUGGED**
- **X-Y STACKABLE**
- **FLUSH MOUNTABLE**
- **CAN BE USED WITH PANEL AND LEGEND MOUNTS**
- **LIGHT EMITTING SURFACE SUITABLE FOR LEGEND ATTACHMENT PER APPLICATION NOTE 1012**
- **SUITABLE FOR MULTIPLEX OPERATION**
- **I.C. COMPATIBLE**

Applications

- **BUSINESS MACHINE MESSAGE ANNUNCIATORS**
- **TELECOMMUNICATIONS INDICATORS**
- **FRONT PANEL PROCESS STATUS INDICATORS**
- **PC BOARD IDENTIFIERS**
- **BAR GRAPHS**

Description

The HLMP-2300/-2400/-2500/-2600/-2700/-2800 series light bars are rectangular light sources designed for a variety of applications where a large, bright source of light is required. These light bars are configured in single-in-line and dual-in-line packages that contain either single or segmented light emitting areas. The -2300/-2400/-2600/-2700 series devices utilize LED chips which are made from GaAsP on a transparent GaP substrate. The -2500/-2800 series devices utilize chips made from GaP on a transparent GaP substrate.

Selection Guide

Light Bar Part Number HLMP-			Size of Light Emitting Areas	Number of Light Emitting Areas	Package Outline Outline		Corresponding Panel and Legend Mount Part No. HLMP-
High Efficiency Red	Yellow	Green					
2300	2400	2500	8.89 mm x 3.81 mm (.350 in. x .150 in.)	1	A	▭	2599
2350	2450	2550	19.05 mm x 3.81 mm (.750 in. x .150 in.)	1	B	▭	2598
2600	2700	2800	8.89 mm x 3.81 mm (.350 in. x .150 in.)	2	D	▭	2898
2620	2720	2820	8.89 mm x 3.81 mm (.350 in. x .150 in.)	4	F	▭	2899
2635	2735	2835	8.89 mm x 19.05 mm (.150 in. x .750 in.)	2	G	▭	2899
2655	2755	2855	8.89 mm x 8.89 mm (.350 in. x .350 in.)	1	C	▭	2898
2670	2770	2870	8.89 mm x 8.89 mm (.350 in. x .350 in.)	2	E	▭	2899
2685	2785	2885	8.89 mm x 19.05 mm (.350 in. x .750 in.)	1	H	▭	2899

Courtesy Hewlett Packard

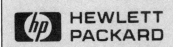
HEWLETT PACKARD

HEXADECIMAL AND NUMERIC INDICATORS

5082-7300
5082-7302
5082-7304
5082-7340

TECHNICAL DATA JANUARY 1984

Features

- **NUMERIC 5082-7300/-7302**
  0-9, Test State, Minus
  Sign, Blank States
  Decimal Point
     7300 Right Hand D.P.
     7302 Left Hand D.P.
- **HEXADECIMAL 5082-7340**
  0-9, A-F, Base 16
  Operation
  Blanking Control,
  Conserves Power
  No Decimal Point
- **DTL/TTL COMPATIBLE**
- **INCLUDES DECODER/DRIVER WITH 5 BIT MEMORY**
  8421 Positive Logic Input
- **4 x 7 DOT MATRIX ARRAY**
  Shaped Character, Excellent Readibility
- **STANDARD .600 INCH x .400 INCH DUAL-IN-LINE PACKAGE INCLUDING CONTRAST FILTER**
- **CATEGORIZED FOR LUMINOUS INTENSITY**
  Assures Uniformity of Light Output from
  Unit to Unit within a Single Category

Description

The HP 5082-7300 series solid state numeric and hexa-decimal indicators with on-board decoder/driver and mem-ory provide a reliable, low-cost method for displaying digital information.

The 5082-7300 numeric indicator decodes positive 8421 BCD logic inputs into characters 0-9, a "-" sign, a test pattern, and four blanks in the invalid BCD states, The unit employs a right-hand decimal point. Typical applica-tions include point-of-sale terminals, instrumentation, and computer systems.

The 5082-7302 is the same as the 5082-7300, except that the decimal point is located on the left-hand side of the digit.

The 5082-7340 hexadecimal indicator decodes positive 8421 logic inputs into 16 states, 0-9 and A-F. In place of the decimal point an input is provided for blanking the display (all LED's off), without losing the contents of the memory. Applications include terminals and computer systems using the base-16 character set.

The 5082-7304 is a (± 1.) overrange character, including dec-imal point, used in instrumentation applications.

Package Dimensions

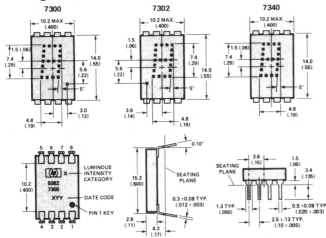

PIN	FUNCTION	
	5082-7300 and 7302 Numeric	**5082-7340 Hexadecimal**
1	Input 2	Input 2
2	Input 4	Input 4
3	Input 8	Input 8
4	Decimal point	Blanking control
5	Latch enable	Latch enable
6	Ground	Ground
7	V_{cc}	V_{cc}
8	Input 1	Input 1

NOTES:
1. Dimensions in millimetres and (inches).
2. Unless otherwise specified, the tolerance on all dimensions is ±.38mm (±.015")
3. Digit center line is ±.25mm (±.01") from package center line.

Courtesy Hewlett Packard

HEWLETT PACKARD

LOW INPUT CURRENT, HIGH GAIN OPTOCOUPLERS

6N138 6N139

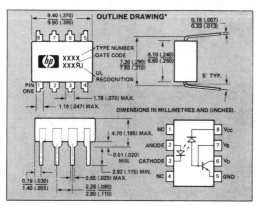

DIMENSIONS IN MILLIMETRES AND (INCHES).

SCHEMATIC

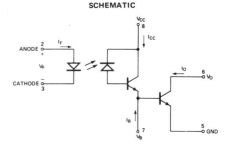

Features

- **HIGH CURRENT TRANSFER RATIO — 800% TYPICAL**
- **LOW INPUT CURRENT REQUIREMENT — 0.5 mA**
- **TTL COMPATIBLE OUTPUT — 0.1 V V_{OL} TYPICAL**
- **HIGH COMMON MODE REJECTION — 500 V/μs**
- **PERFORMANCE GUARANTEED OVER TEMPERATURE 0°C to 70°C**
- **BASE ACCESS ALLOWS GAIN BANDWIDTH ADJUSTMENT**
- **HIGH OUTPUT CURRENT — 60 mA**
- **100K BITS/SEC TYPICAL SPEED AT I_F = 0.5 mA**
- **DIELECTRIC WITHSTAND TESTED AT 3000 Vdc FOR A WORKING VOLTAGE OF 220 Vac**
- **RECOGNIZED UNDER THE COMPONENT PROGRAM OF UNDERWRITERS LABORATORIES, INC. (FILE NO. E55361)**

Description

These high gain series couplers use a Light Emitting Diode and an integrated high gain photon detector to provide extremely high current transfer ratio between input and output. Separate pins for the photodiode and output stage result in TTL compatible saturation voltages and high speed operation. Where desired the V_{CC} and V_O terminals may be tied together to achieve conventional photodarlington operation. A base access terminal allows a gain bandwidth adjustment to be made.

The 6N139 is suitable for use in CMOS, LSTTL or other low power applications. A 400% minimum current transfer ratio is guaranteed over a 0-70°C operating range for only 0.5 mA of LED current.

The 6N138 is suitable for use mainly in TTL applications. Current Transfer Ratio is 300% minimum over 0-70°C for an LED current of 1.6 mA [1 TTL unit load (U.L.)]. A 300% minimum CTR enables operation with 1 U.L. in, 1 U.L. out with a 2.2 kΩ pull-up resistor.

Applications

- Ground Isolate Most Logic Families — TTL/TTL, CMOS/TTL, CMOS/CMOS, LSTTL/TTL, CMOS/LSTTL
- Low Input Current Line Receiver — Long Line or Party line
- EIA RS-232C Line Receiver
- Telephone Ring Detector
- 117 V ac Line Voltage Status Indicator — Low Input Power Dissipation
- Low Power Systems — Ground Isolation

Absolute Maximum Ratings *

Storage Temperature	−55°C to +125°C
Operating Temperature	0°C to +70°C
Lead Solder Temperature	260°C for 10s
	(1.6mm below seating plane)
Average Input Current — I_F	20mA [1]
Peak Input Current — I_F	40mA
	(50% duty cycle, 1ms pulse width)
Peak Transient Input Current — I_F	1.0A
	(≤ 1μs pulse width, 300 pps)
Reverse Input Voltage — V_R	5V
Input Power Dissipation	35mW [2]
Output Current — I_O (Pin 6)	60mA [3]
Emitter-Base Reverse Voltage (Pin 5-7)	0.5V
Supply and Output Voltage — V_{CC} (Pin 8-5), V_O (Pin 6-5)	
6N138	−0.5 to 7V
6N139	−0.5 to 18V
Output Power Dissipation	100mW [4]
	See notes, following page.

CAUTION: The small junction sizes inherent to the design of this bipolar component increases the component's susceptibility to damage from electrostatic discharge (ESD). It is advised that normal static precautions be taken in handling and assembly of this component to prevent damage and/or degradation which may be induced by ESD.

*JEDEC Registered Data.

Courtesy Hewlett Packard

186

EXAR

XR-555

Timing Circuit

GENERAL DESCRIPTION

The XR-555 monolithic timing circuit is a highly stable controller capable of producing accurate timing pulses. It is a direct, pin-for-pin replacement for the SE/NE 555 timer. The circuit contains independent control terminals for triggering or resetting if desired, as shown in the functional block diagram of Figure 1.

In the monostable mode of operation, the time delay is controlled by one external resistor and one capacitor. For astable operation as an oscillator, the free-running frequency and the duty cycle are accurately controlled with two external resistors and one capacitor (as shown in Figure 2).

The XR-555 may be triggered or reset on falling waveforms. Its output can source or sink up to 200 mA or drive TTL circuits.

FEATURES

Direct Replacement for SE/NE 555
Timing from Microseconds Thru Hours
Operates in Both Monostable and Astable Modes
High Current Drive Capability (200 mA)
TTL and DTL Compatible Outputs
Adjustable Duty Cycle
Temperature Stability of 0.005%/°C

APPLICATIONS

Precision Timing	Missing Pulse Detection
Pulse Generation	Pulse-Width Modulation
Sequential Timing	Frequency Division
Pulse Shaping	Pulse-Position Modulation
Clock Generation	Appliance Timing

ABSOLUTE MAXIMUM RATINGS

Power Supply	18 volts
Power Dissipation (package limitation)	
Plastic Package	300 mW
Derate above +25°C	2.5 mW/°C
Power Dissipation (package limitation)	
To 99	600 mW
Storage Temperature Range	−65°C to +150°C

AVAILABLE TYPES

Part Number	Package	Operating Temperature
XR-555MT	TO-99	−55°C to +125°C
XR-555CP	Plastic	0°C to +75°C
XR-555CT	TO-99	-0°C to +75°C

EQUIVALENT SCHEMATIC DIAGRAM

FUNCTIONAL BLOCK DIAGRAM

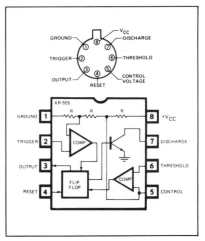

Courtesy EXAR Integrated Systems, Inc.

187

Programmable Timer/Counter

PRINCIPLE OF OPERATION

The XR-2240 Programmable Timer/Counter is a monolithic controller capable of producing ultra-long time delays without sacrificing accuracy for time delays from micro-seconds up to five days. Two timing circuits can be cascaded to generate time delays up to three years. The circuit is comprised of an internal time-base oscillator, a programmable 8-bit counter and a control flip-flop. The time delay is set by an external R-C network and can be programmed to any value from 1 RC to 255 RC.

In astable operation, the circuit can generate 256 separate frequencies or pulse-patterns from a single RC setting and can be synchronized with external clock signals. Both the control inputs, pins 10-11, and the outputs, pins 1-8, are compatible with TTL and DTL logic levels.

The timing cycle for the XR-2240 is initiated by applying a positive-going trigger pulse to pin 11. The trigger input actuates the time-base oscillator, enables the counter section, and sets all the counter outputs to "low" state. The time-base oscillator generates timing pulses with its period, T, equal to 1 RC. These clock pulses are counted by the binary counter section. The timing cycle is completed when a positive-going reset pulse is applied to pin 10.

In most timing applications, one or more of the counter outputs are connected back to the reset terminal. In this manner, the circuit will start timing when a trigger is applied and will automatically reset itself to complete the timing cycle when a programmed count is completed. If none of the counter outputs are connected back to the reset terminal, the circuit would operate in its astable or free-running mode, subsequent to a trigger input.

FEATURES

Timing from micro-seconds to days
Programmable delays: 1 RC to 255 RC
Wide supply range: 4V to 15V
TTL and DTL compatible outputs
High accuracy: 0.5%
External Sync and Modulation Capability
Excellent Supply Rejection: 0.2%/V

APPLICATIONS

Precision Timing
Long Delay Generation
Sequential Timing
Binary Pattern Generation
Frequency Synthesis
Pulse Counting/Summing
A/D Conversion
Digital Sample and Hold

ABSOLUTE MAXIMUM RATINGS

Supply Voltage	18V
Power Dissipation	
Ceramic Package	750 mW
Derate above +25°C	6 mW/°C
Plastic Package	625 mW
Derate above +25°C	5.0 mW/°C
Storage Temperature	−65°C to +150°C

AVAILABLE TYPES

Part Number	Package (16 Pin DIP)	Operating Temperature
XR-2240M	Ceramic	−55°C to +125°C
XR-2240N	Ceramic	0°C to +75°C
XR-2240P	Plastic	0°C to +75°C
XR-2240CN	Ceramic	0°C to +75°C
XR-2240CP	Plastic	0°C to +75°C

SIMPLIFIED SCHEMATIC DIAGRAM

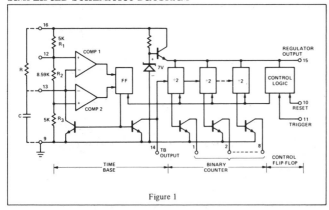

Figure 1

FUNCTIONAL BLOCK DIAGRAM

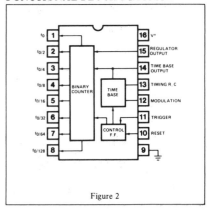

Figure 2

Courtesy EXAR Integrated Systems, Inc.

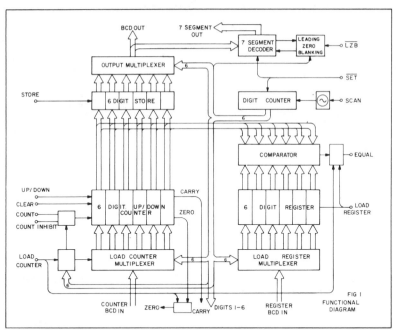

FIG I
FUNCTIONAL
DIAGRAM

The MOSTEK MK 50395 has been developed, after careful counter application analysis, as a counting system for most needs. The functional diagram, figure 1, shows that the system consists of six, synchronous, up down decade counters with a data store and an auxiliary storage register that may be compared with the counter value. The circuit is relatively insensitive to power supply variation, and can interface with CMOS logic using power supplies in the 10 to 15 volt range. Counting speeds up to 1.0 MHz are permissable and the circuits are readily cascaded.

Positive logic, i.e., logic 1 is the more positive level in the following description:

The Counter

The positive going edges of a pulse train at the COUNT input (pin 36) are standardized by an internal monostable to a fixed pulse width thereby giving only a minimum value to the time for which the input pulse must stay high. This pulse is applied synchronously to the six decades and if the UP/DOWN input is a logic 1 the counters will be incremented, if at logic 0 then the counters will be decremented. At any time the value in the counter will be set back to zero if the CLEAR COUNTER input goes to a logic 1 for 2 μs or longer. This resetting action occurs whether or not there is a counting input pulse train by forcing the counters directly to 0.

In addition to resetting it is also possible to preset any desired value into the counter. This is done sequentially decade by decade, under control of the LOAD COUNTER command in the following manner. The internal digit counter signal cycles from the most significant decade (decade 6) to the least significant decade (decade 1) and at each step from decade to decade the LOAD COUNTER input is checked. If it is at a logic 1 as the digit counter steps on then the corresponding decade will be reset to the value currently at the COUNTER BCD INPUTS. It is thus possible to load each of the 6 counters individually if required. While the counter is being loaded the counting input is inhibited. Internally the low counter command is synchronized to the scan oscillator. Thus if load counter is brought to a logic zero in the middle of a digit strobe, the counter will be inhibited until the next interdigit blanking time. A separate COUNT INHIBIT control is provided to stop the applied count inputs from being accepted while this signal is a logic 1.

The counter section has two control outputs, a CARRY from the most significant decade and a ZERO SIGNAL that indicates when the counter contents are zero. This signal is suppressed during LOAD COUNTER operations to avoid a spurious output being given during a counter presetting operation.

Courtesy Mostek Corp.

189

120/240 VOLT AC LINE
DC CONTROL VOLTAGE

10 AMP
POWER SERIES

Tolerances .XX ±.020, .XXX ±.010

THERMAL RATINGS

● Free Air

■ Mounted on
6" x 6" plate (2°C/watt)

▲ Mounted on
12" x 12" plate (1°C/watt)

☐ Photo isolation
☐ Zero voltage turn on
☐ Built-in snubber
☐ 4000 volt isolation
☐ Die cast mounting base
☐ UL recognized
☐ CSA certified
☐ 200% tested at rated current
   at .5 power factor
☐ TTL compatible
☐ High PRV rating

CONNECTION DIAGRAM

	MODEL	
	120D10	**240D10**
AC Line Voltage — nominal	120	240
Operating Voltage Range	12-140	24-280
Peak Repetitive Voltage	500	500
Current Rating Nominal — amps rms	10	10
1 Cycle Surge — amps peak	110	110
Output Voltage Drop — peak	1.6	1.6
Off-state Leakage — ma rms at nominal voltage — 60 Hz	7	14
I^2t Rating, t = 8.3 ms	50	50
Dissipation — watts/amp	1.6	1.6
θjc^* — °C/Watt	1.3	1.3
Isolation Voltage — Vrms	4000	4000
Control Pick-up Voltage	3 VDC	3 VDC
Control Drop-out Voltage	1 VDC	1 VDC
Control Voltage Range	3-32 VDC	3-32 VDC
Control Input Impedance	1000 Ohms ±10%	1000 Ohms ±10%

ADDITIONAL SPECIFICATIONS — ALL MODELS

Operating Frequency: 25–65 Hz (400 Hz permitted with off-state leakage approximately 6 times above value)

Operating Temperature: –40°C to 100°C

Turn-on Time: 1/2 cycle maximum — zero voltage

Turn-off Time: 1/2 cycle maximum — zero current

DV/DT-Off-State: 200 V/μsec

DV/DT-Commutating: snubbed for rated load at .5 power factor.

*Thermal resistance junction-to-base.
 Maximum junction temperature 110°C.

Courtesy Opto-22

190

SINGLE CHANNEL I/O MODULES
AC OUTPUT MODULES — BLACK CASE
120 VOLT AC LINE

AC OUTPUT
OAC5, OAC15, OAC24

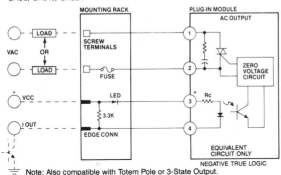

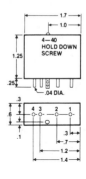

Note: Also compatible with Totem Pole or 3-State Output.

	MODEL		
	OAC5	**OAC15**	**OAC24**
Control Voltage	**5 VDC**	**15 VDC**	**24 VDC**
Line Voltage — nominal	120 VAC	120 VAC	120 VAC
Operating Voltage Range	12 to 140 VAC	12 to 140 VAC	12 to 140 VAC
Peak Repetitive Voltage	500 V	500 V	500 V
Current Rating — at 45°C Ambient	3 amps	3 amps	3 amps
at 70°C Ambient	2 amps	2 amps	2 amps
1 Cycle Surge — amps peak	80	80	80
Minimum Load Current	20 ma	20 ma	20 ma
Output Voltage Drop — max peak	1.6 V	1.6 V	1.6 V
Off-state Leakage at nominal voltage — 60 Hz	5 ma rms	5 ma rms	5 ma rms
Isolation Voltage — Input-To-Output	4000 Vrms	4000 Vrms	4000 Vrms
Control Pick-up Voltage	2.5 V	9 V	18 V
Control Drop-Out Voltage	1 V	1 V	1 V
Control Voltage Range	2.5 to 8	9 to 16	18 to 32
Control Resistance (Rc in Schematic Diagram)	220 ohms	1K ohms	2.2K ohms
Control Input Current at nominal control voltage (I out in Schematic Diagram)	12 ma	15 ma	18 ma

ADDITIONAL SPECIFICATIONS — ALL MODELS

Compatible with Opto 22 input modules for load status indication (outputs may drive inputs)
Directly compatible with PIA type ICs (6821, 6522, 8255A as typical), i.e., buffering not required.

Operating Frequency: 25-65 Hz

Operating Ambient Temperature: −30°C to + 70°C

Turn-on Time: 1/2 cycle maximum — zero voltage

Turn-off Time: 1/2 cycle maximum — zero current

DV/DT-Off-State: 200 V/μsec

DV/DT-Commutating: snubbed for rated load at .5 power factor

Courtesy Opto-22

SINGLE CHANNEL I/O MODULES
AC INPUT MODULES — YELLOW CASE
120 VOLT AC OR DC LINE

AC INPUT
IAC5, IAC15, IAC24

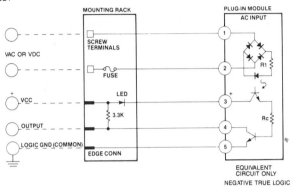

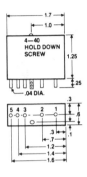

	MODEL		
	IAC5	**IACl5**	**IAC24**
Control Voltage	**5 VDC**	**15 VDC**	**24 VDC**
Input Line Voltage — nominal	120 VAC/DC	120 VAC/DC	120 VAC/DC
Input Voltage Range	90-140 VAC/DC	90-140 VAC/DC	90-140 VAC/DC
Input Current at Max. Line	11 ma	11 ma	11 ma
Input Allowed for No Output	3 ma (45 V)	3 ma (45 V)	3 ma (45 V)
Isolation Input-To-Output	4000 Vrms	4000 Vrms	4000 Vrms
Output Transistor	30 V Breakdown	30 V Breakdown	30 V Breakdown
Output Current	50 ma	50 ma	50 ma
Output Leakage — 30 VDC — no input	100 microamps max.	100 microamps max.	100 microamps max.
Output Voltage Drop	.4 V at 50 ma	.4 V at 50 ma	.4 V at 50 ma
Logic Supply Voltage (Vcc)	4.5 to 6	12 to 18	20 to 30
Logic Supply Current — at nominal logic voltage	12 ma	15 ma	18 ma
Input Resistance (R1 in Schematic Diagram)	14K ohms	14K ohms	14K ohms
Control Resistance (Rc in Schematic Diagram)	220 ohms	1K ohms	2.2 K ohms

ADDITIONAL SPECIFICATIONS — ALL MODELS

Compatible with Opto 22 output modules for load status indication (outputs may drive inputs)

Turn-on Time: 20 milliseconds maximum

Turn-off Time: 20 milliseconds maximum

Operating Ambient Temperature: −30ºC to +70ºC

Courtesy Opto-22

SINGLE CHANNEL I/O MODULES
DC OUTPUT MODULES — RED CASE
60 VOLT DC LINE

DC OUTPUT
ODC5, ODC15, ODC24

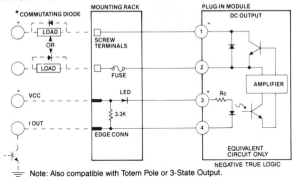

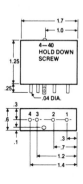

Note: Also compatible with Totem Pole or 3-State Output.

*Must be used on inductive loads.

	MODEL		
	ODC5	ODC15	ODC24
Control Voltage	5 VDC	15 VDC	24 VDC
Line Voltage — maximum	60 VDC	60 VDC	60 VDC
Operating Voltage Range	5 to 60 VDC	5 to 60 VDC	5 to 60 VDC
Current Rating — at 45°C	3 amps	3 amps	3 amps
at 70°C	2 amps	2 amps	2 amps
1 Second Surge	5 amps	5 amps	5 amps
Output Voltage Drop	1.6 max.	1.6 max.	1.6 max.
Off-state Leakage at maximum voltage	1 ma	1 ma	1 ma
Isolation Voltage — Input-To-Output	4000 Vrms	4000 Vrms	4000 Vrms
Control Pick-up Voltage	2.5 VDC	9 VDC	18 VDC
Control Drop-Out Voltage	1 VDC	1 VDC	1 VDC
Control Voltage Range	2.5 to 8	9 to 16	18 to 32
Control Resistance (Rc in Schematic Diagram)	220 ohms	1K ohms	2.2K ohms
Control Input Current at nominal control voltage (I out in Schematic Diagram)	12 ma	15 ma	18 ma

ADDITIONAL SPECIFICATIONS — ALL MODELS

Compatible with Opto 22 input modules for load status indication (outputs may drive inputs)

Directly compatible with PIA type ICs (6821, 6522, 8255A as typical), i.e., buffering not required.

Turn-on Time: 100 microseconds

Turn-off Time: 750 microseconds

Operating Ambient Temperature: −30°C to +70°C

Courtesy Opto-22

SINGLE CHANNEL I/O MODULES
DC INPUT MODULES — WHITE CASE
10-32 VOLT DC OR AC LINE

DC INPUT
IDC5, IDC15, IDC24

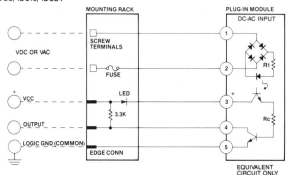

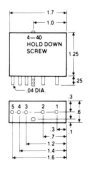

EQUIVALENT
CIRCUIT ONLY

NEGATIVE TRUE LOGIC

	MODEL		
	IDC5	IDC15	IDC24
Control Voltage	**5 VDC**	**15 VDC**	**24 VDC**
Input Line Voltage	10-32 VDC/AC	10-32 VDC/AC	10-32 VDC/AC
Input Voltage Range	10-32 VDC	10-32 VDC	10-32 VDC
	15-32 VAC	15-32 VAC	15-32 VAC
Input Current at Max. Line	25 ma	25 ma	25 ma
Input Allowed for No Output	1 ma (3 V)	1 ma (3 V)	1 ma (3 V)
Isolation Input-To-Output	4000 Vrms	4000 Vrms	4000 Vrms
Output Transistor	30 V Breakdown	30 V Breakdown	30 V Breakdown
Output Current	50 ma	50 ma	50 ma
Output Leakage — 30 VDC — no input	100 microamps max.	100 microamps max.	100 microamps max.
Output Voltage Drop	.4 V at 50 ma	4 V at 50 ma	.4 V at 50 ma
Logic Supply Voltage (Vcc)	4.5 to 6	12 to 18	20 to 30
Logic Supply Current — at nominal logic volts	12 ma	15 ma	18 ma
Input Resistance (R1 in Schematic)	1K ohms	1K ohms	1K ohms
Control Resistance (Rc in Schematic Diagram)	220 ohms	1K ohms	2.2 K ohms

ADDITIONAL SPECIFICATIONS — ALL MODELS

Compatible with Opto 22 output modules for load status indication (outputs may drive inputs)

Turn-on Time: 5 milliseconds maximum

Turn-off Time: 5 milliseconds maximum

Operating Ambient Temperature: −30°C to +70°C

Courtesy Opto-22

6 | Processor-based Control

6.0 Introduction

The integrated circuit provides discrete control functions at low cost and brings sophistication and broader application of control to industry. The integrated circuit solution to control problems requires a redesign effort when new functions are added to a system, and requires a knowledge of electronics as well as control theory to implement and troubleshoot.

Card Logic

As demonstrated by the examples in the previous chapters, the basic functions required for discrete control are the same for the majority of applications. It is the combination of functions and the sequence of function execution that varies from problem to problem. The commonality of control applications suggests a way to reduce the electronic knowledge required for control design and also to simplify the troubleshooting procedure. The solution provides common control functions on standardized printed circuit cards. Each card contains low-cost integrated circuits to produce the logic function and is therefore called a *logic card* or *module*. A logic-module-based system is illustrated in the block diagram in Figure 6-1.

The interconnection between modules in the logic-card system is provided by a wire-wrap back-plane. Control applications are implemented by unwrapping and/or wrapping jumpers between posts. This system reduces the initial design effort by reducing the implementation to interconnection of existing modules. A commercial system based on this method is illustrated in Figure 6-2.

195

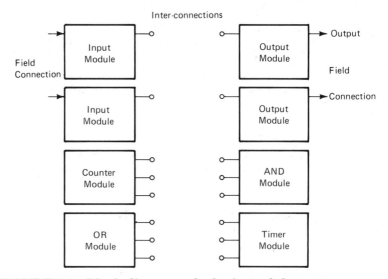

FIGURE 6-1. Block diagram of a logic module system

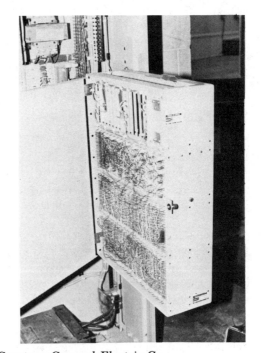

Courtesy General Electric Co.

FIGURE 6-2. Logic card module system

Selector-based Logic

The logic-module system requires extensive documentation to specify the interconnection of modules and is almost as labor-intensive to construct as a custom system. The problem of system modification still plagues the card-based system in addition to the mechanical problem of multiple wire-wrap connections.

An alternative to card logic is a selector-based logic system, as introduced in Chapter 4. The selectors may be used with logic cards by connecting the inputs and outputs of functional modules together through the selector in response to selection inputs. Each selector receives its selection information from the wiring of a plug-in jumper block. The jumpers define the functions of a particular application by defining the selector select-line logic. This system chooses the proper output from a wired set of responses by using variable inputs to select which response is connected to the output. This system is similar to assembling a train in a train yard by selecting which mechanical switches are to close or open as a railroad car is rolled down a hill into the yard. Changing a control scheme in the selector system requires changing jumper blocks in place of rewrapping back-plane jumpers in the logic module system. A block diagram of such a system is shown in Figure 6-3.

In the selector-based system in Figure 6-3, the input and output lines for the modules are shared to reduce the total number required. The same method is used for the selector control lines. The shared lines are termed a *bus*. A bus-based system gates the information from one element of the system to another by providing control signals to three-state AND gates at each of the necessary devices.

The information that controls the system can be separated from the logic circuitry used in selector-based control. Separation of the

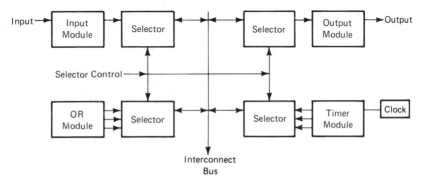

FIGURE 6-3. Selector-based control

control configuration from hardware occurs in relay-based control in the tape controlled machine. These devices store a time sequence of operations as holes punched in paper or Mylar tape. The hole punches are sensed by photoelectric cells or switches as the tape is mechanically advanced past the read head. The control sequence is altered just by changing the tape. The concentration of the control configuration information as a tape, separate from the hardware that performs the control operation, permits easy alteration of the control scheme.

The control sequence of operation is often determined by variable inputs as well as time. The total set of variable input conditions and control system outputs at any one time is termed the status or *state* of the system. The state of a control system provides a picture of the system at that instant and is used to determine the next state.

Programmable Logic Arrays

The control schemes possible with selectors and logic-function modules can be performed by a combination of AND and OR gates arranged as in Figure 6-4. By selecting which input and output lines are gated together, the function of the entire gate array is determined.

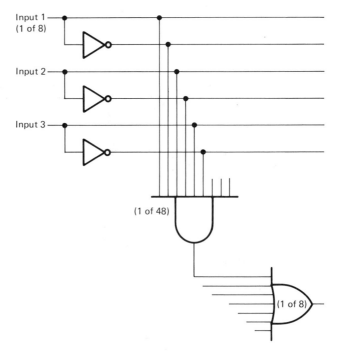

FIGURE 6-4. Programmable logic gate array

An array such as is shown in Figure 6-4 consists of a number of input lines and their complements. Every line and complement is available to the inputs of a series of AND gates. The outputs of the AND gates are then made available to the inputs of a set of OR gates. The outputs of the programmable logic array (PLA) are the outputs of the OR gates. The programming of an output is accomplished by determining which sets of input conditions should produce a logic output for a particular output line. The necessary OR gate and AND gate ties are then either manufactured into the device or selected by blowing fuse links in the unwanted lines. This method of characterizing the PLA to a particular control problem replaces the jumper block as well as the logic modules of the selector system. The PLA provides a general-purpose device that is compact, electrically alterable, and permits the use of the same hardware for many applications.

All the basic discrete control functions may be implemented by a PLA. However, this method is awkward for large systems and is time consuming to change in the field. The PLA is also programmable only once and then must be replaced if a new application is required. The PROM-based logic of Chapter 4 helps this problem by storing the interconnection of logic gates in its erasable memory as binary ones and zeros. The stored ones and zeros are used with a general purpose logic device, such as a full-adder, to produce specific control outputs in response to variable inputs applied to the address lines of the PROM. New applications are programmed into the PROM by analyzing the control problem, determining which control functions are needed, then converting these functions and connections into PROM/gate equivalents and finally programming and testing the PROMs required. The control intelligence is contained in the PROM and can be separated from the hardware in discussion. This control information is termed *software* since it, unlike hardware, is variable or "soft." The separation of the control system into hardware and software permits the control engineer to concentrate on the control aspects of a problem first and the conversion of the solution to electronics second.

6.1 Computer-based Control Architecture

PROM system configuration still requires that the control engineer and instrument technician have some background in digital electronics as well as a grasp of control fundamentals. In addition, the development cycle for a control application is often long and rocky, since new PROMs must be made for every development change. An ideal solution to the problem of rapidly changing control applications would be not to change the hardware at all, but instead change only the control intelligence of the hardware by a means that is easy to understand by human beings.

A computer is a close-to-ideal solution that provides powerful and easily alterable control logic. Under computer control, the application may be altered without reconfiguration of the system hardware. The computer may also communicate the control intelligence of the system in humanly recognizable form by converting word statements of data and commands into the logic ONEs and ZEROs necessary for electronic hardware. The application is changed by altering word statements during development or by the creation of new applications.

Until recently, however, computers were a very complex and costly solution to most common control problems. In the 1950s, computers were out of the question in all but very large applications. The 1960s produced smaller-sized and lower-priced minicomputers that successfully controlled large processes, but the mini was still expensive and delicate when compared to individual circuit solutions for small control applications. The development of the microcomputer in the 1970s eliminated these objections. This device is rugged, compact, and inexpensive, and provides a system for handling small and large control problems.

How does a computer—mainframe, mini, or micro—perform control functions? During operation, information and commands are input as ones and zeros to a standardized logic circuit upon which the circuit performs a stored logic function. The process of control is then reduced to the execution of very simple steps, stored in memory devices, which in combination produce the desired control action. This is very similar to the PROM-based control described earlier. However, in PROM-based designs the logic circuitry is special-purpose and may use the PROM itself to provide the logic. In computer-based control the logic circuitry—such as a microprocessor—is standardized, general purpose, and capable of performing the same action as the PROM-based design.

The structure of the computer, whether mainframe, mini, micro, business, personal, or control machine, is based upon the same functional organization as pictured in Figure 6-5. The blocks represent groups of functionally related components, while the arrows show the flow of information.

The input and output blocks represent the computer interfaces to the external environment of the industrial world, including instrumentation, output drivers, and human controls and indicators. The memory block contains the instructions that are to be executed by the control and arithmetic blocks, as well as the information upon which

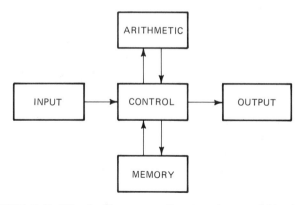

FIGURE 6-5. Block diagram of computer architecture

the instructions are performed. The arithmetic block is the logic engine of the computer. This block has a repertoire of logic functions it can perform. These small instructions, used repeatedly, are the building blocks upon which all the capabilities of the computing system rest. The control block acts as the traffic director for the system. It contains the basic logic that directs instruction information and data from the memory, as well as information from the input block to the arithmetic block. It then directs the results produced by the arithmetic block to the memory and output blocks.

6.2 Microcomputer Hardware

Just as the small motor changed the control industry following World War II, the microprocessor has invaded all areas of control. The microcomputer, based upon the microprocessor, presents a compact example of the functional elements described above.

The power of computer hardware is often evaluated by the following parameters:

- The speed of step execution
- The size of memory
- The number of bits used at a time.

The microcomputer has historically been based on eight-bit microprocessors that address up to 64 kilobytes of memory while operating at master clock speeds of 2 to 8 megahertz. Since microcomputers use many small sequentially executed steps to produce control functions, these seemingly large parameters may restrict the use of microcomputers to small applications. One microsystem architecture uses multiple microcomputers performing orchestrated subtasks in a larger, interconnected system to overcome the limitations of microcomputer size. In recent times, both the power and speed of microcomputers have increased. Inexpensive 16- and 32-bit microprocessors are now available in microcontrol computers. These devices directly address many megabytes of memory. Clock speeds for all sizes of microprocessors have also increased to 14 megahertz and beyond, while both memory packaging and prices have diminished. With the improvements in microcomputing power, many formerly minicomputer applications are now being accomplished by microcomputers while, more importantly, much more intelligence is being incorporated into all aspects of control hardware.

One-Board Computer Control

In many microsystems, the entire computer system is contained on a single printed circuit board. The arithmetic and control functions are contained in the microprocessor while the memory resides in a number of RAM and ROM chips. Additional peripheral support chips handle the input and output interfaces while providing the control block functions of clock generation and other "housekeeping" chores. An example system appears in Figure 6-6.

In the one-board control computer, the entire application is contained in the resident memory of the board. This includes both the instructions common to all applications, such as input and output

Courtesy Divebliss Corporation

FIGURE 6-6. One-board control computer

steps, as well as the applications information. A battery backup to the power supply is required to prevent loss of information during power outages. The common instructions are contained in ROM chips to further safeguard against information loss.

General-Purpose Computer Control

An alternative to the one-board system is the general-purpose control computer. This system is based upon the use of a bus to communicate between the block elements of the computer, and off-line storage to hold copies of the RAM memory to expand the system capabilities.

Bus Structures

The bus structure is implemented using a back-plane. The back-plane is a printed circuit board that contains, in its minimum configuration, the lines of the bus and many sockets into which printed circuit boards are plugged. The boards contain the components that perform the functions shown in the blocks in Figure 6-5. The boards often contain only one of the functions (e.g., RAM memory). The back-plane will, at most, contain the power supplies and processor as well as the bus wiring.

The buses contain three groups of lines. The first group contains the address lines that select the device to be allowed access to the bus. The second group, the data lines, contains the information to be transferred. The last group are the control lines that determine the type of transfer (such as read or write). The control lines may also perform many other miscellaneous functions, such as system clocking. Bus width, in bits, is most often determined by the processor used for the system; the address width is generally twice as wide as the data-line width.

Some buses have become standards that permit many manufacturers to produce compatible function boards. Among the most popular for control applications are the Q-BUS (Digital Equipment Corporation), the MULTI-BUS (Intel Corporation, adopted as IEEE-796), and the STD bus (Pro-log Corporation).

Traditionally, microcomputers were based around a single bus, but the newer, more powerful machines now have multiple buses that divide the burden of system communications. A separate bus may be used for memory devices, another for analog input and output data, and a third for general-purpose device communications.

Off-Line Storage

The general-purpose control computer uses off-line storage. Off-line storage commonly consists of a magnetic media, such as magnetic

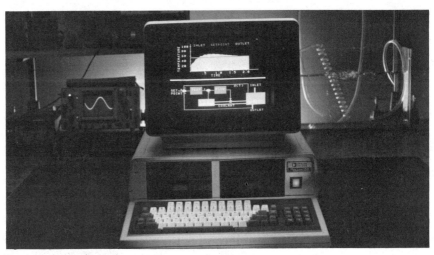

Courtesy Analog Devices, Inc.

FIGURE 6-7. General-purpose microcomputer for control

tape or disk that holds copies of the internal RAM of the computer. This system permits applications to be written that are larger than the working memory size of the computer and allows regeneration of the memory contents after power shutdown. The most often used off-line storage medium is the magnetic disk, either as removable floppy diskettes or larger, hard-disk units. In disk-based systems, both basic utilities and applications are contained on the disk. Only the basic instructions for self-testing and loading of the disk information into memory are contained in PROM memory of the computer. The disk-based system has an additional advantage in that application instructions can be developed on separate machines and the results copied into many machines, which saves time and effort when many identical applications are required. A general-purpose microcomputer for control use is illustrated in Figure 6-7.

Microcomputer Communications

In general, computers do not perform all the functions required for a particular application, and control computers are no exception. Special input devices and output devices (such as printers, modems, and analog-to-digital convertors) are termed *peripherals* and require special means to communicate with the computer. Information is exchanged between computer and peripheral in two forms: parallel and series links. Series links generally have longer usable distances, while parallel links have higher speed capabilities. Standards have emerged for each form, thus permitting different manufacturers to produce compatible equipment. The most popular serial interface (one bit at a time) is EIA standard RS-232C and its newer descendants, RS422 and RS423. Two popular parallel interface (8-16 bits at a time) have evolved. The first is the Centronics parallel interface and the second is the IEEE-488 standard. The IEEE-488 was developed by the Hewlett Packard Corporation as the HPIB bus specifically for communication between intelligent measuring devices and was expanded for general use.

Special communications structures have recently developed that permit linkage of computing devices together rather than the "host/ slave" relationship of the computer and its peripheral equipment. These communication systems are often termed *highways* or *local area networks*. It is these networks that enable many computers to work together as a hierarchy, permitting control schemes to be accomplished that are not possible by individual devices (e.g., a fully automated factory). Some of the most popular networks are DECNET (Digital Equipment Corporation) and Ethernet (Xerox Corporation). Some manufacturers of control equipment have popularized internal networks that have become standards in themselves, such as MOD-WAY (Modicon Corporation) and the Allen Bradley Data Highway.

The hardware selected for control information exchange is only half of the necessary elements. Whether point-to-point or networked, serial or parallel, this remaining half, termed *protocol* is necessary. Protocol, like its counterpart in diplomacy, is the set of rules by which information is exchanged between parties. This includes lengths of messages, special characters, and rules for breakdowns. Some of the popular protocols are X.25, SDLC, HDLC, BISYNC, and DDCMP.

Computer-Based Control Limitations

Mini- and microcomputers have some marked environmental disadvantages when compared to special-purpose control circuits. The largest problem is the sensitivity of computer electronics to temperature. General-purpose computing hardware is designed to operate at a temperature of approximately 25 to 30 degrees Celsius. When the temperature rises above 35 degrees Celsius, most computing hardware becomes unreliable, exhibiting unpredictable, intermittent faults. General-purpose computing units often use forced-air ventilation or air-conditioning units to circumvent this problem. In addition to temperature sensitivity, disk drives are particularly susceptible to dirt. Even smoke or dust of only one micron in diameter may damage the magnetic media or the pickup heads of a disk device. To prevent failures, many disk units use forced air and an elaborate filter system to exclude dirt. Computer electronics is exceptionally susceptible to electrical noise and requires stable ac power feeds to ensure predictable operation.

Industrial conditions cannot often meet the stringent environmental requirements of general-purpose computer hardware, but recent advances in microcomputers have eased the previous restrictions. Operating temperature ranges have been widened by reducing power dissipation of components in the computer enclosure and by the use of improved integrated circuit manufacturing techniques. Hard-disk memories, in tens of megabytes, are now small, inexpensive, and are manufactured in sealed, inert-gas filled modules. Power supplies now contain internal line-conditioning transformers, filters, surge suppressors, and battery backups made possible by the decrease in power requirements of the computing circuitry. These improvements have served to make the computer more practical for industrial use.

Industrial computer equipment is subject not only to the operating conditions of the shop floor, but also to rougher physical treatment than the office environment. Much more equipment handling is required in the plant due to the necessary changes in input and output needs and the increased probability of input/output failure. Protection of input and output assemblies is accomplished by housing these circuits in universal plug-in metal modules. This packaging allows rapid troubleshooting, replacement, and reconfiguration while increasing heat dissipation, noise immunity, and physical ruggedness.

Programmable Controllers

The programmable controller is a good example of a microcomputer outfitted specifically for industrial use. A programmable controller system produces all the functions of relay control at an installed price competitive with relays, while providing all the advantages of programmability. Stemming from before the microcomputer revolution, the programmable controller (PC) has been refined over a period of years and has become a standard in manufacturing equipment and machine tools where rapid setup changes are needed. Hallmarks of the programmable controller are:

- Hardware modularity, for easy reconfiguration and fault isolation
- Rugged component packaging
- Full enclosure shielding to improve noise immunity
- Internal battery backup

- Extensive power supply filtering and wide input voltage range
- Optical isolation of input and outputs
- Wide temperature operating range
- Relay ladder logic programming easily understood by service personnel
- Interfacing to ac power system line voltages, such as 120, 220, and 440 volts ac.

The programmable controller was originally designed as an alternative to relay control, but has evolved into a general-purpose control device that now has calculation, communication, and continuous-control capabilities. These gradual changes have brought the programmable controller closer to the computing power of a general-purpose computer, while maintaining the industrial ruggedness that makes it viable on the shop floor.

Microcomputer Control Software

The hardware of the microcomputer is useless without instructions to execute, just as a tape player does not produce music without a tape. It is the step-by-microstep instructions called software, that permit the hardware to accomplish control functions. As with any digital device, this information, internal to the hardware, is in the form of electrical ones and zeros. The information content is not directly observable as a whole, but is accessible using specialized input and output devices.

The basic software used for input and output transfers and the like is often written in ROMs at the time of the computer's manufacture. Such information, which is not alterable, is termed *firmware*.

The sequence of small steps that form a control application is called a *program*. The program, in its machine-usable form, is a list of ones and zeros called a *machine language object module*. The production of such a module can be done directly by a human programmer, although it is a cumbersome process. The steps to directly code an application include the following:

1. Analysis of the control problem
2. Formulation of a potential solution
3. Breakdown of the solution into small, functional steps
4. Breakdown of the functional steps into machine-executable steps
5. Translation of the machine-executable steps into binary form
6. Loading the binary code into the memory of the computer

7. Connecting the necessary inputs and outputs (peripherals)

8. Testing the potential solution and repeating the steps above until the solution is complete and working.

Coding control applications in this manner is not necessary. Instead, a set of instructions can be placed in memory which will translate control steps, written as symbols, into machine code. This method accomplishes steps 4 through 6 of the above procedure and speeds the development of an application. The set of symbols that are used to represent a series of machine instructions is called a *language*. The closer the symbols are to the machine code they represent, the simpler and faster they are for the machine program to translate, but the more difficult they are for humans to use. Therefore, languages close to machine level are known as low-level languages, while those close to human languages are called high-level languages. Languages need not be human words, but may be symbols where each word or symbol defines a control function. The symbols or words of a high-level language represent the following functions in a control program:

- Input and Output Operations

    Process

    Operator

    Machine self-monitoring

- Logic Operations

    Sequence

    Selection

    Do while

    Do until

    Do case

These operations form an information flow regardless of the control language, and serve to unify, simplify, and optimize control programs.

The use of a language frees the control designer to concentrate on the first three of the programming steps: problem analysis, solution creation, and translation of the solution in an algorithmic form suitable for coding in a language.

A language interfaces with the hardware through a special program called an *operating system*. The operating system contains instructions that identify the binary addresses for every hardware element of the system. In addition, the operating system provides the link of the machine to the operator through a control panel or terminal. This link allows the operator to select which control application will be executed by the machine. The operating system also permits a language to be truly hardware-independent. The language accomplishes this independence by relying on the operating system to route commands to the particular hardware locations necessary to cause the programmed action to occur. Sadly, manufacturers often use nonstandard techniques for interfacing a supposedly universal language to the control hardware, making any application program written under the language hardware-specific.

Languages are not restricted to control applications for computers. Instead, control languages are often built upon, or are extensions of, existing languages. The most popular general-purpose languages that have been adopted for control are FORTRAN, Pascal, FORTH, and BASIC.

The extension for these languages usually includes special commands for process control input and output, special real-time clock routines, multi-tasking, and special process data display routines.

FORTRAN (formula translator) was introduced in 1957 and became a major force in scientific and mathematic computing. Although over 25 years old, FORTRAN still remains a strong control language in the minicomputer applications area.

Pascal, like BASIC, was originally a demonstration language for college use. Its powerful structured approach to programming has made it very popular for control purposes. This is due in part to the advantages of enforced structuring in the creation of long and complex control programs.

FORTH is a language originally written to increase the productivity of its author. One of its first applications was for control of an observatory. This language produces small, fast programs that fit special control devices well. This fit is possible because this language is extendable, allowing the control engineer to define new commands as needed. This powerful ability also makes this language somewhat more difficult to learn and requires a greater knowledge of the electronics of the computer on which the program will run.

BASIC (Beginner's All-Purpose Instruction Code) is a language developed to teach programming to students at Dartmouth College. Its simplicity and ease of use has made BASIC the most popular general-purpose language used for control.

Extended languages are not the only vehicles for control; many special-purpose languages have evolved around specific hardware. Special languages for control include APT and Ladder logic. APT (Automatically Programmed Tools) is a numerical control language used for the programming of machine tools. This language grew from the need for a method of producing instructions for automated part manufacture. Ladder logic is a symbolic language in which electrical drafting symbols are used to program a computer to perform relay logic. This method grew from the need for a common thread between relay controls and computer-based systems. Ladder logic has been expanded to include much more than relay functions and now has symbols for calculation and communications.

Software START-STOP Station Example

As an example, consider our old friend the START-STOP station. The problem is to provide a means for a human operator to start a motor and stop a motor while permitting the motor starter to stop itself or prevent itself from starting if certain conditions are violated.

As a comparison, the functions to be performed by the station can be succinctly shown in the relay solution from Chapter 2 shown in Figure 6-8. The advantages of the software solution lie in the ability to add, subtract, or modify the functionality of the control algorithm, and to test the result in minutes versus the hours of labor involved in hardware-based systems. The steps involved in this software solution are as follows:

1. Analysis of the control problem
2. Formulation of a potential solution
3. Breakdown of the solution into small, functional steps
5. Translation of the machine-executable steps into a form understandable by the machine
6. Connecting the necessary inputs and outputs (peripherals)
7. Testing the potential solution and repeating the steps above until the solution is complete and working.

The problem analysis step is often the most abused of all the steps involved in the creation of a successful control solution, and yet

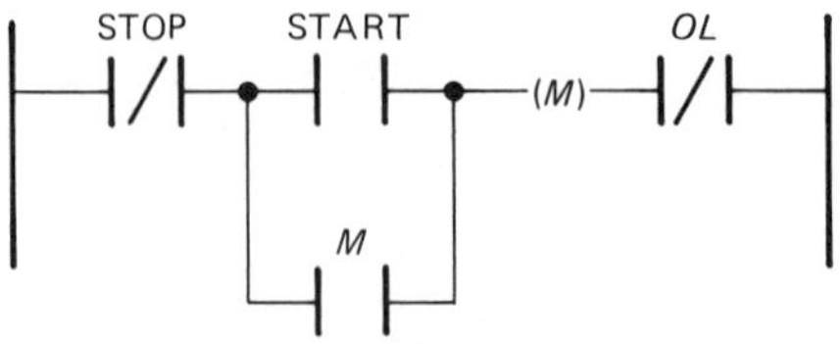

FIGURE 6-8. Relay START-STOP station

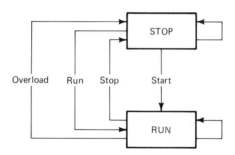

FIGURE 6-9. State diagram for a START-STOP station

it is this step upon which all remaining work depends. It is often estimated that in a successful control solution, 50 percent of the time expended is used identifying the problem and its environment.

The analysis of a control problem consists of determining the inputs and outputs of the system and the functions to be performed using these inputs and outputs. The inputs to a START-STOP system include a start command (START), a stop command (STOP), and a running status from the motor starter (MIN). The output from the system is a motor START command (MOUT).

The functions performed by the START-STOP station are to command a motor starter to open or close when instructed to do so by a human operator, and to automatically open the starter when an overload condition is detected or power is lost to the control system. This word description is easy to express, but the computer can only perform control functions by executing very small steps sequentially in time. When creating code for the computer, the programmer emulates the machine and considers each tiny step in its time sequence of occurrence for each possible condition (state) of the machine. The first step in this process is to determine the states for the station. The states in this example are RUN and STOP. These appear in diagram form in Figure 6-9.

In the STOP state, the motor contactor is shut off, the run lamp is turned off, and a STOP lamp is illuminated. The STOP state remains until a START request is detected. This must be the state immediately after power is applied to the system.

In the RUN state, the contactor is turned on, the STOP lamp is turned off, and the RUN lamp is illuminated. The RUN state remains until a STOP request is given or if contactor drop-out is detected. The state conditions are converted to a time sequence of events in the following algorithm.

Read the condition of the START, STOP, OVERLOAD and RUN switches.

If the RUN switch is active, then

Turn off the STOP light.

Turn on the RUN light

Else

Turn on the STOP light.

Turn off the RUN light.

If

The START push button is pushed (START) or the run contacts *(M)* are made

AND

the STOP push button is not pushed,

AND

the overload contacts are not made,

Then

Turn on the motor contactor

Return to READ switches

Else

Turn off the motor contactor

Return to READ switches

The steps of the completed algorithm can be converted into any language or PROM code as needed to meet the requirements of the intended control hardware. One possibility is the control BASIC program, which follows:

```
100 REM *** A DEMONSTRATION PROGRAM IN BASIC ***

110 REM * THIS  PROGRAM  DEMONSTRATES  THE  USE
    OF BASIC TO PERFORM THE                    *

120 REM * FUNCTIONS OF A START-STOP MOTOR CON-
    TROL STATION.                              *

130 REM * READ THE FIELD SWITCHES (START, STOP,
    OVERLOAD, AND RUN).                        *

140 REM * THE SWITCHES OCCUPY THE 1,2,4,8 BITS RE-
    SPECTIVELY IN THE INPUT                    *

150 REM * WORD  CALLED  SWITCH  IN  CARD  SLOT-2
    CHANNEL-1 WORD-0.                          *

160 INPUT(2,1,0);SWITCH

170 REM * TURN ON OR OFF THE INDICATOR LIGHTS
```

```
         RUN AND STOP PER THE INPUT                    *
180 REM * WHERE THE RUN LIGHT IS CARD SLOT-3
    CHANNEL 13 AND THE STOP                            *
190 REM * LIGHT IS CARD SLOT-3 CHANNEL 14.
200 RUNL=SWITCH AND 8
210 OUTPUT(3,13);RUNL
220 STOPL=NOT(SWITCH AND 8)
230 OUTPUT(3,14);STOPL
240 REM * TEST THE WORD;SWITCH FOR THE PRESENCE
    OF START OR RUN CONDITION                          *
250 REM * AND THE ABSENCE OF A STOP OR OVERLOAD
    CONDITION.                                         *
260 IF ((SWITCH AND 8) OR (SWITCH AND 1)) AND NOT
    (SWITCH AND 2) AND NOT (SWITCH AND 4) THEN
    GOTO 320
270 REM * TURN OFF THE OUTPUT TO THE CONTACTOR
    CARD SLOT-3 CHANNEL 15                             *
280 MOUT=0
290 OUTPUT(3,15);MOUT
300 GOTO 340
310 REM * TURN ON THE OUTPUT TO THE CONTACTOR
    CARD SLOT-3 CHANNEL 15                             *
320 MOUT=1
330 OUTPUT(3,15);MOUT
340 GOTO 160
350 END
```

The REM statements in this program form the documentation of the logic of the program and cause it to be maintainable by persons unfamiliar with the system under control. This documentation is an absolute necessity, but requires a large amount of space. Often listings like the one above are kept for development and maintenance, while a shortened version is actually compiled for execution. The shortened version is as follows:

```
100 INPUT(2,1,0);SWITCH : OUTPUT(3,13);(SWITCH AND 8):
    OUTPUT(3,14);(NOT(SWITCH AND 8)) : IF ((SWITCH
    AND 8) OR (SWITCH AND 1)) AND NOT(SWITCH AND
    2) AND NOT(SWITCH AND 4) THEN OUTPUT(3,15);1
    ELSE OUTPUT(3,15);0
110 GOTO 100
```

6.3 Control System Architecture Using Computers

An industrial control system requires the interfacing of discrete and continuous control as well as instrumentation and human interfaces. The control computer, the data logger, relays, and analog controllers are often all present in a single system. The functions of a control system are similar from system to system and are summarized as follows:

- Data acquisition
- Discrete control
- Safety interlocks
- Continuous control.

The control system architecture determines the interconnection of these elements into a functioning whole. The role of the computer in the control system varies from performing a single, required function in a simple architecture to incorporation of all the system needs under its control in an integrated system.

A common control architecture is the parallel system. This system structure uses parallel, but not interconnected, elements. The data acquisition system can be a data logger that records values at pre-assigned intervals. The discrete control system can be a programmable controller that handles sequencing and basic logic. The safety system can consist of relays and switches due to their simplicity and reliability, while the continuous control elements may be analog controllers. A block diagram of the parallel architecture is illustrated in Figure 6-10.

The hierarchical architecture is a more sophisticated scheme than the parallel system. In this architecture, the computer commands other system elements. Analog controller setpoint values, for example, are sent as voltages from a programmable controller to

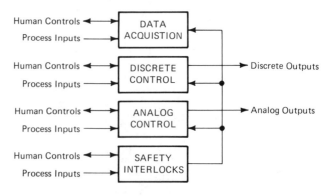

FIGURE 6-10. Parallel system architecture

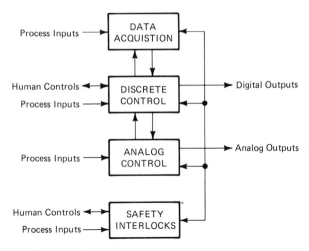

FIGURE 6-11. Hierarchical system architecture

analog controllers. This feature allows automatic coordination of the discrete and continuous control systems. The data acquisition system can also be commanded to record data in concert with the discrete controller. To provide feedback to the discrete controller, the data acquisition and analog controllers may provide contact closures that indicate the status of each device. The operator now interfaces directly with only the discrete control computer. The safety system is still independent in order to maintain system integrity. The hierarchical system is shown in Figure 6-11.

The integrated control architecture is a logic extension of the hierarchical system. In this architecture, the data acquisition and discrete and analog control are incorporated into a single computer. This method, illustrated in Figure 6-12, reduces the number of field interfaces by eliminating redundant sensors, and also improves the

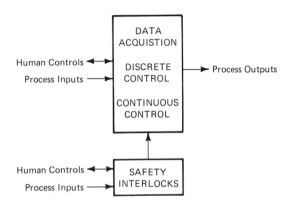

FIGURE 6-12. Integrated computer-based control

flexibility of the system by interconnecting the functions of the system by software. In some systems, even the safety interlocks are under computer control. This is possible due to built-in computer self-testing, redundant logic circuitry, and fault-tolerant computing hardware.

Discrete Control of Continuous Processes

How is an integrated, computer-based control architecture possible? Up to this point, computer-based control has been an extension of discrete control, which traces its roots back to relay-based systems. The use of high-speed computer circuitry permits digital circuitry to appear to control continuously. For instance, a computer system may examine a series of switches so often that each switch appears to be examined continuously with respect to the rate of change of the system under control. This effect is similar to the smooth appearance of motion seen on a television screen, although the picture is actually changing about 60 times a second and the picture itself is composed of hundreds of dots scanned only one at a time.

The ability of a computer to scan switches rapidly implies that a computer could emulate the analog control principles presented in Chapter 9. The use of a computer for analog control requires representation of the continuous signals of the control system as digital values. The analog input values are converted to digital values and then processed by the computer system. Conversely, digital values are converted back to analog when continuous output signals are needed.

Digital-to-analog conversion (DAC) is the simpler of the two conversion processes. A popular method uses a number of power sources that may be switched on or off by the computer and summed together to form an output. Binary numbers are converted to analog voltages by switching source voltages that are binary multiples of one another. Integrated circuit converters (DACs) of twelve to thirty-two bits are popularly used for this purpose as computer peripherals.

Analog-to-digital conversion (ADC) is a bit more difficult than its counterpart. The heart of most conversion methods is based upon creating, by summing discrete steps, a duplicate scaled voltage internal to the converter. The numeric equivalent is determined by counting the steps at the time that the internal voltage equals the input. Methods commonly used include successive approximation, stepped comparison, and dual-slope conversion. The trade-offs in conversion methods occur between speed of conversion, accuracy, and cost.

The usable bandwidth of computer-based analog control is dependent upon the sampling rate of the system. The Nyquist sampling criterion states that the sampling frequency must be twice the highest input signal frequency. In actual practice, the sampling rate is most often three to five times the highest analog frequency. Failure to sample at a high enough rate produces an effect known as *aliasing,* which creates a false signal from the data of the sampled input.

Analog control is based upon correction of the error between a desired value (setpoint) and a measured value (measurement). The correction uses both the magnitude of the error and the variation of the error with time. The error corrections based upon magnitude are easily calculated by the computer, but the computations of integration and differentiation with respect to time require special consideration. The software used by a computer for analog control is based upon algebraic approximations for the derivative and integral functions. The derivative is approximated by finding the difference between two samples and dividing by the time period between them. The integral function is approximated by defining an integration period in terms of the number of samples it contains and finding the weighted sum of the samples. By these methods, the continuous control equations of Chapter 9 can be adequately emulated by a control computer.

Computer-based control is not limited to one microcomputer, but may incorporate literally hundreds. These microcomputers may not only be interconnected among themselves, but also may be tied to supervisory minicomputers and mainframe corporate business machines. This interconnection permits information exchange within an organization from the production floor to the highest levels of management.

The programs used by computer-based control systems have been unable to modify themselves, and therefore are unable to incorporate past experience. However, *artificial intelligence* is beginning to find application in industry as evidenced in self-tuning controllers. In the near future, control systems may be able to modify and improve control schemes independently, based on the experience of operating a process.

Problems

6.1 What are the drawbacks and advantages of integrated-circuit-based control circuits as compared to programmable control?

6.2 Changes to card-based logic systems are accomplished through what mechanism?

6.3 How is a selector-based control system modified?

6.4 Sketch a diagram of a selector-based system for control of a time-based traffic light.

6.5 How are the number of wires reduced in a selector-based system versus an integrated circuit-based system?

6.6 What are the benefits and penalties of separating control configuration data from control hardware?

6.7 What logic gate type typically connects a device to a bus?

6.8 What is the effect of a speed variation in the mechanism that advances the Mylar tape in a tape-based controller?

6.9 What term is used to define the total set of variable input and control output conditions of a system at any one time? Why is this information important?

6.10 How are the OR and AND gates connections of a PLA programmed?

6.11 What are the advantages of a PLA-based system over an integrated circuit logic design?

6.12 The PROM-based system contains what information within the PROM and how is this information read?

6.13 A computer-based control system has what two advantages and what two disadvantages in comparison with a PROM-based system?

6.14 What are the objections to processor-based control in the industrial environment?

6.15 What are the advantages of a microprocessor-based control design as opposed to a logic-card-based system?

6.16 Sketch a block diagram of a control computer showing the directions of information flow between functional elements.

6.17 What are the functions of the control elements of the control computer?

6.18 What are three measures of the functional capabilities of a control computer?

6.19 A one-board computer is best applied in what control situations?

6.20 A general-purpose control computer is based upon the use of what mechanism to communicate between computing elements?

6.21 What are three types of buses used in general-purpose control computers?

6.22 Name three common buses used for real-time control purposes.

6.23 Modern systems are based upon multiple buses. What are advantages of such an architecture?

6.24 What is off-line storage and what is the most common storage media?

6.25 In the general-purpose control computer, what information is contained in PROM?

6.26 What are two forms of electrical communication between control computers and input/output devices?

6.27 What is designated by the term RS422?

6.28 What is designated by the term IEEE-488?

6.29 Intelligent control devices are linked by local area networks. What are two types presently in use?

6.30 What is meant by the term *protocol* in computer terminology?

6.31 What are two protocols in current use?

6.32 What is the largest problem involved with the use of computers in an industrial environment?

6.33 How are control computers avoiding the environmental problems of the plant floor?

6.34 What is a programmable controller and what distinguishes it from the desk-top microcomputer?

6.35 What is the relationship of hardware to software?

6.36 What are the steps in the creation of a control program?

6.37 What is a language and what steps of problem 6.36 are accomplished by its use?

6.38 What is the difference between a low- and high-level language?

6.39 What is the purpose of an operating system and what advantages does an operating system provide?

6.40 What are three control languages and how does a control language differ from a general-purpose language?

6.41 Give an example of a language specifically for control applications.

6.42 Does the analysis of a control problem often consume a large or small portion of the total time of a project?

6.43 What are the four functions most commonly required of an industrial control system?

6.44 Sketch a parallel control architecture using a programmable controller.

6.45 Should a safety interlock system be included as a computer-based control function? Why or why not?

6.46 Sketch a hierarchical control architecture and describe its advantages and disadvantages over a parallel structure.

6.47 How is continuous control possible by a binary-value computing system?

6.48 What is a DAC and what are two methods of operation?

6.49 What is an ADC and how does one operate?

6.50 What is the Nyquist sampling criterion and what is the effect if it is violated?

6.51 How are time-based integrations and differentiations performed by computer logic?

6.52 Programs that modify themselves based upon experience are termed *artificially intelligent*. What are some applications for control systems that incorporate such an ability as opposed to those designed for specific purposes?

7 | Programmable Control

7.0 Introduction

This chapter is concerned with the character and application of the programmable controller (PC). PCs are microprocessor-based controllers that produce output functions by electronically scanning input signals, processing the signals according to the user program instruction set, and setting the outputs in accordance with the inputs and program. PCs are widely used to replace or displace relay controls, but PCs have capabilities that far exceed relay control in terms of complexity and flexibility. An example of a PC with its program panel is shown in Figure 7-1.

Courtesy Gould Electronics

FIGURE 7-1. A programmable controller with its program panel

7.1 History

Although vacuum-tube-based control systems were used in industry and military applications, vacuum-tube controllers were not competitive with relay-based controllers for the vast majority of control systems applications. A major reason, among others, was that the vacuum tube lacked the ruggedness and long life of the relay. With the advent of the solid-state era and semiconductor devices such as transistors, diodes, phototransistors, SCRs and triacs, and integrated circuits, a new technology came into being that had a strong competitive edge over relays in a wide range of applications (but certainly not all applications).

As an alternative to relay or vacuum-tube control systems, solid-state logic circuits were implemented. In the early applications of these solid-state industrial control systems, severe problems were encountered. The original solid-state controls experienced random failures due to lack of quality control. The sensitivity of these controls caused them to be receptive to false signals and noise, due in part to a lack of signal conditioning. Also, replacement parts were not easily available, nor were they universally replaceable as were relays. In addition, solid state controls made of gates, flip-flops, counters, registers, etc., were a strange and unfamiliar technology to the industry workforce.

Clearly, there was a need for a solid-state controller that was reliable, compact, and versatile. It also had to have the acceptance of the industry workforce; that is, it had to use the logic of a ladder diagram in the same way that relay logic did. In the late 1960s the development of computers had progressed to the point where high-volume production industries—especially the automotive industry that had to cope with annual model changes—were searching for a better way than relay logic to control assembly lines. Due to the finite lifetime of mechanically operating devices, equipment failures were frequent and caused costly downtime. In addition, annual model changes required virtually total relay replacement. At this time, programmable controllers were introduced to serve the purpose of relay replacement. Some of the key innovations were:

> *1969.* PCs were applied to industry operations such as assembly machines, transfer lines, and turning machines.
>
> *1971.* PCs were extended to other industries as relay-logic replacement.
>
> *1973.* PCs became "intelligent," including arithmetic and data manipulation functions. PCs also became more compact for rack mounting, and programmers were developed with keyboard input and CRT display.

1975. PCs' capabilities were expanded to include operator communication, analog control, positioning control, and machine-fault detection. PCs thus had capability overlap with minicomputers and numerical control. Also, "mini" PCs were introduced.

1977. PCs were expanded into system control, i.e., machine lines, production testing, and batch chemical plant control, where multiple "slave" PCs were used with a supervisory PC or minicomputer.

1979. PCs entered their fourth generation, with new technology in communications, improved and versatile languages, fault diagnostics, inventory and data processing, mathematical function capability, and packaging improvement.

7.2 PC Definition and Articulation with Related Equipment

The definition of a PC has evolved with the advancement of PCs. Originally, the PC was a software replacement for relays. As shown by tracing the history above, the PC has evolved into a computer system with a wide assortment of capabilities: arithmetic operations, digital-to-analog conversion, data comparison, word manipulation, complex functions, and equation solving. Two additional capabilities include communications with the operator and communications within a distributed control system. The uniqueness of a PC is related to its interface capability and its ability to survive an industrial environment. Various languages are used in PC programming. Initially, ladder logic was used almost exclusively, then new models were introduced that used other languages such as Boolean functions, BASIC, and other high-order languages.

In summary, according to NEMA Standards, a PC is a digitally operating electronic apparatus that uses a programmable memory for the internal storage of instructions that implement specific functions, such as logic, sequence, timing, counting, and arithmetic, to control machines and processes.

The place of PCs in the control world can be seen by realizing how they articulate with related hardware.

1. PCs must receive a signal from an input device such as a voltage state from a limit switch. Other inputs include voltage states from other switches, analog signals, and BCD (binary coded decimal) data. The appropriate input interface is required for each type of input.

2. PCs must drive output devices such as relay coils, solenoid valves, indicator lamps, and motor starters. The output is

through an internal switching device such as a triac powered by user-supplied power. In terms of relay logic, the PC essentially supplies a contact closure.

3. PCs differ from numerical control (NC) and computer numerical control (CNC) in that these units are position-control oriented whereas PCs are sequence-control oriented, although these distinctions are less clear-cut than they have been historically, since more sophisticated PCs have position-control capability.

4. PCs differ from computers in that PCs are designed and constructed to interact directly with the industrial environment in terms of hardware input/output and in terms of familiar software.

5. PCs can be used to replace as few as eight logic relays and be cost-effective, depending on the application, but even the smallest PCs have far greater capability than simply relay replacement.

6. PCs can be used to support an entirely new job with only software changes, as opposed to a possible total tear-down of a relay system.

7. PCs can communicate troubleshooting information to the operator as well as input/output and inventory data to a supervisory computer.

7.3 Industry Use of PCs and Technical Skills Required of Users

Tens of thousands of PCs are in use in the United States alone and the growth rate is high. Table 7-1 shows a sample list of industrial uses of PCs.

Full utilization of programmable controllers requires a commanding grasp of the use, maintenance, and design application of

TABLE 7-1. Industry uses of PCs

Machine Tools	Conveyor Systems
Automatic Warehouses	Energy Management
Petrochemical Process Control	Paint Spraying Equipment
Automated Test Stands	Automatic Weighing
Steam Burner Control	Time Card Monitoring
Automated Wheel Balancing	Facilities Monitoring

PC-operated equipment. Familiarity with the following areas is needed:

1. *Motor and motor starters.* The characteristics of motors and motor starters are important to PC operation. Important considerations include inrush current, starting transients, and overload protection. The PC must interface with the motor starter and the motor to be assured of proper operation.

2. *Relay logic.* PCs are usually designed with the concept of ladder diagrams and relay logic.

3. *Digital logic.* Some success may be obtained in ignoring the fact that a PC is a digital logic device, but for more comprehensive involvement it will be necessary for the individual to understand gates, flip-flops, registers, number systems, and Boolean algebra.

4. *Power electronics.* The PC output will not only interface with power devices such as SCRs and triacs, but its output is also made up of these devices; thus, familiarity with the operation of power electronics devices is important in the understanding of PCs.

5. *Noise suppression techniques.* In the area of high-impedance solid state electronics, the handling of noise suppression is critical, unlike the relay logic predecessor, which is practically noise immune.

6. *Software programming.* Regardless of whether the medium is the ladder diagram, Boolean algebra, BASIC, or some other language, the competent user must be aware of how to program the computer for the application.

7.4 The Block Structure of a PC

The PC is a microprocessor-based controller in that its monitoring of inputs and directions to outputs depends on the instruction set that is processed by the microprocessor. Thus, the PC is based on digital logic; it is essentially a microcomputer with specialized input/output and logic structure.

Any computing unit can be diagrammed in four basic blocks. A block diagram is shown in Figure 7-2. An example of the structure is an arithmetic logic unit (ALU). Figure 7-3 shows an 8-bit ALU. In this figure, the A input is an 8-bit binary number, the B input is also an 8-bit binary number, and the S input is a 4-bit control input. The A and B

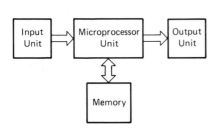

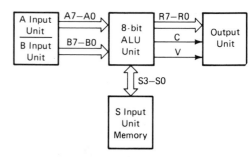

FIGURE 7-2. Block structure of a computing unit

FIGURE 7-3. Block structure of an 8-bit ALU

inputs may be in the form of a voltage bias from a supply, from a switch, from a flip-flop, or from a memory unit. The output is an 8-bit binary number, R, a carry (or borrow) bit, C, and an overflow bit, V. The output could be LED displays, flip-flops, memory cells, etc. This unit is capable of carrying out several arithmetic operations. If the value of the control S3-S0 is 0010, then the operation is addition of A and B; for example, if A and B are as given below, then R could be found by addition:

$$A = 0101\ 0101$$
$$\underline{B = 1001\ 0010}$$
$$R = 1110\ 0111$$

Other operations that are controlled by the value of S are subtraction, complementation, negation, incrementation, decrementation, ANDing, ORing, EORing (exclusive ORing), and maximum selection. Thus it can be seen that several operations are possible in this simple unit.

7.5 The Structure of the Central Processing Unit

The major difference between the gated logic control that was presented in Chapter 3 and PC control is that the logic used here is programmed. In the case of logic gates, flip-flops, counters, and registers, the operation is solely determined by the hardwired elements. If this operation is hardwired, then in contrast, the operational control of a microprocessor is "soft," namely, the operation also depends on the stored program in memory. The program is a sequence of code words, and thus the system is "programmable" by inserting the desired code words.

Another difference between hardwired digital systems and programmable digital systems is the degree of complexity. Certainly it is possible to start with the basic building blocks of gates, flip-flops, registers, etc., and build a microcomputer, but the likelihood of doing so satisfactorily is about the same as building a space shuttle from nuts, bolts and bathroom tile. The point is that an enormous concentration of logic elements is currently available in today's integrated circuit technology. A recent news release stated that a prototype 64K memory unit the size of a pinhead has been manufactured. The importance of this technology can be realized by visualizing the problems involved in storing 64K of memory by wiring vacuum tubes. Thus, without high storage density in modern integrated circuits, modern microcomputers would not be possible.

In its operation, the microprocessor is similar to the ALU discussed above in that it performs one operation at a time depending on the control word. The difference is that the microprocessor has many more possible operations defined by a larger selection of code words.

7.6 The Structure of the Memory

The memory is typically dynamic CMOS (Complementary Metal Oxide Semiconductor) and has battery backup (which should have several months' to years' program retention capability).

The memory unit of programmable controllers usually consists of two types of semiconductor integrated circuits. Read/write memory (R/WM, also called RAM for Random Access Memory) is a volatile storage element that contains the created logic sequence and "scratch pad" calculation work space. The second type of memory is ROM (Ready-Only Memory), which is nonvolatile and contains the elemental instructions required for the execution of any field-created (user) logic program. Typically, both types of memory are made up of words of two bytes each which, in turn, consist of four to 16 bits each. A typical size of user memory in a small PC is in the range of 512 bytes to 1K bytes.

The memory stores the sequence of code words that make up the program. By placing the code words in successive addresses, a program counter keeps track of the next code word to be addressed. The code word for the operation to be performed, the address of the data, and the storage address (for the result of the operation) are stored in successive locations of memory. The CPU performs the programmed logic by execution of the contents of successive memory locations.

The R/WM memory is divided into two major sections: the data section and the user program. The data section has several subsections. A typical breakdown follows.

Output Image Memory

The output image memory is an exact image of the conditions of the output states. Its purpose is to control the status of outputs on the output modules. If a bit in the output image memory is set high, then the corresponding output on the output board is set ON. Conversely, if that same bit is set low, then the corresponding output is set OFF.

Input Image Memory

The input image memory is an exact image of the conditions of the input states. Its purpose is to duplicate the status of inputs at the input modules. If an input is ON, then the corresponding bit in the input image memory is set high. Conversely, if that input is OFF, then the same input bit is set low.

Counter/Timer Storage Memory

Each timer and counter requires that a preset value and an accumulated value stored for counter/timer operation. Thus, two words must be stored for each counter or timer. There is typically a reserved location for each of these values, and a timer must be given an address consistent with this reserved location.

User Storage Memory

Another area of memory is provided for user storage of such items as look-up tables and data. This is usually available on a bit basis or on a word basis. Naturally, the program must provide instructions that permit accessing this table on a bit/word basis.

Processor Storage Memory

In addition, the processor will reserve a portion of memory for work and storage areas. These areas will not generally be available to the user. Thus the user cannot use addresses for input/output or other devices that correspond to these reserved areas.

7.7 Input/Output Modules

In many PCs, input and output modules can be moved from one location to another or be replaced by another module to match the I/O voltage and current requirements. Input modules are available in several ranges. The following are typical:

dc 12-24 V	analog (8-bit)
dc 48 V	analog (12-bit)
ac 120 V	analog (16-bit).
TTL	

Output modules are typically available in the following ranges:

dc 12-24 V	TTL
dc 48 V	digital to analog.
ac 120 V	

The input module operates by sensing the voltage level of the input device and providing the processor with a conditioned signal from that input, namely, a one or zero level in one bit in a word. The input can be from any combination source and switch (or other device) that is consistent with the voltage specification of the input module.

The output module operates by a logic-level command from the processor directing it to provide an ON or OFF condition to the output terminal. By connecting the source voltage to the module and the load to the designated terminal, the voltage is conducted to the load when the processor so specifies.

Each manufacturer provides a different method of addressing the I/O to the external world of switches, relays, and so forth, but each method must identify whether the I/O is input or output and the location of that particular I/O device. One addressing scheme is given below:

For input: *1FGXX*

For output: *0FGXX*

where F stands for a single-digit octal number whose value is 2 for the designation of an I/O address, G stands for a single-digit octal group number, and XX stands for a two-digit octal terminal number. Thus, an address of 11307 would mean that the device is an input that is attached to the third group at the seventh terminal. Other addresses where the F value is not 1, such as 02307, are used for internal storage and could be used for a logic device, but without physical output.

Section 7.13 on Boolean algebra shows another addressing scheme. This scheme is based on *X1, X2, X3*, etc., being input addresses; *Y1, Y2, Y3*, etc., being output addresses; and *C1, C2, C3*, being internal storage or logical devices (as if these were relays used for logic but not I/O).

7.8 Operation of the Processor Unit

The controller continuously monitors the status of devices connected as inputs, and then, following the instruction program in its memory, controls the status of the devices connected to its output terminals. Its purpose is scanning of the I/O devices, timing and counting functions, data comparison and transfers, arithmetic operations, and self-checking diagnostic routines.

Processors typically have two or three modes of use:

1. *Program Mode.* The PC is connected to the program panel, the memory-protect function (often a hand-operated key) is turned off, and the program is entered through the program panel in the form of ladder elemental symbols, Boolean functions, or other logic as required by the program panel.

2. *Run Mode.* The PC monitors inputs and sets outputs in accordance with the program.

3. *Test Mode.* Some PCs have the capability of operating the internal logic provided by the program and in accordance with inputs, but the outputs are not enabled. This mode is useful for testing and debugging the program logic.

For the processor to function, it must be provided regulated and filtered power, typically 5 volts, by the system power supply. If the power system voltage has dropped below a preset level, the processor typically disables all output devices and stops receiving input data. The processor also indicates when there is an internal fault that interferes with processing.

7.9 The Program Panel

The program panel is connected by cable to the processor unit. It can be used to program the processor, to edit an existing program, to alter the condition of an I/O state by forcing it to a desired state, and to change a programmed data value. It can be cable-connected to a data terminal for recording/loading a copy of the entered program, possibly in ladder-diagram form. The keyboard provides all the control functions. Displays are of several kinds, the least expensive one being the single-line display using LEDs (light-emitting diodes) or fluorescent elements that display a single device at a time. Another style displays an array of the logic diagram through the use of LCD (liquid crystal display) but does not show the detail of each element, which is shown in a separate area of the display. In this style, only the power flow condition is shown by the LCD array. More expensive units provide CRT output wherein a large section of the ladder diagram can be

Courtesy Gould Electronics

FIGURE 7-4. A program panel

displayed and the device that is being addressed is highlighted. An example of a program panel is shown in Figure 7-4.

7.10 Programming and Hardwiring the PC

PC control may be implemented in three steps:

1. Enter the control program (such as a ladder diagram)
2. Test the programmed instructions
3. Wire the accompanying hardware.

Thus, the first step is to program the ladder diagram using the program panel. The desired component (contact, coil, etc.) is activated by programming the appropriate I/O address. More instructions are required for timers, counters, etc.; these are covered later.

The second step of software testing is elective but highly recommended in early experiences with PCs. It consists of testing the software by using the program panel editing capability to force the various input functions. In this manner, the functions that later will be implemented with hardware are simulated in software.

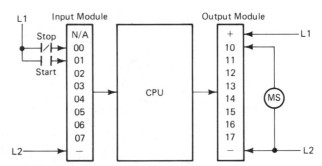

FIGURE 7-5. Diagram of I/O for START-STOP control

The third step is the actual physical wiring installation connecting the input and output devices to the I/O boards. Figure 7-5 is an example of the I/O wiring for a three-wire START-STOP station motor control. Although addresses and wiring conventions differ among manufacturers, the figure is representative. The input is provided by wiring the power supply to one side of the switches used as input devices, such as push buttons, limit switches, etc.; the other side of the line is tied to the common terminal on the input board, just as the other side of the switches are tied to their respective addressed locations. On the output side of the I/O, the power supply is wired to the specified grounded line terminal on the output board (i.e., the "hot" side), and the other side of the line is connected to the common terminal on the board. The output devices are connected from their respective addressed locations and the output common terminal.

7.11 Programming Languages

The language of the PC is preprogrammed into the PC processor memory unit at the time of the manufacture of the PC. A variety of languages are used. The user should consider the application to determine the appropriate language.

- For primarily mathematical and communications applications, high-order languages (HOLs) are appropriate. These include BASIC, various modified BASIC versions, and others.
- For applications that call for Boolean algebra, a Boolean algebra-type language is appropriate. Boolean algebra-based PCs are usually of the smaller type.
- For elementary programming, the most popular languages involve ladder-diagram programming. Advantages are clarity and familiarity to persons in the control field.

7.12 High-Order Languages

Several HOLs are applied to PCs: BASIC, FORTRAN, SYBIL (which is similar to BASIC), and MCL. Although not the most efficient code, BASIC is probably the most popular due to its simple, English-like commands. Familiarity with BASIC can be obtained from the vast amount of manuals published on it.

As an example, following is a BASIC program that provides proportional control. The feedback control system error E is determined by finding the difference between the setpoint S and the feedback variable F. (Note that in BASIC each line must begin with a line number. The program is executed in the line-number sequence.)

> 60 E = S − F

Next, the output C is determined by multiplying the error E by the gain G and allowing for an offset correction T.

> 70 C = G • E + T

To get the data S and F prior to the above statements, special functions would need to be exercised in BASIC. For example, if the setpoint S was available at port 12 and feedback F was available at port 13, they could be retrieved in byte form by the command

> 40 S = INP(12)
>
> 50 F = INP(13)

To get the value of offset correction T, several approaches could be used, depending on the need to revalue T. If T is changed frequently, it could be input from a thumbwheel switch (as could S). If T is set at the start of each run of the PC operation, it could be initialized by the user through the use of an INPUT statement at the beginning of the BASIC program. If T is essentially constant, then it could be set in a data statement or in a line statement:

> 20 T = 123

The output C could be sent through port 16 to the outside world for digital-to-analog conversion and for operating a servomotor by the command

> 80 OUT 16,C

Special considerations will be necessary to assure that C is properly scaled to fit in the allowable range for the output port.

The above program can be made to operate continuously if it ends with a loop back to the beginning:

90 GOTO 30

However, it may be useful to cause the operation to wait until the desired datum is available on port 12 to assure that the operator is ready. The WAIT function will suspend program execution while monitoring the status of the input port:

30 WAIT 12,1

This statement will cause the program to continuously monitor port 12 until bit 0 (the least significant bit) is set to 1, and then it will continue with the next line.

In summary, the above program is given as

10 REM PROPORTIONAL CONTROL WITH OFFSET
11 REM CORRECTION
20 T = 123
30 WAIT 12,1
40 S = INP(12)
50 F = INP(13)
60 E = S − F
70 C = G * E + T
80 OUT 16,C
90 GOTO 30
100 END

The result is control output C. Many other considerations would be added to the above in terms of scaling the input and output, providing start-up procedure, stopping procedure, etc., but the example shows the basic elements of programming in HOL for proportional feedback.

Additional control strategies can readily be implemented once the HOL is used to write the control algorithm. Deadband can be implemented by simply providing a line that sets E to 0 if the absolute value of E is less than some deadband range. Timing of resets can be controlled by a clocked function such as WAIT. Proportional, integral, and derivative control can be implemented by numerical integration and differentiation of the error signal. These matters will be taken up more fully in Chapter 9.

7.13   Boolean Language

Returning to the principles of Boolean algebra expressed in Chapters 2 and 3, ladder logic can be expressed in terms of Boolean functions. Consider a ladder diagram of contacts and an output as shown in Figure 7-6. The Boolean equation is

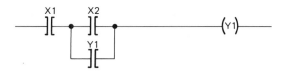

FIGURE 7-6. Logic diagram to Boolean expression example

$Y1 = X1\ AND\ (X2\ OR\ Y1)$

The start of the rung is designated by a START command (STR), followed by the name of the input device (e.g., *X1*), followed by an ENTER of the instruction command:

STR X1 ENTER

Next, provision is made for the branch to the *Y1* contacts by using another START command, followed by the one of the parallel contacts:

STR X2 ENTER

The parallel contacts provide a Boolean OR function; the command is followed by the other parallel contacts:

OR Y1 ENTER

Next, provision is made for the Boolean AND arrangement of the *X1* contacts and the parallel *X2-Y1* contacts by ANDing them. The STR command is used to designate the end of the most recent STR command at the beginning of the branch:

AND STR ENTER

Finally, the output device must be programmed:

OUT Y1 ENTER

In summary, the commands for programming a START-STOP station are given together:

STR X1 ENTER
STR X2 ENTER
OR Y1 ENTER
AND STR ENTER
OUT Y1 ENTER

Other commands are available. If the *X2* contacts in the above example were normally closed, then the symbol *NOT X2* would be used in place of *X2*.

7.14 Ladder Logic

Some common symbols of ladder diagram programming are given here:

] [The *open contact* symbol designates an OFF (i.e., zero) condition that can be set ON (i.e., to one) by an external input or by a programming instruction.

]/[The *closed contact* symbol designates an ON, or one, condition that can be set OFF, or to zero, by either an external input or a programming instruction.

( ) The *coil* symbol designates an output device that can be set to a one condition by establishing a connecting set of contacts that are ON, or one. In turn, the contact devices under its control will be set to their energized or held condition.

L The *output latch* operates similarly to the coil above; however, it will not de-energize upon losing the path of continuity to it.

U The *output unlatch* is the device used to unlatch the above latch. An example of the use of a latch is shown in Figure 7-7. The addressing is the same as that given in Section 7.7. When the initiating contacts 10001 are made, the latch will be set TRUE and all the 02000 contacts throughout will be latched on. In the case of temporary power shutdown, upon renewal of power, the latch will remain just what its name says, i.e., "latched." A necessary condition to unlatch the latch is the making of contacts 10002, in which case the 02000 contacts are opened throughout the circuit. Incidentally, if the 10001 contacts and 10002 contacts are both made at the same time, the latch will only be latched for the time it takes the PC processor to process from one line to the next; or, in the case where there are rungs between the two lines, the latch would be set TRUE

FIGURE 7-7. Example of the use of a latch

for the time that the in-between rungs were being executed.

⊤ The *branch start* is the logic unit that permits branching. It is used to designate the node wherever the branch begins, and it is used where that new ladder rung connecting to that node is programmed.

⊥ The *branch end* is the logic unit that completes a set of branches.

MCR The *master control relay* instruction provides for the control over all output within the MCR zone, in that all the outputs are de-energized when the conditions that control the MCR relay are FALSE. A ladder diagram illustrating the MCR and other symbols is shown in Figure 7-8. In addition to the software MCR, it is good practice, if not a requirement, for the installation to include a hardwired master control relay for emergency I/O power shutdown. This consideration depends on the process being controlled and the hazards associated with it.

ZCL The *zone control logic* instruction provides for the control over all output within the ZCL zone, in that all the outputs are held in their last state when the conditions that control the ZCL relay are FALSE. The difference between the ZCL and the MCR is that the ZCL-controlled states are held following a power interruption to the processor, whereas the MCR-controlled states are set to OFF during and following a power interruption.

JMP The *jump* command permits jumping around all rungs that are located beneath the JMP command and above the LBL instruction that must follow; that is, the com-

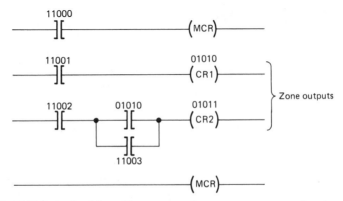

FIGURE 7-8. Ladder diagram using master control relay

mand "jumps" the program logic to the LBL instruction without executing the in-between lines.

LBL The *label* instruction is the landing place for the JMP.

JSB The *jump to subroutine* allows the programmer to use a single routine accessed from various locations of the program without repeating it at each location where it is needed. After jumping to a particular rung that has the LBL instruction and exercising those subroutine rung instructions, the program pointer is set back to the statement following the original JSB statement.

RET The *return* instruction is the last instruction in the subroutine.

An example of a ladder diagram using a subroutine is shown in Figure 7-9. In the case where 11000 contacts are not TRUE, the instructions are followed down to, but not including, the LBL rung; rather, the next instruction is the first line of the main program. In the case where the 11000 contacts are TRUE, the next line that is executed is the LBL rung. Following the execution of other rungs preceding the RET rung, if they exist, the execution is transferred to the line following the JSB rung, the *CR1* rung. By this logic, it is possible to build a hierarchy of instructions, depending on external and internal logic conditions.

Single-Line Timers and Counters

Both timers and counters require two values: the accumulated value that is being timed or counted, and the preset value, which is the value that the accumulated value times or counts to, at which time the status

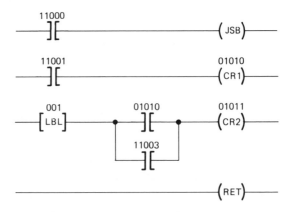

FIGURE 7-9. Ladder diagram using a subroutine

bit goes high. A single counter or timer has a limited counting capability—999 is typically the largest timer or counter value; however, use can be made of the overflow bit to cascade counters and/or timers to achieve large quantities of time or count.

There are two kinds of counters: up counters (CU) and down counters (CD). The counting action takes place whenever the rung logic condition to the counter coil symbol goes from FALSE to TRUE. When the accumulated count (AC) reaches the preset count (PR) in the CU or zero in the CD, the counter stops counting and the status bit goes high. When the accumulated value goes above 999 in the CU or below zero in the CD, the overflow bit in the accumulated value word goes high. This overflow bit can be used to trigger the next counter in a string of cascaded counters. There is also a designated bit in the AC that is enabled for the down counter, and a designated bit that is enabled for the up counter.

A timer is similar to a counter except that it counts elapsed time intervals. The time scale may be one of several values. When the count of the programmed time interval as stored in the accumulated value (AC) reaches the preset value (PR), the timer stops counting and the status bit goes high. There are three kinds of timers available: timer on delay (TON), timer off delay (TOF), and retentive timer (RTR). A typical timer ladder diagram is shown in Figure 7-10.

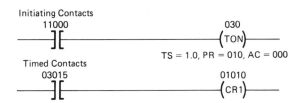

FIGURE 7-10. Ladder diagram using a timer.

Single-Line Data Manipulation Instructions

Data manipulation instructions that operate on words are the following: get from a memory location (GET), put in a memory location (PUT), less than or equal to (LES), equal (EQU), addition (+), and subtraction (−). These word instructions are described below:

GET   Used to transfer a three-digit address of a memory word for use in another operation.

PUT   Used to transfer a word from one data table location to another; must be preceded by a GET, which addresses the word (useful with a BCD thumbwheel switch).

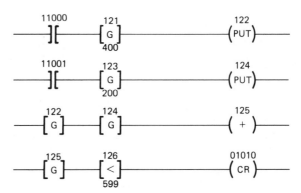

FIGURE 7-11. Ladder diagram for a data instruction

EQU Used to determine if two BCD words are equal; must be used with GET.

LES Used to compare two BCD words for "less than" or "equal to"; must be used with GET.

$+/-$ Used to add or subtract two BCD words; must be preceded with two GETs.

An example ladder diagram of word data manipulations is given here in Figure 7-11. In this example, the contents of registers 125 and 126 are being compared for an LES condition to be a TRUE condition to set *CR* TRUE. In the case that neither contacts 11000 nor 11001 have been set TRUE, the initial values of registers 122 and 124 in the first and second lines will be left at their initial values, which will be zero at start-up. These two numbers are then added in the third line and the sum is stored in register 125 for comparison with register 126. In the case where both contacts 11000 and 11001 are closed, 400 is stored in register 122 and 200 is stored in register 124, causing the sum stored in register 125 to be 600. In this case, the LES test will fail, i.e., it is not true that $600 < 599$; thus, output 01010 will change to FALSE.

In addition to data manipulation instructions that operate on words, there are data manipulation instructions that operate on bytes. Examples are GET BYTE and LIMIT TEST.

7.15 Functional Block Unit

The above single-line instructions are limited in their ability to handle more complicated instructions such as word and file manipulations. In addition, some PC manufacturers choose to use block style for timer

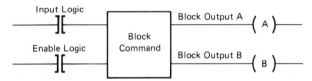

FIGURE 7-12. Form of the block command

and counter instructions. The form of the block command is shown in Figure 7-12.

The input to the block may be a contact or possibly a series-parallel combination of contact logic. Depending on the block structure and type, the other input to the left side of the block may be the ENABLE logic. For example, if the ENABLE logic to a block timer is TRUE, then the timer times as long as the input logic is TRUE and holds its value when the input logic is FALSE. The block output A is TRUE when the block condition is satisfied (e.g., when the timer reaches the preset value). Block output B is another possible output, depending on the block structure and type. Examples follow.

Block Counters and Timers

An example of a block counter is provided in Figure 7-13. The block is enabled by the RESET/ENABLE logic, which must be TRUE for block operation. In the case where the upcount logic is TRUE, the counter counts up 1, 2, 3, etc., and in the case where the downcount logic is TRUE, the counter counts down 3, 2, 1, etc. Block output A is TRUE whenever the count equals zero if the ZERO flag is on; alternately, block output A is TRUE whenever the count equals the preset value if the ZERO flag is OFF. Block output B is TRUE whenever the count is not equal to the preset value.

The above description of block counters carries over to block timers with the condition that timers are clock-driven rather than

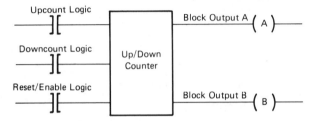

FIGURE 7-13. Form of an up/down counter command

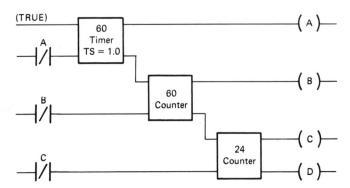

FIGURE 7-14. Using timers and counters for a 24-hour clock

event-driven, and count up only. For flexibility of timing, time scaling is provided. As an example of how timers can be cascaded to time beyond the 999 BCD count that is common to many PCs, Figure 7-14 shows how a timer and two counters are used to form a 24-hour clock. The timer is reset every 60 seconds by the use of the *A* coil being set TRUE at the end of 60 seconds and it, in turn, opening its normally closed *A* contacts in the ENABLE/RESET line of the timer. Each of these events of a 60-second period is used by connecting the NOT EQUAL output of the timer to the first counter. Whenever the 60-second count is reached, the counter input is FALSE, and one count is accumulated at the time that the counter input returns to TRUE. This minute counter in turn drives the second counter, the hour timer, so that an event is recorded every 60 minutes. Finally, the hour counter counts to 24 hours and resets.

Note that the 24-hour clock in this example will tend to run slightly slower than real time, due to the time required for one scan cycle as the 60-second timer is reset. This time lost is dependent upon the scan time of the processor, which depends on program size. Self-correcting clocks can be programmed in those situations where this inaccuracy is significant.

Other Block Instructions

The block form is useful for performing arithmetic instructions. For example, Figure 7-15 shows an addition block. The input to the block may be a contact or possibly a series-parallel combination of contacts. The operation of adding the contents of Register 1 to Register 2 and placing the sum in Register 3 occurs when the input logic is TRUE. The outcome is stored in Register 3; however, the possibility of overflow of

FIGURE 7-15. Addition block

the fixed word length does exist, and the block output A is set TRUE whenever overflow does exist.

Other arithmetic block operations occur in a similar way to addition blocks.

Data-manipulation blocks allow words and tables of words to be moved, set to specified values, shifted, compared, placed in stack registers, and manipulated in other ways. An example of the usefulness of a data-move operation is that sets of preset values for timers could be stored in data tables. When it is desired to change the speed of operation of the PC-controlled process through an input communication, one of the sets of preset times could be transferred into the preset timer addresses, causing each timer to time to the table of preset values. The point of this example is that data manipulation provides the capability for powerful commands. These commands are applicable primarily in large, sophisticated operations.

Another valuable operation of a programmable controller is the sequencer. The electromagnetic equivalent of a sequencer is a drum controller wherein many outputs can be set ON or OFF by the electromagnetically controlled rotation of the drum through the individual drum steps in a cyclical manner. In a similar way, the input to a sequencer causes the stepping of the sequencer; the output is stored in registers for I/O or for data manipulation.

7.16 Programming for the Future

The PC functions of relay replacement, counting and timing, and data manipulation have been discussed here. Another topic of PC control is PID control. This topic requires the development of control concepts of proportional, integral, and derivative feedback. In addition, the use of PCs for PID control requires the mating of a discrete controller and a continuous process. Another consideration is that it is no longer possible to conceive of the response of the controlled system as an on/off response; rather, it is necessary to consider the dynamics of the response. For this reason, in Chapter 8 we will turn our attention to dynamic systems.

Problems

7.1 Give the definition of a PC.

7.2 Using Figure P7.2, identify the basic units of a PC.

7.3 a. What year marked the beginning of the use of PCs in industry?

    b. What year marked the beginning of "intelligent" PCs that have capabilities beyond relay replacement?

    c. What year marked the beginning of networking of PCs?

7.4 State two differences between a PC and a microprocessor board.

7.5 What does a PC provide to a motor starter circuit that is attached to the PC's input/output devices?

7.6 What are the two kinds of memory used in PCs and what is the purpose of each?

7.7 What are the six sections of Read/Write memory used in the PC and what is the purpose of each?

7.8 State the functions of an input module of a PC.

7.9 State the functions of an output module of a PC.

7.10 a. Given the schematic of inputs and outputs for the PC in Figure P7.10, show the I/O wiring for a three-wire, START-STOP station motor control.

    b. Consider that the group for the input module is 1, the group for the output module is 2, and that the address consists of the following digits

        For input: 11GXX

        For output: 01GXX

where G stands for "group" and XX stands for "terminal number." Draw a logic diagram for the START-STOP station that provides addresses consistent with the I/O wiring.

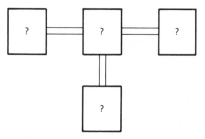

FIGURE P7.2. Block structure of a computing unit

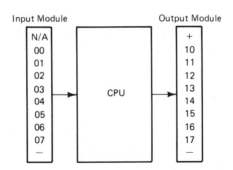

Input Module ... Output Module

Input Module	Output Module
N/A	+
00	10
01	11
02	12
03	13
04	14
05	15
06	16
07	17
—	—

CPU

FIGURE P7.10. Diagram of I/O for START-STOP control

c. Given the relay symbols for ladder logic presented in this chapter, write a list of the keystrokes to program the START-STOP station.

7.11 Repeat problem 7.10 a) through c) for a PC that uses Boolean language, with input addresses *X9* through *X20* and output addresses *Y1* through *Y8*.

7.12 Repeat problem 7.10 a) through c) for a PC that uses BASIC language, with input ports 12 through 15 and output ports 16 through 20. Assume a logical TRUE is 00000000 and a logical FALSE is any other value.

7.13 Give the three major steps for implementing a PC program after the design stage is completed.

7.14 The SMASH Company has had trouble with fork trucks pulverizing motor starter enclosures, which prevents proper motor-starter operation. They wish to design a PC program for a motor-starter circuit such that the holding contact of the motor starter provides the instruction for the holding action in the PC logic circuit. In this way, the PC will detect a physical contact closure (or lack of one in the case of a fork truck collision). With this in mind, redesign the circuit in problem 7.10 and repeat parts a through c.

7.15 Repeat problem 7.10 a) through c) for converting the water-level control circuit of problem 2.13 in Chapter 2 to a PC implementation.

7.16 It is desired to latch on an output for as long as the logic input called Flag 1 is TRUE, unless logic input called Flag 2 is FALSE, in which case it is desired to unlatch the output. The NO logic contacts of the latch are used to operate coil *M*. Using the addressing suggested in problem 7.10 show the logic circuit

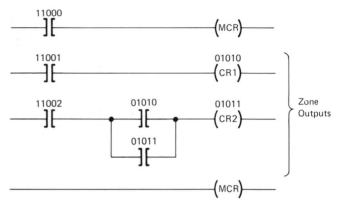

FIGURE P7.20. An MCR problem

that will operate with a START-STOP station and provide a coil output *M*. (*Hint:* It is necessary to both prevent the latch and cause the unlatch in order to unlatch.)

7.17 The JUMP command is to be used such that the PC will scan the logic diagram alternating between outputs *M1* and *M2* on each scan. Show the logic diagram to achieve this.

7.18 Use a single-line timer to provide a cyclical output of 10-seconds duration so that the clock output can drive a counter. After the counter reaches a count of 5, the *M* coil should be energized. Show the logic diagram.

7.19 Use single-line data manipulation instructions to subtract the contents of register 220 from register 221 and compare the result with the contents of register 222 to see if equality is achieved, in which case the *M* coil is energized. Show the logic diagram.

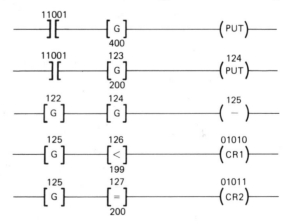

FIGURE P7.21. Ladder diagram for a data instruction

7.20 The circuit in Figure P7.20 is to be used to control *CR1* and *CR2* outputs. Explain the manner that *CR1* and *CR2* would be TRUE with respect to the parameters 11000, 11001, 11002, and MCR. Also explain the effect of a power outage.

7.21 Analyze the circuit in Figure P7.21 to determine what the consequence would be of 11001 first being open and then closing in terms of *CR1* and *CR2* outputs.

7.22 It is desired to use a block counter of the form shown in Figure P7.22 so that the counter will count pulses on the *X* contact until the count reaches the preset value of 12, or until a contact *Y* is opened. In the case that the count reaches the preset value, a warning light should be energized.

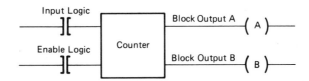

FIGURE P7.22. A block counter command

8 Dynamic Response of Basic Systems

8.0 Introduction

Early in control system history, control system applications were limited to discrete-valued events. For example, a relay control system had the capability to turn one or more motors on, and when the requirements were satisfied, to turn the motors off.

Within recent decades, increased demand and improved technology created increasingly sophisticated control applications. These applications required that the controlled output be continuous over all values from off to on. This new era of control technology was heralded by the development of radar-controlled gun positioning during World War II, which was instrumental in determining the outcome of the war. These weapons required that the controlled motors run in proportion to the control position required.

An example of the contrast between on-off control and continuous control is a heating temperature control system. In the case of on-off control, the thermostat contacts turn the heater on whenever the temperature is below the level required. When the desired temperature level is reached, the thermostat contacts open such that the heater is turned off. Thus in on-off control, the control system provides a control signal that is simply on or off, depending on whether the output is at a "close-enough" value. The "closeness" of the output is controlled by the construction of the thermostat.

In the case of continuous temperature control, the heat sensor, such as a thermocouple, provides a control signal that is proportional to the difference between the desired temperature and the actual temperature. Then the heater produces a quantity of heat that is proportional to this thermocouple signal. Thus in continuous control, the control system provides a control signal that is proportional to the amount of correction that is to be made. Obviously, the continuous control system requires more sophisticated sensors and actuators, but that is the price that is to be paid for a control system that provides more exact control than on-off control provides.

Other examples of applications where continuous control may be necessary include controlling a valve, positioning a machine tool, and aligning a satellite antenna. In all these cases, it may not be adequate for the control system to simply turn the actuator on and off—it may be necessary to control the valve, the tool, or the antenna position to reduce the error to a minimum.

The study of continuous control systems brings about a different set of problems than the study of discrete control systems. These systems operate in a continuous and dynamic mode where the controlled response may not satisfy the intended precise response. The response may be unstable due to an undesirable feedback problem. Even if the response is stable, it may be too oscillatory, or on the other hand, the response may be too sluggish. These are some of the concerns that must be addressed in control system analysis and design.

This chapter is concerned with building the tools necessary to understand control systems used to control the continuous operation of dynamic systems. Such systems include those involved in process controls, machine controls, and military systems, where the output is in proportion to the input.

The chapter covers simple exponential transient responses, proceeds to more complicated oscillatory responses, and discusses characteristics of desirable and undesirable system responses.

8.1   Simple Transient Response

The dynamic systems that are the topic of this chapter are characterized by having responses that change exponentially with time. The simplest example is a decreasing exponential decay. The form of this response is

$$x(t) = x(0)e^{-t/\tau}, t > 0 \tag{8-1}$$

where

t = the independent variable time,

x = the dependent variable,

$x(0)$ = the initial value of $x(t)$ at $t = 0$,

τ = the system time constant.

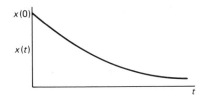

FIGURE 8-1. Decreasing exponential response of a first-order, linear, constant coefficient system

A graph of the decreasing exponential response is given in Figure 8-1. This response is characteristic of a system that is linear, first order, and has constant coefficients. These terms can be understood as follows:

- The linear system response is proportional to the input, e.g., if the value of $x(0)$ were doubled, then the value of $x(t)$ at any point in time would be doubled. An example of a linear system is an RC circuit with an initial charge on the capacitor. The current through the resistor is proportional to the initial charge. If the charge and thus the voltage were doubled, then the current at any point in time would also be doubled.
- The first-order system consists of a single energy-storing element such that only an exponential response is possible. An example is an electrical circuit that consists of a single capacitor and one or more resistors.
- The constant coefficients system has parameter values that do not change in time, e.g., in a resistor-capacitor circuit, the resistor value and capacitor value are constant.

Example 8-1

Determine the decaying exponential response of an RC circuit as shown in Figure 8-2.

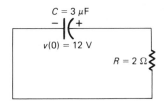

FIGURE 8-2. A resistor-capacitor circuit with an initial charge voltage on the capacitor

Solution. For an unforced resistor-capacitor circuit with an initial charge voltage on the capacitor of 12 V, the exponential response of the voltage on the capacitor is found as follows:

1. For a resistor-capacitor circuit, the time constant is the RC product, i.e., $\tau = RC = 2$ ohms $\bullet 3~\mu F = 6~\mu s$ (microseconds).

2. The initial value of voltage on the capacitor is 12 V, i.e., $v(0) = 12$ V.

3. The response of the voltage on the capacitor as a function of time is written

$$v(t) = 12e^{-t/6\mu s},~t > 0 \qquad\qquad (8\text{-}2)$$

A graph of this voltage function is shown in Figure 8-3.

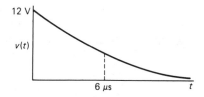

FIGURE 8-3. The exponential response of a resistor-capacitor circuit with an initial charge voltage on the capacitor

A function that is closely related to the decreasing exponential decay is the increasing exponential decay. This function is also the response of a linear, first-order, constant-coefficient system. However, in this case the increase is due to a forcing function causing the response to climb to a nonzero final value. A unit-step forcing function can be written as

$$u(t) = \begin{cases} 1 \text{ for } t > 0 \\ \\ 0 \text{ for } t \leq 0 \end{cases}$$

which simply stated means that the applied forcing function is zero until a certain point in time, called the *zero time,* and then it becomes unity, as shown in Figure 8-4. For a step function different than unity, the unit-step function is multiplied by the magnitude of the step. For example, connecting a 12-volt battery to a circuit could be represented by a forcing function 12 *u(t).*

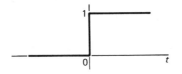

FIGURE 8-4. Unit-step function

With the step function applied, a frequent outcome is that the response is an increasing exponential decay function. The expression for the increasing exponential decay function starting at $t = 0$ is

$$x(t) = x(\infty) - [x(\infty) - x(0)]e^{-t/\tau}, \, t > 0 \qquad (8\text{-}3)$$

In the case that the initial value $x(0)$ is zero, the above can be rewritten as

$$= x(\infty)[1 - e^{-t/\tau}], \, t > 0$$

where

$$x(\infty) = x \text{ as } t \longrightarrow \infty$$

A graph of the increasing exponential response is given in Figure 8-5.

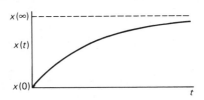

FIGURE 8-5. Increasing exponential response of a first-order, linear constant coefficient system

Example 8-2

Determine the exponential response of an RC circuit with a forcing function as shown in Figure 8-6.

Solution. For a resistor-capacitor circuit as shown in Figure 8-6 with a voltage source of 12 V, the exponential response of the voltage on the capacitor is found as follows:

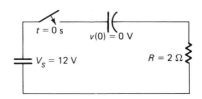

FIGURE 8-6. A resistor-capacitor circuit with a voltage forcing function

1. For a resistor-capacitor circuit, the time constant is the RC product, i.e., $\tau = RC = 2$ ohms $\cdot$ 3 μF $= 6$ μs (microseconds).
2. The initial value of voltage on the capacitor is 0 V, i.e., $v(0) = 0$ V.
3. The final value of voltage on the capacitor is 12 V, i.e., $v(\infty) = 12$ V.
4. The response of the voltage on the capacitor as a function of time is written as

$$v(t) = 12[1 - e^{-t/6\mu s}], t > 0 \tag{8-4}$$

A graph of this voltage function is shown in Figure 8-7.

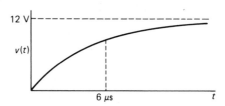

FIGURE 8-7. The exponential response of a resistor-capacitor circuit with a voltage forcing function

In summary, analyzing the exponential response $x(t)$ depends on evaluating the time constant, τ, the initial value, $x(0)$, and the final value, $x(\infty)$. The symbol x may signify almost any variable including current, voltage, position, and velocity.

8.2 Time Constants

The time constant is a measure of the rate of change of the variable of a first-order system. It is defined as the ratio of the variable to the rate of change of the variable (for the unforced system response).

For example, if the velocity of a friction-mass system were changing at a rate of 15 meters per second and the acceleration were 5 meters per second per second, then the time constant could be measured to be

$$\tau = \frac{\text{variable}}{\text{rate of change of variable}} = \frac{\text{velocity}}{\text{acceleration}}$$

$$= \frac{15 \;\; \text{meters/second}}{5 \;\text{meters/second/second}} = 3 \;\text{seconds}$$

A small time constant means that the variable has a large rate of change relative to the size of the variable. This means that the variable will reach its final value quickly.

The following time constants are very common and frequently used:

Resistance(R)-inductance(L) system:	$\tau = L/R$	(8-5)
Resistance(R)-capacitance(C) system:	$\tau = RC$	(8-6)
Friction(B)-inertia(M or J) system:	$\tau = M/B$ or J/B	(8-7)
Spring(K)-friction(B) system:	$\tau = B/K$	(8-8)

From the above relationships, it can be seen that mechanical systems and electrical systems have similar time constant relationships. The time relationships of mechanical systems will be covered in more detail in later sections. The similarity between the role of the mechanical components and the electrical components is the basis for using electrical systems to model mechanical systems in design and analysis work. This "analogy" is the basis for the analog computer that uses RC time constants and operational amplifiers to model mechanical and other systems.

To illustrate the significance of the time constant, an example of transient analysis follows:

Example 8-3

For a forced resistor-inductor series circuit as shown in Figure 8-8, determine the inductance voltage and current for $t > 0$.

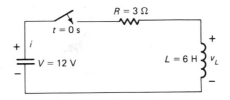

FIGURE 8-8. A forced R-L circuit

Solution. The time constant is $\tau = L/R = 6$ henries/3 ohms $= 2$ seconds. The initial value of current is zero, since no initial current is established. The final value of current is $i(\infty) = 12$ V/3 ohms $= 4$ amperes since the resistor is the only element that opposes the continued current as $t \to \infty$. Thus the circuit current expression from (8-3) is

$$i(t) = 4[1 - e^{-t/2\ sec}]A, \, t > 0 \; sec$$

The expression for inductor voltage follows (8-1). The time constant has been found to be 2 seconds. The initial value of voltage is 12 V. Thus the inductance voltage expression is

$$v(t) = 12e^{-t/2\ sec}, \, t > 0 \; sec$$

The waveforms for the RL example are shown in Figure 8-9. In both graphs, the waveform is a decaying exponential: in the case of the current waveform, the exponential is subtracted from the constant value of 4 A, such that the waveform starts at a value of 0 A and decays to a final value of 4 A. It is also noted that only exponential decaying waveforms are possible in passive circuits like the one in this example. If the waveform were exponentially growing, such as $e^{+t/\tau}$, then an active device would necessarily be present to put energy into the system to cause the growing exponential.

For a response that is a decaying exponential, the response converges to its final value as time grows to infinity. Fortunately, it is not necessary to wait infinitely long to find the final value. By measuring the response in terms of time constants, the closeness of the response to the final value can be defined. In terms of integer time constants, the relationship between the time constant and the percentage of the final value (see Figure 8-9(a) for an example) can be shown in Table 8-1. The response for many purposes is considered

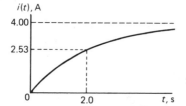
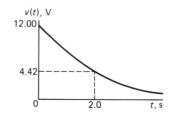

FIGURE 8-9. (a) Current waveform and (b) voltage waveform for R-L example

TABLE 8-1. Response of exponential function as a percentage of its final value

TIME IN TIME CONSTANTS	CURRENT IN PERCENT OF FINAL VALUE
0.0	0.0%
1.0	63.2
2.0	86.5
3.0	95.0
4.0	98.2
5.0	99.3

to have reached its final value at three time constants; for more precise needs, possibly five time constants would be used to measure when the final condition is achieved. This conclusion is an important point in control theory, since the speed of response of a control system is measured either by its time constant, or by an equivalent time constant as explained in Section 8.14. The time constant is a valuable measure of the speed of response of the system. A fast system has a small time constant and a slow system has a large time constant.

8.3 An Introduction to Mechanical Systems

An important attribute of control systems is that both the insights of the electrical and mechanical engineering disciplines are necessary to understand the operation of the overall control system. Fortunately, there are many similarities. An example of a simple mechanical system consisting of mass, friction, and a spring constant is shown in Figure 8-10. A positive force is applied from the left, which causes an acceleration to the right, at least until the restoring force of

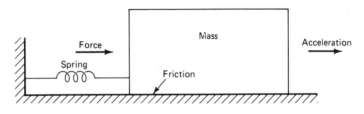

FIGURE 8-10. Friction-mass example

the spring, the friction force, and the effect of the inertia matches the applied force.

This section gives a brief outline of some of the characteristics of mechanical systems. Just as the starting point in understanding electrical circuits is understanding the v versus i operating characteristics of inductance, resistance, and capacitance, the starting point of understanding mechanical circuits is understanding the force versus motion characteristics of inertia, friction, and spring components. But first, a review of motion variables is given.

The relationship between velocity (v) and acceleration (a) is that acceleration is the time rate of change of velocity. If the velocity is constant, then the acceleration is zero. If the velocity is changing at a constant rate, then the acceleration is constant:

$$a = \frac{\text{change in velocity}}{\text{change in time}} = \frac{dv}{dt} \tag{8-9}$$

where

$$dv = \text{change in velocity}$$
$$dt = \text{change in time}$$

Similarly, the velocity is the time rate of change in displacement or position, x. If the position is constant, then the velocity is zero. If the position is changing at a constant rate, then the velocity is constant:

$$v = \frac{\text{change in position}}{\text{change in time}} = \frac{dx}{dt} \tag{8-10}$$

where

$$dx = \text{change in position}.$$

Conversely, the reverse relationship can also be expressed. If the acceleration is constant, then the expression for velocity is

$$v = at \tag{8-11}$$

If the velocity is constant, then the expression for position is

$$x = vt \tag{8-12}$$

Finally, for constant acceleration the position grows at an ever-increasing rate due to the increasing velocity. If the initial position is

$x(0)$ and the initial velocity is $v(0)$, then the expression for position with constant acceleration is

$$x(t) = x(0) + v(0)t + \frac{at^2}{2} \qquad (8\text{-}13)$$

where t^2 is the square of the time during which the acceleration has occurred.

Example 8-4

Relationship of acceleration, velocity, and position. Given that a machine tool is accelerating along a straight line at an average acceleration of 0.4 feet per second per second, starting from an initial position described as $+1$ foot from the zero position and with an initial velocity of 0.3 feet per second, determine the displacement of the tool at the end of 2 seconds.

Solution. Using the equation provided by (8-13), it is found that the displacement at 2 seconds is

$$x(2) = 1.0 + 0.3 \bullet 2.0 + 0.4 \bullet \frac{(2.0)^2}{2}$$

$$= 1.0 + 0.6 + 0.8$$

$$= 2.4 \text{ feet}$$

The relationship of position, velocity, and acceleration is important in various control topics. Examples are gyroscopes, accelerometers, motor control, and feedback control, especially where integral and derivative control are used. Following is a description of the basic mechanical parameters of any control system that has a mechanical output or component.

8.4 The Mass Parameter

Every high school physics student is familiar with the expression

$$f = Ma$$

and has some understanding of this law of physics. It states that for a nonchanging mass, there is a proportionality between the acceleration of an object of mass M and the force that is applied to it, and

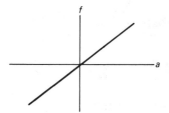

FIGURE 8-11. Friction force vs. acceleration for a mass parameter

furthermore that that proportionality constant is the mass *M*. *M* is measured in kilograms in the metric system and in slugs (lb sec ^{2}/ft) in the English system. In terms of a graph, this relationship between force and acceleration is shown in Figure 8-11.

The extension of the line into the third quadrant where force and acceleration are negative is the representation that the action is bilateral; that is, along a line, mass can be accelerated to the right or to the left. Deceleration is a negative acceleration. For example, if an object is traveling at a given velocity and then that velocity is reduced due to the forces acting upon it, then the object is decelerating.

8.5 The Friction Coefficient Parameter

Friction forces are manifested by different sources and have different characteristics. One friction force is *kinetic friction*, wherein the friction force is constant for a given direction of velocity. A graph of kinetic friction is shown in Figure 8-12. This figure shows that in the case of kinetic friction, the friction force is independent of the force applied other than the sense of the force.

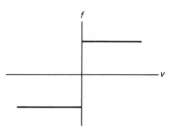

FIGURE 8-12. Friction force vs. velocity for a kinetic friction parameter

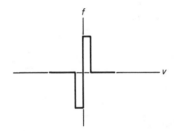

FIGURE 8-13. Friction force vs. velocity for a stiction
parameter

In the case of static friction forces, called *stiction,* a phenomenon similar to a partial welding of the two contacting surfaces occurs. A friction force is present at standstill that must be overcome to induce motion. A graph of stiction is shown in Figure 8-13. This figure shows that once the initial welding or static forces holding the surfaces together is overcome, the friction force is independent of the force applied other than the sense of the force.

In the case of viscous friction, the force of friction is proportional to the velocity between the contacting surfaces, as shown in Figure 8-14. This kind of friction coefficient is called viscous friction because it represents the kind of coefficient expected from two viscous surfaces, e.g., a well-lubricated bearing of a motor shaft. The expression for this relationship is given by

$$f = Bv$$

where B is the viscous friction coefficient. Since viscous friction is the most common friction in control components such as motors, we will concentrate on it in the remainder of the work here; nonetheless, stiction and kinetic friction are also present in many applications and must be considered in the analysis and design.

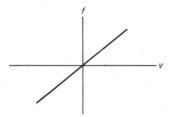

FIGURE 8-14. Force vs. velocity for a viscous friction
parameter

8.6 The Spring Coefficient Parameter

The third and last mechanical parameter that is considered here is the spring. The ideal spring component obeys Hooke's Law, i.e., that the force and displacement are linearly related by the spring coefficient K, as shown in Figure 8-15. The third quadrant represents the opposite of the first quadrant, e.g., the operation of the spring under compression as opposed to the operation of the spring under tension. The expression for the force of a spring is

$$f = Kx$$

where it is assumed that the spring works equally under tension and compression. An example of such a symmetric spring is a zero-center electrical meter movement spring as used in a galvanometer.

In summary, a system with mass M, friction (viscous) B, and a spring K, and with an applied force f, could be represented as

force applied = force due to mass + force due to friction
+ force due to spring

or

$$f = Ma + Bv + Kx$$

If only mass and friction are present or only friction and spring are present, the response due to a step input can be solved by the inspection method. On the other hand, if both mass and spring are present, the problem is second order and the response is not a simple exponential.

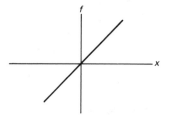

FIGURE 8-15. Force vs. displacement for a spring parameter

Example 8-5   Friction-Mass System

Determine the expression for velocity for the friction-mass system in Figure 8-16, where a step function of force is applied at $t = 0.0$ seconds as denoted by the $u(t)$ (unit step) notation.

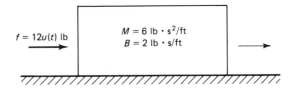

FIGURE 8-16. Friction-mass example

Solution. The expression for velocity is an increasing exponential similar to (8-3). The time constant and the final velocity are found as follows:

$$\tau = M/B = \frac{6 \text{ lb sec}^2/\text{ft}}{2 \text{ lb sec}/\text{ft}} = 3 \text{ sec}$$

$$v(\infty) = \frac{12 \text{ lb}}{2 \text{ lb sec}/\text{ft}} = 6 \text{ ft}/\text{sec}$$

Therefore, the solution for velocity is given as

$$v(t) = 6[1 - e^{-t/3sec}] \text{ ft}/\text{sec}, \, t > 0 \text{ sec}$$

The sketch of the velocity is shown in Figure 8-17.

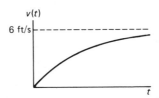

FIGURE 8-17. Graph of velocity for mass-friction example

8.7 Angular Motion

In addition to the motion of mechanical systems along a straight line (rectilinear motion), frequently the motion under study is angular. An example of an angular system is shown in Figure 8-18. The extension of the previously covered concepts of motion and system parameters to the angular system is straightforward. Instead of measuring displacement in meters (feet), it is measured in revolutions (radians, degrees). A similar change is necessary for velocity and acceleration. The angular equivalent to mass is moment of inertia J measured in Newton meter sec^2. Likewise, the angular equivalent to friction

TABLE 8-2. Comparison of electrical and mechanical systems

CONCEPT	ELECTRICAL SYSTEM	MECHANICAL SYSTEM	
application	series RLC ckt	rectilinear motion BKM circuit	angular motion BKJ circuit
forcing function	applied voltage $v(t)$ [V]	applied force $f(t)$ [N]	applied torque $T(t)$ [Nm]
response variable	charge $q(t)$ [Q]	displacement $x(t)$ [m]	angular displacement $\theta(t)$ [rad]
response rate of change	current $i(t)$ [A]	velocity $v(t)$ [m/s]	angular velocity $\omega(t)$ [rad/s]
response rate of rate of change	rate of change of current [A/s]	acceleration $a(t)$ [m/s^2]	angular acceleration $a(t)$ [rad/s^2]
inertia	inductance L [H]	mass M [kg]	moment of inertia J [Nms^2]
damping	resistance R [ohm]	viscous friction B [Ns/m]	angular viscous friction B [Nms]
spring	elastance 1/C [1/F]	spring constant K [N/m]	angular spring constant K [Nm]

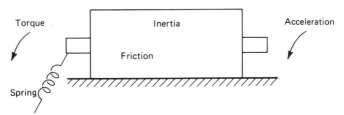

FIGURE 8-18. Friction-mass angular system

coefficient is angular-friction coefficient, measured in Newton meter sec. Finally, the angular equivalent to spring force is angular-spring force, measured in Newton meters. A comparison of the mechanical and electrical concepts of motion and system parameters is shown in Table 8-2 for the series RLC circuit, the rectilinear mechanical circuit, and the angular mechanical circuit.

8.8 An Introduction to the *s* Operator

Although the inspection method of solution covered so far in this chapter has importance in its own right, its usefulness is limited. This inspection method does not provide the solution of second-order systems and it does not permit the solution of systems with other than constant forcing functions. Furthermore, it does not provide the insight available in using the *s* operator. The *s* operator provides a method for representing both integral and differential equations as simpler algebraic expressions. This method provides solutions of higher-order equations with other than constant forcing functions without resorting to differential equation methods. In addition, the *s* operator is used extensively in the analysis and design of electrical and mechanical systems in the form of transfer functions and derivative and integral operators. The mathematical basis for the *s* operator method of representing systems is Laplace transform analysis. The *s* operator is used without showing the derivation from the Laplace transform. The rationale is that the results of the Laplace transform can be useful without the theory or the mathematics.

8.9 The *s* Operator Approach

The principle of using the *s* operator is that functions of time (t) involving derivatives and integrals can be transformed to functions of complex frequency (s) as illustrated:

Time domain   Frequency domain
$f(t)$ ←→ $F(s)$

The s operator is used as a multiplier to express the derivative relationship. An important example is the relationship between position and velocity. Earlier, the velocity was expressed as the time rate of change of position, or in terms of calculus, $v = dx/dt$. In the Laplace transform approach, the s operator replaces the derivative operator d/dt, and the relationship between the Laplace transform of velocity $V(s)$ and position $X(s)$ is

$$V(s) = sX(s) \qquad\qquad (8\text{-}14)$$

Another example is that the acceleration is the time rate of change of velocity. Thus the calculus expression is $a = dv/dt$. In the Laplace transform approach, the s operator replaces the derivative operator d/dt, and the relationship between the Laplace transform of acceleration $A(s)$ and velocity $V(s)$ is

$$A(s) = sV(s) \qquad\qquad (8\text{-}15)$$

The benefit of using the s operator here is that the derivative operation is replaced with a multiplication operation.

Another important property of the s operator is that the calculus operation of integration can be replaced by the operation of dividing by s in the Laplace transform expression. For example, (8-14) can be written as

$$X(s) = \frac{V(s)}{s} \qquad\qquad (8\text{-}16)$$

and (8-15) can be written as

$$V(s) = \frac{A(s)}{s}$$

In these examples, the benefit of using the s operator is that the integral operator is replaced with a division operation.

The same benefits exist in the analysis of electrical circuits. An example is the relation between voltage and current in an inductance. The voltage is proportional to the time rate of change of current where the proportionality constant is the inductance L. Expressed as a transformed expression, this relationship becomes

$$V(s) = LsI(s) \qquad (8\text{-}17)$$

and conversely,

$$I(s) = \frac{V(s)}{Ls}$$

The voltage versus current relationships will be developed more fully later after some of the properties of the s operator are covered.

8.10 Properties of the *s* Operator

The following properties of the *s* operator are important:

- The constant multiplier. When the function to be transformed includes a constant multiplier, that multiplier can be carried over the transformed quantity. For example, if the voltage across a 2 H inductor is

$$V(s) = 2sI(s)$$

then if the inductor is changed to 4 H, by the above property the voltage would become

$$V(s) = 4sI(s)$$

- Sum of operators. The *s* operator terms can be added directly. For example, the total voltage $V_T(s)$ across both a 2 H inductor and a 4 H inductor in series is simply

$$V_T(s) = 2sI(s) + 4sI(s) = 6sI(s)$$

- Derivative operator. This property is important in solving differential equations in that the operation of taking the derivative can be replaced by multiplication by *s* in the frequency domain, namely,

$$d(f(t)) \longleftrightarrow sF(s) \qquad (8\text{-}18)$$

In simple terms, this property states that the derivative operator d/dt is replaced by the *s* multiplier when the transform is taken. This property is the reason that the voltage across an inductor is expressed by multiplying *s* times the inductance-current product, as shown above.

- Integral operator. This property is important in solving inter-grodifferential equations in that the operation of taking the integral can be replaced by division by s in the frequency domain, namely,

$$\int f(t)dt \longleftrightarrow F(s)/s \qquad (8\text{-}19)$$

In simple terms, this property states that the integral operator is replaced by the $1/s$ multiplier when the transform is taken.

In summary, the operations of constant multiplication, adding, finding the derivative, and finding the integral using the s operator are given in Table 8-3. The usefulness of these properties is shown by reducing the differential and integral relationships that describe the v-i relationships of inductors and capacitors to multiplication and division by s, respectively, as shown in the next section.

TABLE 8-3. s **operator properties**

PROPERTY	$f(t)$	$F(s)$
1	$Kf(t)$	$KF(s)$
2	$f(t) + g(t)$	$F(s) + G(s)$
3	$d/dt\, f(t)$	$sF(s)$
4	$\int f(t)dt$	$F(s)/s$

8.11 Component Relationships using the s Operator

For a resistance, the transformed relationship of Ohm's law is straightforward:

$$v(t) = Ri(t), \qquad i(t) = \frac{1}{R}\, v(t) \qquad (8\text{-}20)$$

The transforms of these equations are

$$V(s) = RI(s), \qquad I(s) = \frac{1}{R}\, V(s) \qquad (8\text{-}21)$$

from property 1. Thus, the impedance and admittance of a resistance are

$$Z(s) = \frac{V(s)}{I(s)} = R \qquad Y(s) = \frac{I(s)}{V(s)} = \frac{1}{R} \tag{8-22}$$

For an inductance of L henries, the v-i relationship is

$$v(t) = L \frac{di}{dt}, \qquad i(t) = \frac{1}{L} \int v(t)\, dt \tag{8-23}$$

The transforms of these equations are

$$V(s) = LsI(s), \qquad I(s) = \frac{1}{Ls}\, V(s) \tag{8-24}$$

from properties 1, 3 and 4. Thus, the impedance and admittance of an inductance are

$$Z(s) = \frac{V(s)}{I(s)} = Ls, \qquad Y(s) = \frac{I(s)}{V(s)} = \frac{1}{Ls} \tag{8-25}$$

For a capacitance of C farads, the v-i relationship is

$$v(t) = \frac{1}{C} \int i(t)dt, \qquad i(t) = C \frac{dv}{dt} \tag{8-26}$$

The transforms of these equations are

$$V(s) = \frac{1}{Cs} I(s), \qquad I(s) = Cs V(s) \tag{8-27}$$

from properties 1, 3, and 4. Thus, the impedance and admittance of a capacitance are

$$Z(s) = \frac{V(s)}{I(s)} = \frac{1}{Cs}, \qquad Y(s) = \frac{I(s)}{V(s)} = Cs \tag{8-28}$$

With regard to other relationships of variables, such as motion relationships, the transformation to the time domain is straightforward. For example, consider the relationship between position x and velocity v:

$$v = \frac{dx}{dt}, \qquad x = \int v dt \tag{8-29}$$

The transforms of these equations are

$$V(s) = sX(s), \qquad X(s) = \frac{1}{s} V(s) \tag{8-30}$$

from properties 1, 3, and 4.

Finally, apply properties 3 and 4 twice (as well as property 1) to solve for the transform of $f = Ma$ in terms of x:

$$f(t) = M\frac{d^2x(t)}{dt^2}, \qquad x(t) = \frac{1}{M}\int\int f(t)\, dt\, dt \tag{8-31}$$

The transforms of these equations are

$$F(s) = Ms^2 X(s), \qquad X(s) = \frac{F(s)}{Ms^2} \tag{8-32}$$

from properties 1, 3, and 4.

The impedance and admittance of mechanical components can be handled in the same manner as electrical impedances and admittances are. For example, the impedance and admittance functions for force versus displacement of a mass are

$$Z(s) = \frac{F(s)}{X(s)} = Ms^2, \qquad Y(s) = \frac{X(s)}{F(s)} = \frac{1}{Ms^2} \tag{8-33}$$

By writing impedance and admittance functions of electrical and mechanical components, it is possible to solve electromechanical problems without resorting to differential equations. Some examples of using the s operator are found in Section 8.12.

8.12 Using the s Operator

All of the methods that apply to solving circuits—including series-parallel reduction, mesh analysis, nodal analysis, current and voltage division, superposition, and Thevenin's and Norton's equivalents—can be applied by using the s operator to reduce the circuit to a dc equivalent. Only a few simple steps will be taken here to show that more complicated systems can be reduced to a simplified representation.

Consider a simple approach here, the equivalent of dc circuit analysis, only with the use of the s operator to express the dynamic nature of the response of the inductor and capacitor voltage versus current response. For electrical circuits, the impedance can be found in a few simple steps.

Step 1. Replace circuit components by their frequency-domain impedances:

$$R \longrightarrow R$$
$$L \longrightarrow Ls$$
$$C \longrightarrow \frac{1}{Cs}$$

Step 2. Find the circuit impedance by any of the methods listed above. For simple circuits, series-parallel reduction of imped-ance elements is a desirable method.

Example 8-6   An RC Circuit

Determine the impedance of the RC network shown in Figure 8-19.

Solution.   Following the steps as given above,

Step 1. $R \longrightarrow 4$ ohms, $C \longrightarrow 1/2s$

Step 2. Solve for the impedance

$$Z(s) = 4 + \frac{1}{2s} = \frac{8s + 1}{2s}$$

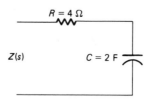

FIGURE 8-19. An RC circuit

Example 8-7   A Series RLC Circuit

Find the impedance of the circuit shown in Figure 8-20.

Solution.   Following the steps as given above,

Step 1. $R \longrightarrow 50$ ohms, $L \longrightarrow 2s$, $C \longrightarrow 200/s$

Step 2. Solve for the impedance.

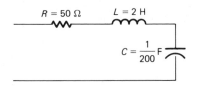

FIGURE 8-20. An RLC circuit

$$Z(s) = 2s + 50 + \frac{200}{s} = \frac{2s^2 + 50s + 200}{s} = \frac{2(s^2 + 25s + 100)}{s}$$

Example 8-8   A Parallel LC with Series R Circuit

Find the impedance of the circuit shown in Figure 8-21.

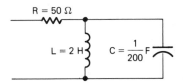

FIGURE 8-21. A parallel LC with series R circuit

Solution.   Following the steps as given above,

Step 1. $R \longrightarrow 50$ ohms, $L \longrightarrow 2s$, $C \longrightarrow 200/s$

Step 2. Solve for the impedance.

$$Z(s) = 50 + \frac{2s(200/s)}{2s + 200/s} = 50 + \frac{400s}{2s^2 + 200} = \frac{50s^2 + 200s + 5000}{s^2 + 100}$$

Thus, parallel circuit elements can be represented by the impedance function as well as series circuit elements.

Example 8-9   A Friction Mass Circuit

Find the impedance (ratio of position to force) of the mechanical circuit shown in Figure 8-22.

Solution.   Following the steps as given above,

Step 1. $B \longrightarrow 10s$, $M \longrightarrow 30s^2$

Step 2. Solve for the impedance.

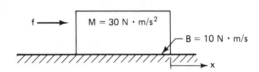

FIGURE 8-22. An MB circuit and determining its impedance

$$Z(s) = 30s^2 + 10s$$

Thus, impedance expressions can be found for mechanical components as well as for electrical components. The impedance of the mechanical circuit is the ratio of the forcing function to the response, such as force-to-displacement ratio.

8.13 Transfer Functions

With the understanding of the s operator, a new and powerful tool can be made available for understanding the input/output relations of systems, namely, the *transfer function* (TF). The TF is defined as the ratio of the transformed output to the transformed input with no initial conditions:

$$TF = G(s) = \frac{\text{output as a function of } s}{\text{input as a function of } s} = \frac{O(s)}{I(s)}$$

Since the TF can be determined from the circuit or from the manufacturer's specifications, it is useful to determine the output from the TF and a specified input:

$$O(s) = G(s)I(s).$$

The TF can be the ratio of voltage-out to voltage-in, the ratio of voltage to current, the ratio of displacement to force, or the ratio of speed to applied voltage, just to name a few possibilities. Its value in control systems is that the contributions of all the components, regardless of whether they are electrical or mechanical, can be incorporated into the overall TF.

In the case of a two-port electrical network, the voltage TF can be found by voltage division in many cases—namely, where the impedance components can be divided into two parts, those across the output and those in series with the output, as shown in Figure 8-23. Then the TF is found as

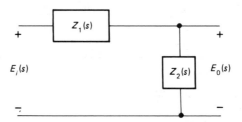

FIGURE 8-23. Transfer function by voltage division

$$TF = G(s) = \frac{E_o(s)}{E_i(s)} = \frac{Z_2(s)}{Z_1(s) + Z_2(s)}$$

where $Z_1(s)$ and $Z_2(s)$ are transformed impedances.

Example 8-10 Transfer Function of the $R_1 R_2 C$ Network

Find the TF of a network represented by Figure 8-23, where Z_1 consists of $C = 1/3$ F capacitance in parallel with $R_1 = 6$ ohms, and Z_2 consists of a $R_2 = 3$ ohms.

Solution. The impedances are found as

$$Z_1(s) = \frac{\dfrac{6 \times 3}{s}}{6 + \dfrac{3}{s}} = \frac{18}{6s + 3} = \frac{6}{2s + 1}$$

$$Z_2(s) = 3$$

Then the TF is found by voltage division to be

$$TF = G(s) = \frac{3}{3 + \dfrac{6}{2s + 1}} = \frac{3(2s + 1)}{3(2s + 1) + 6} = \frac{2s + 1}{2s + 3}$$

Thus, the TF can be found in a rather straightforward manner. Further examples of its significance will be provided later in this chapter.

Example 8-11 Transfer Function of a Friction-Mass Circuit

Find the transfer function (ratio of position to force) of the mechanical circuit shown in Figure 8-22.

Solution. In Example 8-9, the impedance of this circuit was found. The definition of impedance was given as

$$Z(s) = \frac{\text{force as a function of } s}{\text{position as a function of } s} = \frac{F(s)}{X(s)}$$

and it was also found that

$$Z(s) = 30s^2 + 10s$$

The definition of TF is given as $X(s)/F(s)$. Thus, we have the result that

$$G(s) = \frac{X(s)}{F(s)} = \frac{1}{Z(s)} = \frac{1}{30s^2 + 10s} = \frac{1/10}{s(3s + 1)}$$

Two points can be made by looking at this example. One is that the TF of the mechanical system can be determined as simply as the electrical system. The second point is that the TF is determined by defining the involved variables. For example, if the TF had been defined as the ratio of velocity to force, then the result of the above calculation would have been

$$G(s) = \frac{V(s)}{F(s)} = \frac{1}{30s + 10} = \frac{1/10}{3s + 1}$$

Once again, the significance of these representations is presented later.

8.14 Time Domain Response of First- and Second-Order Systems

Even with the aid of tools like the Laplace transform and the s operator, determining the total response of a system to a particular input is time-consuming and laborious. Many times, more important than finding the exact response is finding the general nature of the response to a typical input, such as a step input. For this reason, the treatment here is to determine the general form of the response of the control system rather than to determine the exact system response. See the Appendix for a more detailed treatment of the Laplace transform.

First-Order System Response

Recalling from the discussion of first-order systems at the first of this chapter, the form of the response of first-order systems is given by exponential functions. For example, a general representation of the response of the first-order system to a step input of magnitude A is

$$x(t) = A + B \cdot e^{-at} = A + B \cdot e^{-t/\tau} \tag{8-34}$$

where the time constant τ is $1/a$. The constant term A of the response can be thought of as an exponent with an infinitely long time constant. Thus, it is possible to fully describe the dynamics of the response by the size of the time constant. The time constant is used as a common method of describing the system; e.g., the time constant of the servo-drive system is 2.5 seconds, or the delay time to a step input is 2.5 seconds. Of course, if it is desired to know when the response has virtually completed its transient portion, then the response could be described as complete at the end of 7.5 seconds (or 12.5 seconds if a more exact answer is required).

In terms of the transfer function, the first-order system can be given as

$$G(s) = \frac{K}{s + a} = \frac{K/a}{\frac{s}{a} + 1} = \frac{K'}{\tau s + 1} \tag{8-35}$$

This representation also shows the time constant of the system τ, once the transfer function is manipulated into a recognizable form.

Second-Order System Response

The second-order system cannot be described by a single time constant. In fact, the second-order system has the capability of having a large variety of responses different from the exponential function. The kinds of responses all stem from the general representation of the second-order system in the form of a transfer function

$$G(s) = \frac{\omega_n^2}{s^2 + 2\zeta\omega_n s + \omega_n^2} \tag{8-36}$$

where

ω_n = the natural resonance frequency
of the system in radians/sec

ζ = the damping ratio (unitless)

These responses can be described in the following three categories.

Overdamped Response

The response to a step input of magnitude A is the sum of two exponentials plus a constant term:

$$x(t) = A + B \bullet e^{-at} + C \bullet e^{-bt} \qquad (8\text{-}37)$$

where

A = magnitude of the input step

B = constant

C = constant

$a = \zeta \bullet \omega_n - \omega_n \sqrt{\zeta^2 - 1}$

$b = \zeta \bullet \omega_n + \omega_n \sqrt{\zeta^2 - 1}$

The above a and b are inverse time constants. The response is similar to the first-order system response except there are two time constant terms.

Critically Damped Response

The response to a step input is an exponential and a ramp-exponential product plus a constant term:

$$x(t) = A + B \bullet e^{-\omega_n t} + C \bullet t \bullet e^{-\omega_n \cdot t} \qquad (8\text{-}38)$$

This response is between the response of an overdamped system and an underdamped system. It is the limiting case of the underdamped system case where the response has the smallest damping possible without exhibiting overshoot.

Underdamped Response

The response to a step input is the product of an exponential and a sinusoidal function plus a constant term:

$$x(t) = A + B \bullet e^{-\zeta \cdot \omega_n \cdot t} \bullet sin\,(\omega_d t + \phi) \qquad (8\text{-}39)$$

where ζ, ω_n, are given above and

$$\omega_d = \omega_n \sqrt{1 - \zeta^2}, \qquad \zeta < 1 \qquad (8\text{-}40)$$

$$\phi = \arccos\,(\zeta). \qquad (8\text{-}41)$$

This response has great significance in control system work and in designing control systems, since it is a common form of response of control systems.

The step response for all three cases of damping—over, under, and critical—is shown in Figure 8-24. Examination of these response curves reveals that the response is exponential for large values of ζ ($\zeta > 1$), but as ζ is decreased, the curves become more oscillatory. These curves are a general representation of the response of a control system. It is the concern of the control system designer that the response be the best choice possible. For this reason, it is necessary to determine a measure of system response for second-order systems similar to the time constant of the first-order system. In order to determine the form of the response of the second-order system, the transfer function is examined. As given above, the *general expression* (also called the *standard expression* or the *canonical expression*) for the transfer function for any second order system is

$$G(s) = \frac{\omega_n^2}{s^2 + 2\zeta\omega_n s + \omega_n^2} \tag{8-42}$$

where

$$\omega_n = \text{the natural resonance frequency}$$
$$\text{of the system in radians/sec}$$

$$\zeta = \text{the damping ratio (unitless)}$$

The natural resonance frequency is the frequency at which the system will oscillate if all the damping is removed. An example is a pendulum where the friction forces are negligible. The value of ω_n is $2\pi/T$ where T is the period of the oscillation. The natural resonance frequency in hertz is f_n, which is $1/T$. For a system that has damping, in the form of friction or hydraulic shocks, the natural resonance frequency is found by first removing the damping. An example is an RLC series circuit. The natural resonant frequency is

$$\omega_n = \frac{1}{\sqrt{LC}} \tag{8-43}$$

which is independent of the value of R.

The damping ratio in the above expression is a measure of the tendency of the system to oscillate. More damping means that the system will oscillate less. If the value of ζ is greater than one, then the system will not oscillate.

Since the above TF in (8-36) is normalized by the use of a "one" multiplier times the s^2 term, a $2\zeta\omega_n$ times the s term, and an ω_n^2 constant

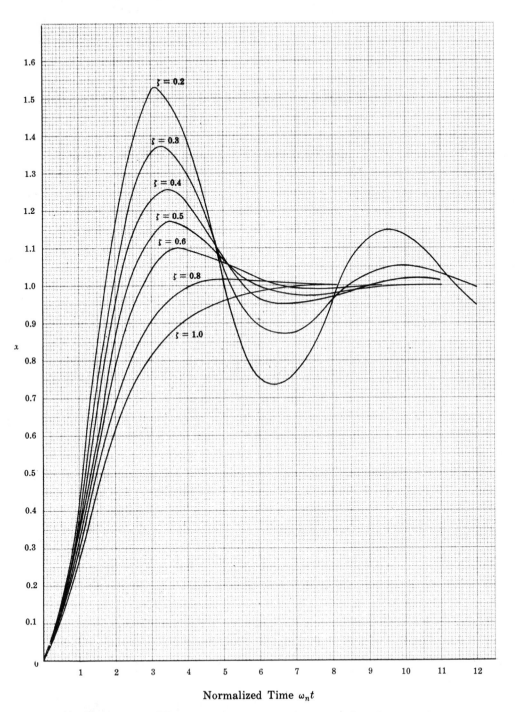

FIGURE 8-24. Time step response of a second-order system

term, the form of the response can be characterized by whether ζ is greater than, equal to, or less than one. The relationship between ζ and the degree of damping is as follows:

$\zeta > 1$ system is overdamped

$\zeta = 1$ system is critically damped   (8-44)

$\zeta < 1$ system is underdamped

The variable ω_n is called the natural radian frequency. It defines the radian frequency of oscillation in the case where the damping is zero, i.e., $\zeta = 0$. In the case that the system is underdamped, the radian frequency of oscillation is called the damped resonant frequency, ω_d, defined as

$$\omega_d = \omega_n \sqrt{1 - \zeta^2}, \qquad \zeta < 1 \tag{8-45}$$

Example 8-12   Determining ζ, ω_n and ω_d

It is desired to find the value of ζ, ω_n, and ω_d for the system described by the following transfer function:

$$G(s) = \frac{12}{3s^2 + 18s + 75}$$

Solution.   Match the TF with the general form

$$G(s) = \frac{\text{Constant}}{s^2 + 2\zeta\omega_n s + \omega_n^2}$$

To match coefficients, first divide the numerator and denominator by three to normalize the expression to match the normal form:

$$G(s) = \frac{4}{s^2 + 6s + 25}$$

Now the s^2 coefficients are one for both the example and the normal form. The other two coefficients are given by

$$\omega_n^2 = 25 \quad \text{and} \quad 2\zeta\omega_n = 6$$

Thus

$$\omega_n = 5 \text{ rps} \quad \text{and} \quad 10\zeta = 6 \quad \text{or} \quad \zeta = 0.6$$

Finally,

$$\omega_d = \omega_n \sqrt{1 - \zeta^2} = 5 \sqrt{1 - 0.36} = 4.0 \text{ rps}$$

Thus, the damping coefficient is 0.6, the natural resonant frequency is 5.0 radians per second, and the damped resonant frequency is 4.0 radians per second. Note that the numerator of the TF does not affect the dynamic response of the system; its effect on the system response is on the magnitude.

For the second-order system, there is no time constant as such; however, a reasonable substitute that can be used for the under-damped exponential response is $\zeta\omega_n$, since $\zeta\omega_n$ is the exponential argument coefficient of the step response of the second-order system, since this exponential acts as an envelope that contains the sinusoidal oscillation. Thus, this value is used as a conservative measure of time-constant response: namely, the time-constant equivalent of a second order underdamped system is

$$\tau_{eq} = \frac{1}{\zeta\omega_n} \tag{8-46}$$

Since the damping information is essentially contained in the damping coefficient ζ, this quantity is commonly used to describe a second-order system, as shown in Figure 8-24. Table 8-4 characterizes the response of the system dependent upon the value of the damping ratio ζ.

From the table and the figure, it can be seen that if ζ is small— say, less than about 0.5—then the response is very oscillatory; if ζ is larger—say about 1.0—then the response is sluggish. For a response that is between these two extremes of sluggishness and oscillation, ζ should be between 0.5 and 0.9. As a rule of thumb, a value for ζ of about 0.7 is ideal for a design goal for control system response.

TABLE 8-4. Second-order system responses

ζ	FORM OF RESPONSE	COMMENT
$= 0$	pure oscillation	good only for building oscillators
< 1	exponential sinusoid	responsive
$= 1$	ramp times exponential	sluggish
> 1	sum of two exponentials	more sluggish

Example 8-13   Determining the Transfer Function from ζ

It is desired that the system described by the following TF should have a damping coefficient of 0.7. Determine the value of the coefficient B.

$$G(s) = \frac{12(s + 2)}{s^2 + Bs + 36}$$

Solution.   Match the TF with the general form

$$G(s) = \frac{12(s + 2)}{s^2 + 2\zeta\omega_n s + \omega_n^2}$$

Then match coefficients (noting that the coefficients of the s-squared terms are already matched as "ones"; otherwise, the TF would need to be so normalized by dividing numerator and denominator by that coefficient):

$$\omega_n^2 = 36 \quad \text{and} \quad 2\zeta\omega_n = B$$

Thus

$$\omega_n = 6 \text{ rps} \quad \text{and} \quad B = 2(0.7)(6.0) = 8.4$$

Thus if the damping parameter B is chosen to have value 8.4, the damping coefficient will be 0.7. Note that the numerator of the TF does not affect the dynamic response of the system; its effect on the system response is that it alters the magnitude of the response.

A few other terms are used commonly in describing the second-order system response. These are listed below:

Delay time. The time required for the system response to travel from 0 percent to 50 percent of the final value.

Rise time. The time required for the system response to travel from 10 percent to 90 percent of the final value.

Peak time. The time required for the system response to travel from 0 percent to the peak response value.

Settling time. The time required for the system response to travel from 0 percent to within a bound of plus or minus 5 percent of the final response.

Peak value. The peak response x_p as given by the expression

$$x_p = 1 + e^{\left(\frac{\zeta \cdot \pi}{\sqrt{1 - \zeta^2}}\right)} \tag{8-47}$$

where the response is normalized such that the final value is 1.

Overshoot. The difference between the peak value and the final value, divided by the final value (usually expressed as a percent).

The student may wonder with some bewilderment at this point that if this much ado has been made over simple first- and second-order systems, what must follow when higher-order systems are pursued? The answer is comforting in that there is not much new in analyzing higher-order systems other than additional complexity and tediousness. The system responses of the exponential and exponential sinusoid are characteristic of that expected in higher-order systems, and are adequate to describe many systems. The typical system response will consist of several different modes of response such as exponentials and exponential sinusoids, but typically one exponential, or exponential sinusoid, will dominate over the others in determining the overall response of the system, and thus the system analysis and design can be centered about that feature. An example of this concept follows.

Example 8-14   Transfer Function Simplification

A servomechanism consists of an amplifier with transfer function $G(s)$ and a servomotor and an inertia load with the TF $M(s)$:

$$G(s) = \frac{200(0.01s + 1)}{0.005s + 1}, \qquad M(s) = \frac{4.0}{s(0.2s + 1)}$$

Determine the character of the dynamic response.

Solution.   One method of solution would be to apply a step input and then use the methods of Laplace transform to determine the response; however, this is more laborious than is necessary here. An alternative method that is less work, but useful, is to note that the time constant associated with the amplifier is $T = 0.005$ seconds and that the time constant of the motor and load is $T = 0.2$ seconds. Thus the exponential response of the amplifier is completed in, say, 0.025 seconds, long before the response of the motor is started. Thus, in this example, but not necessarily in all cases, the dynamics of the amplifier can be ignored and treated as a TF of $G(s) = 200$ and the analysis can be made on the TF

$$G(s)M(s) = \frac{800(0.01s + 1)}{s(0.005s + 1)(0.2s + 1)} \doteq \frac{800}{s(0.2s + 1)}$$

Thus it is possible to use the simplified TF to describe the response of systems, eliminating the need for tedious labor. In this case, the response is exponential with a time constant of 0.2 seconds.

8.15 Frequency Response Characteristics

This section will be limited to a brief review of the frequency response of systems. The frequency response of the linear system can be viewed as the special case where the complex frequency variable s is taken to have zero real part sigma and only the imaginary part $j\omega$. Thus the solution form will have no transient part and will only consist of the sinusoidal steady-state part. Consider the system shown in Figure 8-25, where the TF $G(s)$ is linear. For a sinusoidal input, the TF becomes

$$G(s) \longrightarrow G(j\omega) = \frac{\text{OUT } (j\omega)}{\text{IN } (j\omega)}$$

The output is a sinusoid as the input is a sinusoid. The output can vary from the input only to the extent that it can differ in magnitude and in phase. The ratio of the amplitudes gives the gain of the TF, and the difference of the phases gives the phase angle of the TF:

$$|G(j\omega)| = \frac{|\text{OUT } (j\omega)|}{|\text{IN } (j\omega)|} \quad \text{and} \quad \angle G(j\omega) = \angle \text{OUT } (j\omega) - \angle \text{IN } (j\omega)$$

The most common method of representing the above information in graphical form is by Bode diagrams. The Bode diagram of the magnitude of $G(j\omega)$ is the magnitude in decibels on the ordinate and the logarithmic scale of the frequency on the abscissa. The expression for decibel gain of the magnitude of the TF is

$$G_{db} (j\omega) = 20 \log |G(j\omega)|$$

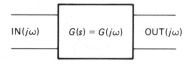

FIGURE 8-25. Frequency transfer function

The Bode diagram of the phase is represented by the phase angle on the ordinate and, as above, the logarithmic scale of the frequency on the abscissa.

It is useful to know how to obtain the Bode diagrams experimentally. We need to use a function generator with variable-frequency sinusoidal output of sufficiently low impedance to drive the system. The frequency is varied over the frequency range of interest. For each frequency setting, the gain is computed by finding the ratio of the magnitude of the output to the magnitude of the input. By plotting the gain for each frequency, the frequency magnitude response is formed. The frequency phase response is similarly formed by measuring the difference in output phase to input phase for each frequency over the range of interest. Together, these curves are called the *Bode diagrams* of the system.

In the case where the analytic expression for the system is known in the form of the TF, then the Bode diagram can be found analytically.

Example 8-15   Frequency Response using the Transfer Function

Determine the frequency response of the TF

$$G(s) = \frac{12}{s^2 + 4s + 8}$$

Solution.   Convert from s to $j\omega$. Since $s = j\omega$, $s^2 = -\omega^2$, and

$$G(j\omega) = \frac{12}{-\omega^2 + j4\omega + 8}$$

To find the magnitude and the phase, the parts are grouped as to whether they are real or imaginary:

$$G(j\omega) = \frac{12}{8 - \omega^2 + j4\omega}$$

where the real part of the denominator of $G(j\omega)$ is given as

$$Re(j\omega) = 8 - \omega^2$$

and the imaginary part of the denominator of $G(j\omega)$ is given as

$$Im(j\omega) = 4\omega$$

The magnitude of $G(j\omega)$ is the magnitude of the numerator divided by the magnitude of the denominator. The magnitude of the numerator is simply 12; the magnitude of the denominator is found by taking the square root of the sum of the squares of the real part and the imaginary part:

$$| G(j\omega) | = \frac{12}{\sqrt{Re^2 + Im^2}} \tag{8-48}$$

The phase shift is found by finding the angle of the denominator:

$$\text{Angle } G(j\omega) = -\arctan \frac{Im}{Re} \tag{8-49}$$

The phasor diagram for this denominator term is shown in Figure 8-26. The overall angle is the negative of the denominator term angle and the overall magnitude is the reciprocal of the $\sqrt{Re^2 + Im^2}$ times the numerator. It is important to sketch the angle to assure that the proper value is being used in the arctangent argument Im/Re, since the arctangent function is only valid for the angle in the first or fourth quadrant (-90 to $+90$ degrees).

For first-order systems, the frequency magnitude response is only capable of a flat response and an increase or decrease in gain at the maximum rate of 20 db/decade equal to 6 db/octave, where a decade is a tenfold increase in frequency and an octave is a twofold increase in frequency. The point where the increase changes from, say, a flat response to a fall-off in response, is called, among other things, the *critical* or *3db frequency*. This critical frequency is inversely related to the time constant of the system. For example, the TF of the first-order system is given above as

$$G(s) = \frac{K}{s + a} = \frac{K/a}{\frac{s}{a} + 1} = \frac{K'}{\tau s + 1} \tag{8-35}$$

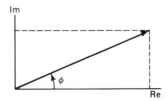

FIGURE 8-26. Phasor diagram for second-order system

Convert the complex frequency to imaginary frequency, namely, let $s = j\omega$:

$$G(j\omega) = \frac{K}{j\omega + a} = \frac{\dfrac{K}{a}}{\dfrac{j\omega}{a} + 1} = \frac{K'}{1 + j\omega\tau} \qquad (8\text{-}50)$$

The magnitude of $G(j\omega)$ is found as

$$|G(j\omega)| = \frac{|K|}{|j\omega + a|} = \frac{\left|\dfrac{K}{a}\right|}{\left|\dfrac{j\omega}{a} + 1\right|} = \frac{|K'|}{|1 + ja\tau|} = \frac{K'}{\sqrt{1 + (\omega\tau)^2}} \qquad (8\text{-}51)$$

The angle of $G(j\omega)$ is found as

$$\text{Angle } G(j\omega) = -\arctan(\omega\tau) \qquad (8\text{-}52)$$

For second-order systems, the frequency magnitude response has several possible responses, as shown in Figure 8-27. The frequency response curve is a function of the damping factor. At low frequencies, the response is flat; i.e., $|G(j\omega)|$ is relatively constant over changes in frequency and is independent of the damping. In the mid frequency range, the response may increase above the unity gain value (0 decibels) and exhibit a peaking response for small damping. At high frequencies, the frequency magnitude response falls off at 40 db/decade. Of special interest is the peaking effect that is obtained when the damping coefficient ζ is less than 0.707. This peak frequency ω_p occurs when the magnitude of the TF

$$G(j\omega) = \frac{\omega_n^2}{(\omega_n^2 - \omega^2) + j2\zeta\omega_n\omega} \qquad (8\text{-}53)$$

is a maximum. The magnitude $|G(j\omega)|$ is a maximum when the frequency is

$$\omega_p = \omega_n \cdot \sqrt{1 - 2\zeta^2}, \qquad \zeta < 0.707 \qquad (8\text{-}54)$$

The maximum value of $|G(j\omega)|$ is called M_p; it can be found from the expression

$$M_p = \frac{1}{2\zeta \cdot \sqrt{1 - \zeta^2}}, \qquad \zeta < 0.707 \qquad (8\text{-}55)$$

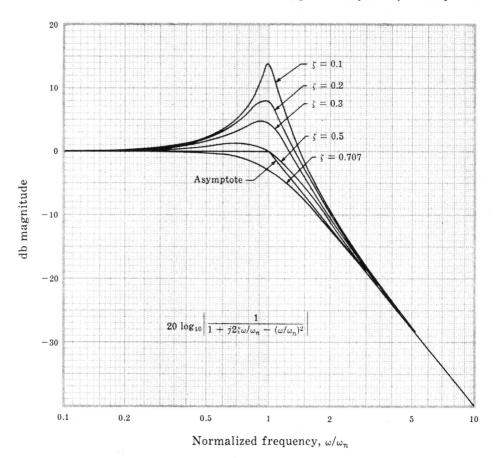

The equation shown on the figure:
$$20 \log_{10}\left|\frac{1}{1 + j2\zeta\omega/\omega_n - (\omega/\omega_n)^2}\right|$$

FIGURE 8-27. Magnitude frequency response of a second-order system

The phase-shift information available from the Bode phase versus frequency curve for the second-order system can be seen in Figure 8-28.

One use of the gain and phase information is in the design of closed-loop systems, where the phase shift and gain around the loop determine the stability and performance of the closed-loop system.

8.16 Block Diagram Analysis

A convenient method of representing several components of a system is by block diagram representation, which includes blocks (operators and multipliers), summing junctions, and pickoff points.

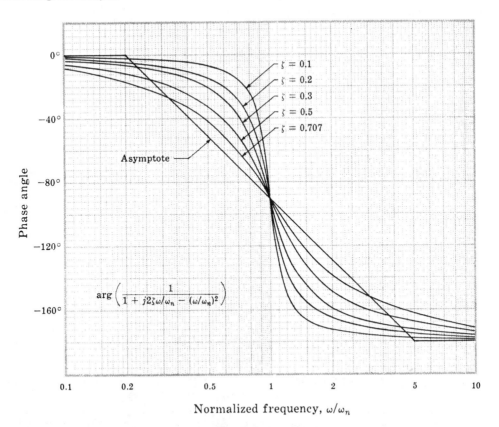

FIGURE 8-28. Phase shift frequency response of a second-order system

Operators. These quantities are simply the operation performed by the block on the input applied to it. Examples are the derivative operator, which can be expressed as d/dt, or preferably as s, a complicated TF, or a constant multiplier such as the gain of an amplifier. See Figure 8-29.

Summing junctions. In a control system, signals that are generated by various means need to be summed algebraically to find a

FIGURE 8-29. Block operator

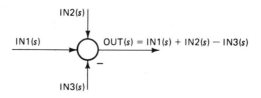

FIGURE 8-30. Summing point

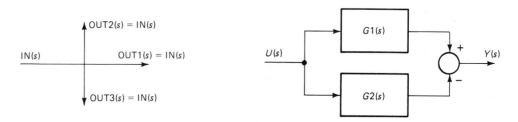

FIGURE 8-31. Pickoff point   FIGURE 8-32. Feedforward block diagram

sum or difference. This operation is represented by a summing junction, as shown in Figure 8-30.

Pickoff points. In order to send a signal to more than one point, a pickoff point is used, as shown in Figure 8-31.

Two classical combinations of block diagrams are examined here. The feedforward diagram is shown in Figure 8-32. The TF of the feedforward system can be derived using the block diagram rules given above:

$$G_{ff}(s) = \frac{Y(s)}{U(s)} = G_1(s) - G_2(s) \tag{8-56}$$

The most important block diagram configuration is where feedback is provided, as shown in Figure 8-33. The TF of the feedback system can be derived using the block diagram rules given above and as shown here. The basic relations are

$$E(s) = U(s) - F(s) \tag{8-57}$$

$$Y(s) = G(s)E(s) \tag{8-58}$$

$$F(s) = H(s)Y(s) \tag{8-59}$$

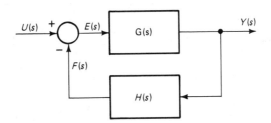

FIGURE 8-33. Feedback block diagram

Combining the above equations, the relationship

$$E(s) = U(s) - G(s)H(s)E(s) \qquad (8\text{-}60)$$

is established, which can be solved to find the expression for the error signal

$$E(s) = \frac{1}{1 + GH(s)} U(s) \qquad (8\text{-}61)$$

or, in terms of a transfer function,

$$\frac{E(s)}{U(s)} = \frac{1}{1 + GH(s)} \qquad (8\text{-}62)$$

To find the total TF across the feedback network, the above two equations are multiplied by $G(s)$ to establish

$$Y(s) = \frac{G(s)}{1 + GH(s)} U(s) \qquad (8\text{-}63)$$

or, in terms of the TF,

$$\frac{Y(s)}{U(s)} = \frac{G(s)}{1 + GH(s)} \qquad (8\text{-}64)$$

which is the closed-loop transform of the entire feedback system. For the system to be a negative feedback control system, the feedback $F(s)$ is subtracted as shown in Figure 8-33. It is left for the reader to determine the effect of using positive feedback on the transfer function.

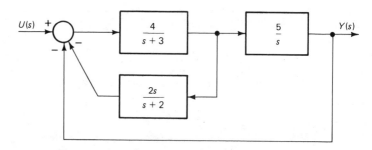

FIGURE 8-34. Feedback block diagram

Example 8-16   Transfer Function for a Feedback Control System

Determine the TFs $E(s)/U(s)$ and $Y(s)/U(s)$ for the negative feedback control system where

$$G(s) = \frac{12}{s+2}, \qquad H(s) = 4$$

Solution.   Use the above expressions to determine that

$$\frac{E(s)}{U(s)} = \frac{s+2}{s+50}, \qquad \frac{Y(s)}{U(s)} = \frac{12}{s+50}$$

Example 8-17   Transfer Function for a Multiple Feedback Control System

Determine the TFs $E(s)/U(s)$ and $Y(s)/U(s)$ for the negative feedback control system given in Figure 8-34.

Solution.   First reduce the inner loop by letting

$$G(s) = \frac{4}{s+3}, \qquad H(s) = \frac{2s}{s+2}$$

and use (8-64) to show that the TF of the inner loop is

$$\frac{\dfrac{4}{s+3}}{1 + \left(\dfrac{4}{s+3}\right)\left(\dfrac{2s}{s+2}\right)} = \frac{4(s+2)}{(s+3)(s+2)+8s} = \frac{4(s+2)}{s^2 + 13s + 6}$$

The above is now used in (8-64) with the following expressions:

$$G(s) = \frac{4(s+2)}{s^2 + 13s + 6} \frac{5}{s} = \frac{20(s+2)}{s(s^2 + 13s + 6)}, \qquad H(s) = 1$$

The overall TF becomes

$$G(s) \text{ overall} = \frac{\dfrac{20(s+2)}{s(s^2 + 13s + 6)}}{1 + \dfrac{20(s+2)}{s(s^2 + 13s + 6)}} = \frac{20(s+2)}{s^3 + 13s^2 + 26s + 40}$$

In summary, this example concludes the building of the analytic tools that are needed to understand the basics of feedback control analysis. These tools are used in the following chapter in the study of dynamic feedback control systems.

Problems

8.1 Given the equation, $x(t) = 1.0 - 1.0e^{-t/2.0 \text{ sec}}$, find the value of x for
   a) $t = 0.0$ sec
   b) $t = 1.0$ sec
   c) $t = 2.0$ sec
   d) $t = 4.0$ sec
   e) $t = 6.0$ sec
   f) $t = 8.0$ sec
   g) $t = 10.0$ sec

8.2 Given the equation, $x(t) = e^{-t/4.0 \text{ sec}}$, find the value of t for
   a) $x(t) = 1.00$
   b) $x(t) = 0.75$
   c) $x(t) = 0.50$
   d) $x(t) = 0.25$
   e) $x(t) = 0.00$

8.3 It is known that the half-life of a capacitance charge is 5.0 sec.
   a) What is the time constant of the capacitance discharge?

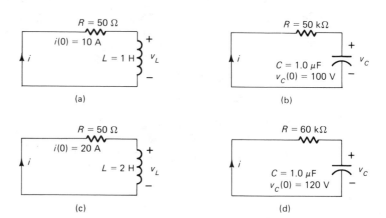

FIGURE P8.4.

b) What is the relationship between time constant, τ, and half-life, hl?

c) How many half-lives should expire to call the process settled by the five time-constant rules?

8.4 Solve for $v(t)$ and $i(t)$ in the circuits given in Figure P8.4.

8.5 Solve for $v(t)$ and $i(t)$ in the circuits given in Figure P8.5.

8.6 Given a constant acceleration of 2 ft/sec^2, an initial velocity of 3 ft/sec at $t = 0$ sec, and an initial displacement of -50 ft at $t = 0$ sec, determine

a) the velocity at the end of 3 sec

b) the displacement at the end of 3 sec

c) the time at which the displacement is 0 feet.

8.7 Consider mechanical systems with the following parameters.

a) In Figure P8.7(a), force $f = 10u(t)$ lb, mass $M = 1$ slug, friction $B = 2$ lb sec/ft. Solve for the velocity $v(t)$ for $t > 0$.

b) Same parameters as part (a). Solve for the displacement $x(t)$.

c) Torque $T = 10u(t)$ Nm (Newton meters), moment of inertia $J = 5$ Nm sec^2, and friction $B = 2$ Nm sec. Solve for the angular velocity $\omega(t)$.

d) Same parameters as part (c). Solve for the angular displacement $\theta(t)$.

e) In Figure P8.7(b), torque $T = 10$ dyne cm, friction $B = 2$ dyne cm sec, spring constant $K = 25$ dyne cm and moment of inertia J is negligible. Solve for the angular position function $\theta(t)$.

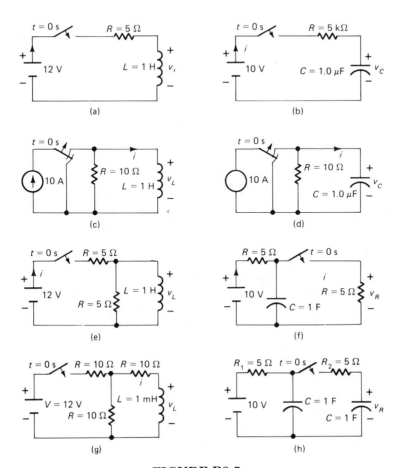

FIGURE P8.5.

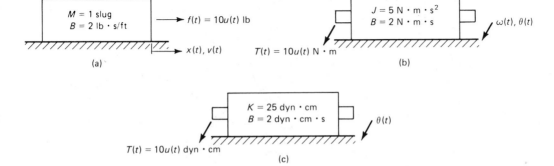

FIGURE P8.7.

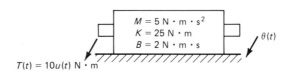

FIGURE P8.8.

8.8 a) For a mechanical system as shown in Figure P8.8, determine the final position.

b) For the spring $K = 0$ in the Figure P8.8, determine the final velocity.

8.9 a) Given a series RLC circuit with a 12 V source, an inductance $L = 2\,H$, a resistance $R = 24$ ohms, and a capacitance $C = 2\,F$, determine an equivalent rectilinear mechanical circuit.

b) Given an angular system such as a meter movement with a spring constant of $2.0(10^{-6})$ Nm, a friction coefficient of $3.0(10^{-6})$ Nm s, and a moment of inertia of $1.0\,(10^{-6})$ Nm s^2, determine an equivalent electrical circuit.

8.10 Convert the following expressions to the s operator domain.

a) For an inductor: $v = 4\,\dfrac{di}{dt}$

b) For a friction: $v = 5\,\dfrac{dx}{dt}$

c) For a capacitor: $v = 3 \displaystyle\int idt$

d) For a resistor: $v = 6i$

8.11 Convert the following expressions to the time domain.

a) For an inductor: $V(s) = 6sI(s)$

b) For a friction: $V(s) = 2sX(s)$

c) For a capacitor: $V(s) = (1/2s)I(s)$

d) For a resistor: $V(s) = 7I(s)$

8.12 For circuits (a) through (h) of problem 8.5, determine the impedance seen looking in at the circuit from the source.

8.13 Find the impedance $Z(s)$ of a series RLC circuit consisting of 10 ohms, 3 H, and 0.02 F.

8.14 For the mechanical systems (a) through (e) in problem 8.7, determine the respective impedances:

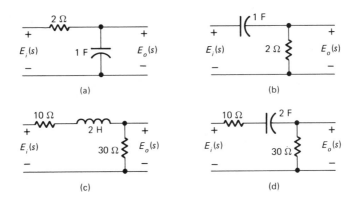

FIGURE P8.15.

a) $Z(s) = F(s)/V(s)$

b) $Z(s) = F(s)/X(s)$

c) $Z(s) = T(s)/\omega(s)$

d) $Z(s) = T(s)/\theta(s)$

e) $Z(s) = T(s)/\theta(s)$

8.15 Solve for the transfer functions $G(s) = E_o(s)/E_i(s)$ for Figures P8.15(a) through (d).

8.16 In problem 8.15 (a) and (b), solve for $E_o(s)$ for $E_i(s) = 10/s$. *(Hint: Use $E_o(s) = G(s)E_i(s)$.)*

8.17 a) Solve for $G(s) = X(s)/F(s)$ in Figure P8.17.

b) Solve for $X(s) = G(s)F(s)$ for $F(s) = 10/s$ in Figure P8.17.

8.18 Reduce the block diagrams in Figures P8.18 (a) through (f) to a single equivalent block.

8.19 Determine the transfer function for Figures P8.18 (c) and (d) if positive feedback is used instead of negative feedback.

8.20 For Figures P8.18 (a), (b), (c), and (d), determine the response $C(s)$ to input $R(s)$ a step input of magnitude 12, i.e., $12/s$.

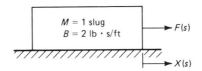

FIGURE P8.17.

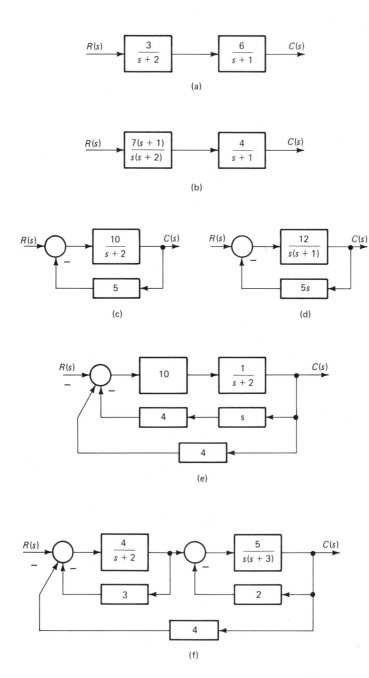

FIGURE P8.18.

9 Dynamic Control

9.0 Introduction

The earliest electrical control systems were static; however, in the evolution of control systems it became necessary to develop systems that could continuously monitor and control the controlled object, both in time and in the measure of the response, be it displacement, velocity, heating, force, torque, or one of many other outputs. The advent of electronics made possible many of the dynamic control systems that are in existence today.

This chapter is titled "dynamic control" because the subject matter is the analysis and design of controls for dynamic systems. The expression *dynamic systems* means that the components of the system—electrical, mechanical, etc.—have a continuum of energy transfer such that the system variables change continuously (as opposed to changing from off to on and on to off).

An example of a dynamic system is a mass-friction system as discussed in the previous chapter; without a forcing function, the velocity will be an exponentially decaying function of time. The control system that controls this friction-mass system must be designed to handle the friction and mass values to provide desirable system response and to avoid problems such as sluggish response.

The subject of dynamic control is in contrast to the control systems—called static systems—in the early chapters of this text, static systems being those systems that can be dealt with on a step-by-step basis. In the static case, there is no need for concern about the consequences of one control act before the next control act is promulgated. In the water tank problem at the end of Chapter 2, the pump motor was simply commanded to turn on and off at the level limits without any concern for the dynamics of the water level and its rate of change. In contrast, if the water level had to be continuously controlled at a specified level, then the control would need to control the water inlet flow at the proper rate of flow. The flow rate would have to be continuously adjusted to match the rate of use. In this case, the dynamics of the control system would have to be analyzed, since it would be a dynamic control problem. Another comparison is that an RC circuit is dynamic in its response, whereas a resistance network with no capacitance is static.

9.1 Concepts of Dynamic Control

Key conceptual aspects of control systems are system functions, feedback, and open- versus closed-loop control.

The Three Basic Functions of a Dynamic Control System

Dynamic control systems consist of three necessary functional elements:

1. The sensor that detects, modulates, and transforms the output response to a measurable signal
2. The amplifier that receives the output of the sensor, amplifies and conditions this sensor output signal, and drives the third element
3. The prime mover that produces the required output response.

A common example of dynamic control is the operation of the hot and cold water valves of the shower faucets to control the water temperature and the water-flow rate. In this example, a human makes up the loop, i.e., the sensor, the amplifier, and the prime mover (the valve is also a part of the prime mover). When the water is too cold or too hot or too fast or too slow, it is controlled as follows:

1. The temperature sensors in the skin sense this condition and a signal is sent through the nervous system.
2. The central nervous system amplifies and conditions the signal to direct the response.
3. The motor action of the muscles corrects this condition.

This example opens up a lot of areas to explore in control technology, but let us define a few more control concepts before this example is carried further. First let us categorize control systems by the concept of feedback.

Feedback Control

In the routine activities of living things such as Homo sapiens, feedback is a necessary, even essential, attribute. In adjusting shower-faucet valves to control water temperature, in lifting a cup of coffee without dropping it, in standing or walking, and in countless other acts, we use perception (i.e., sight, sound, feel, smell, taste) as feedback senses to measure our actions and to direct these actions by our nervous system. The popularity of sports and video games is largely based on the thrill of tuning the human feedback control system to its ultimate capacity to give the optimum dynamic response.

Needless to say, early industrial and other man-made control systems did not exhibit this remarkable feedback capacity. One of the earliest examples of the need for a feedback mechanism was the instability of a steam engine running without feedback. Even with the application of a manually controlled steam valve, the speed of the steam engine was poorly regulated and would vary with its operating condition and with the load to which it was coupled. In an effort to overcome this lack of acceptable control of the operation, James Watt (1736–1819) developed a governor that senses the speed of the steam engine; through the action of centrifugal weights, a slider, and levers, the governor controls the steam valve to "govern" or "regulate" the flow of steam to the engine. Thus, under increased loading when the steam engine would tend to slow down, the governor increases the opening of the steam valve and provides more power to the load. When the load is reduced, the engine speeds up and the governor closes the steam valve.

Today, the examples of industrial and commercial feedback control systems abound. A few that are familiar to many people are demand-controlled traffic controllers, automotive automatic transmission accelerator-controlled shifting, automotive engine speed-controlled ignition timing, line printer printing-head position control, passenger elevator floor-level stopping, automotive cruise control, television antenna-rotor position control, and record player speed control.

Open-Loop vs. Closed-Loop Control

The term *closed loop* essentially designates the same concept as the term *feedback*.[1] The purpose of closed-loop control is to "feed back" a measured value of the output variable to be compared with the setting of a "control command" value, to amplify the difference between them, and to alter the output based on this difference. In open-loop

---

[1]The term *open loop* is not necessarily the same as *without feedback*, since this term may also refer to the total loop from the sensor through the amplifier and prime mover and back to the sensor with the last connection unconnected. In spite of this connotation of open loop, the term "open-loop" gain will be used synonymously with the term "without feedback."

control systems, it is not possible to alter the output based on the difference between the control command and the output.

A commonly experienced example of a closed-loop control system is steering a vehicle. The human eye is the sensor, the human nervous system is the amplifier, and the human, along with the steering mechanism, is the prime mover. In the normal mode of steering, whenever the eye senses that the vehicle is deviating from the desired path, corrective action is taken in a "closed-loop" fashion. This same system becomes "open loop" whenever the eye is taken from the road. The reader that has had a harrowing experience when not adequately observing the road or other vehicles is aware of the need for precise and timely feedback to provide a satisfactory closed-loop steering control system.

It should also be pointed out that application of feedback to a control system, expressed as "closing the loop," does not cause the response of the control system to be perfect. The degree of improvement of system performance depends on several factors. The gain around the loop affects the system performance; if the gain is too small, the error in the output will be too large. The kind of feedback will also affect the system performance. The kinds of feedback include proportional and/or rate and/or integral feedback. The level of gain for each of these feedback loops is also significant.

Dynamic Control System Terminology

The above concepts can be more easily expressed and analyzed by setting them in a block diagram representation, as shown in Figure 9-1.

1. The reference signal $R(s)$ is typically a hand-set value, such as a voltage level at which it is desired that the system should operate. This quantity is also called the *command, set value, or set point.*

2. The error signal $E(s)$ is the difference between the reference signal $R(s)$ and the feedback signal $F(s)$, which is also called the difference signal.

3. The error signal is generated by the summing block, which may be a number of things, including a comparator, a summing amplifier, or a differential operational amplifier.

4. The amplifier/controller block $G(s)$ is sometimes called the forward-loop transfer function. It includes the dynamics not only of the comparator, the amplifier system, and the prime mover, but also of the load, which may have inertial and frictional components.

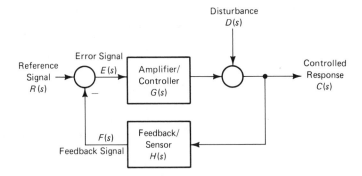

**FIGURE 9-1. General block diagram representation of a
control system**

5. The disturbance *D(s)* is a representation of the nonideal
   forces that enter into a control problem. The disturbance
   D(s) may represent the wind on a radar antenna in a radar
   control system, or it may represent the increase in electrical
   usage in an electrical-power distribution system.

6. The controlled response *C(s)* is the response of the load to
   the control system; it may be position, velocity, temperature,
   etc.

7. The feedback control block *H(s)* is the sensor that converts
   the controlled variable *C(s)* to a usable feedback control
   variable *F(s)*. An example is a feedback potentiometer that
   is wired in parallel with a reference potentiometer such that
   the signal *E(s)* is the difference of voltages at the brush
   connections of the potentiometers. Another example of a
   feedback control block is a synchro pair that provides an
   error signal between the control command and the output.

9.2 Control System Excitation

The operation and performance of any control system can be
examined only under the stimulus of external excitation, what we
have called the *forcing function*. In actual operation, the stimulus to
the control system is a combination of the external input *r(t)* and the
feedback signal *f(t)*, which together form the error signal *e(t)*:

$$e(t) = r(t) - f(t)$$

or, in terms of the *s* operator,

$$E(s) = R(s) - F(s)$$

In operation, the signal *e(t)* is a fluctuating signal that is a consequence of changes in the input reference signal and random changes in the feedback signal; for example, the wind blowing on a radar dish antenna would cause it to travel away from its desired trajectory. However, it is not possible to test the system for such unique and unidentifiable signals. For this reason, dynamic control systems are tested with standard test signals that have sufficient common properties with randomly changing signals, allowing the performance to be specified based on these standard signals.

Unit-Step Test Signal

Possibly the most popular method of testing a control system is applying a step function to the input and then determining the response. As discussed in Chapter 8, the response can be measured in terms of several parameters such as delay time, rise time, peak time, settling time, overshoot, damped resonant response, and the damping coefficient. A feedback control system can be specified in terms of these parameters.

Another reason that the unit step function is a widely used test signal is that the response to the step function represents the response to a wide range of the frequency spectrum. For example, consider a square-wave input that is equivalent to a series of step functions. This square wave can be decomposed into a series of harmonic functions. This series contains all the odd harmonic frequencies of the fundamental frequency of the square wave. For example, if the square wave had a frequency of 10 Hz, then the harmonics would have frequencies of 30 Hz, 50 Hz, 70 Hz, etc. The magnitude of these harmonics would be in inverse magnitude to their frequency. Thus the squarewave, which is a series of step functions, is a useful test signal in that it tests the response of the system to a wide range of the frequency spectrum.

The step input is expressed as

$$u(t) = \begin{cases} 0, & t < 0 \\ 1, & t > 0 \end{cases}$$

which means that the input is zero until time t changes from the negative domain to the positive domain, and then it instantly changes to 1. An illustration of the unit-step function is shown in Figure 9-2. A magnitude that is different than unity is expressed by writing the function as *Ku(t)*, where K is the magnitude.

An example of using the step function is determining the step response at the output *c(t)* for a step input at *r(t)*, and also determining the output *c(t)* for a step input of the disturbance *d(t)*. For these

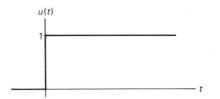
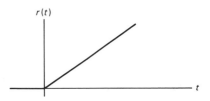

FIGURE 9-2. The unit step input   **FIGURE 9-3. The ramp input**

responses, the above-mentioned parameters of rise time, overshoot, etc., can be measured. Then various system designs can be compared as far as minimizing the effect of the disturbance and optimizing the effect of the reference input.

Unit-Ramp Function

Although the unit-step function response is an adequate measure of the system response for a wide range of considerations, a shortcoming is that after the initial transient is finished, the response settles out to a constant value; thus the unit-step function is called a *position command*. In many control systems, it is important to determine how well the system will follow a changing input, called *rate following*. For this reason, a ramp function is often used to test a control system. Since a ramp can be easily obtained by integrating a step input, it is an easy test signal to generate. A sample application is a radar-aiming servo following a moving target such as an aircraft. Similar applications exist in industrial applications where rate following is needed. The ramp input is expressed as

$$r(t) = Kt$$

where K is the slope constant and t is time. An illustration of the ramp function is shown in Figure 9-3.

Unit-Impulse Function

Closely related to the step function is the impulse function. The concept of an impulse is based on a pulse waveform that in the limit becomes infinitely high and infinitesimally narrow. Thus, the pulse itself is over before the response of the system has taken shape (that is, the period of the impulse is short compared to the equivalent time constant of the system).

The impulse function is particularly useful because the response of the system to an impulse can be readily determined. This convenience is a consequence of the fact that the impulse function as a function of s can be given simply as

$$R(s) = 1$$

and

$$C(s) = \frac{G(s)}{1 + G(s)H(s)}$$

The ease of handling an impulse function analytically is clear; the system output parameters, such as damping coefficient and damped resonant frequency, can be found directly from the system transfer function. An example of this property follows:

Example 9-1   Impulse Response

Determine if the system response is oscillatory and, if so, determine the value of ζ and ω_n.

$$G(s) = \frac{15}{s^2 + 4s + 6}, \qquad H(s) = 2$$

Solution.   The closed-loop system transfer function (TF) $G'(s)$ must first be found from the expression

$$G'(s) = \frac{G(s)}{1 + G(s)H(s)}$$

For the above $G(s)$ and $H(s)$, $G'(s)$ is found to be

$$G'(s) = \frac{15}{s^2 + 4s + 36}$$

$$= \frac{K}{s^2 + 2\zeta\omega_n s + \omega_n^2} = C(s)$$

since the system can be tested by $R(s) = 1$. Thus by matching the terms of the standard form with the given transfer function, the following relations are determined:

$$\omega_n^2 = 36, \qquad \omega_n = 6 \; rps$$

and

$$2\zeta\omega_n = 4, \qquad \zeta = \frac{1}{3}$$

Therefore, the response is oscillatory with a damping factor of $\zeta = 1/3$ and a resonant frequency of 6 rps. As a further exercise, the damped resonant frequency ω_d can be determined to be 5.66 rps.

Sinusoidal Input Function

An alternative approach to time-domain analysis and testing using time-domain signals is the use of frequency-domain analysis and testing using frequency-domain signals. Since the actual fluctuating signal in a feedback control system can have energy in a wide range of the frequency spectrum, the frequency response information will be useful for determining the response of the system in following this signal. A concern is that the control system will exhibit too high a resonant response at a particular frequency. The peak magnitude of the frequency response was given in Chapter 8 as M_p and the frequency was given as ω_p. If the M_p value is too large, then there is a possibility that the control system will exhibit oscillation at ω_p radians per second. By testing the frequency response for the M_p value, the tendency for resonance response will be determined.

Example 9-2   Resonant Response

A control system has a resonant peak at 2.3 radians per second with a peak of 14 decibels. Is the system response satisfactory?

Solution.   From the standard frequency response curves (see Figure 8-27), it can be determined that the damping ratio is 0.1. This small value of ζ means that the system is very resonant to inputs with energy content in the 2.3 rps range, and that the system will be terribly oscillatory, not only for a 2.3 rps sinusoid but also when a step, ramp, impulse, or other input is applied.

By this example, we can see that frequency-domain information can be translated to time-domain information and vice versa. The general form of the analysis is started by letting $s = j\omega$ and then

$$G(j\omega) = G(s)$$

and

$$H(j\omega) = H(s)$$

The closed-loop transfer function $G'(j\omega)$ is

$$G'(j\omega) = \frac{G(j\omega)}{1 + G(j\omega)H(j\omega)}$$

TABLE 9-1. Table of applications of test functions

	STABILITY	TRACKING	RESONANCE	FREQUENCY RESP
unit step	x		x	
unit ramp		x		
unit impulse	x		x	
sinusoid	x	x	x	x

The form that the test would take in the laboratory is to apply a sinusoidal function generator to the input $R(j\omega)$ and then measure the magnitude and angle of the output $C(j\omega)$ by the use of an oscilloscope or other measuring device. The magnitude of $G'(j\omega)$ is determined by forming the ratio.

$$|G'(j\omega)| = \frac{|C(j\omega)|}{|R(j\omega)|}$$

and the phase of $G'(j\omega)$ is determined by forming the difference

$$\angle G'(j\omega) = \angle C(j\omega) - \angle R(j\omega)$$

In practice, specific equipment is commercially available to expedite these tests and show both magnitude and phase information.

Four different test signals have been discussed here; obviously there are many additional ones that could be considered. The most suitable test signal will depend on the particular system, its purpose, and the test setup. Table 9-1 shows by indicating with an "x" the test functions that are suitable for various applications: testing for stability of operation, ability to track a changing signal, determining resonance response, and performing frequency response analysis.

9.3 Measures of Control System Performance

Specific measures are used to determine a control system's quality of performance. Important measures of performance are the system's ability to follow a constant input and its ability to stabilize its output, described here as *offset*, *stability*, and *relative stability*.

Offset

The value of using feedback is to reduce the error to the lowest value possible within the constraints of other system parameter bounds,

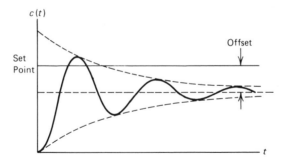

FIGURE 9-4. A system response with offset

such as kind of system feedback and gain in the feedback loops. In spite of feedback control, significant steady-state error may exist after the transient condition is completed. This steady-state error is called the *offset*. Offset is defined as the difference in the output and the reference after transients have decayed. The easiest method of testing for offset is to apply a step input or an impulse, and to measure the difference between the commanded value of the output and the actual value of the output. Figure 9-4 demonstrates a typical servo response with offset.

An example of a system that has offset is an antenna-aiming system that follows a target. Offset may exist due to friction forces, such as stiction or viscous friction, or transport lag. The effect is that the antenna position will be offset from the ideal position, which means that the antenna will have an error in tracking the target. Offset can be decreased by increasing the loop gain, but the increased gain may cause the system to be less stable.

Stability

Feedback is used to reduce the error in output and provide an essential method of obtaining acceptable system performance; however, the use of feedback can cut both ways. Namely, it is possible to start with a control system that has open-loop stability, but with the addition of feedback the system can become unstable. This concept can be easily understood. Any available signal that enters the sytem at any point (including an infinitesimally small noise) can have a particular frequency component that is fed around the loop and back to that starting point; in the case where a phase shift of 360 degrees is present, the feedback signal will be coincident with the original source and will add to it. If the loop gain at this particular frequency is equal to or greater than unity, then the original signal frequency component will be amplified; within a few cycles of this feedback, the

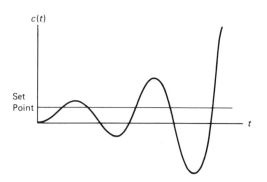

FIGURE 9-5. An unstable system response

system will be running out of control, limited only by mechanical stops or by saturation of electronic amplifiers that limit the buildup of energy to a steady-state oscillation—obviously an unacceptable solution to anyone except oscillator designers. An example of an unstable system response is shown in Figure 9-5.

   The stability problem is easily solved by reducing the gain below the unity loop gain level. This method is called *gain compensation.* Gain compensation may not satisfy the offset requirements in that the offset will be increased proportionally to the decrease in the loop gain. Two other methods of compensation are *lag compensation* and *lead compensation.* In the case of lag compensation, an attenuation network is introduced into the system, which attenuates the loop gain at the frequency that oscillation would otherwise occur; the reduced gain stabilizes the response. In the case of lead compensation, phase lead is introduced to compensate for the phase shift that is causing 360 degrees of phase lag, such that the system does not have sufficient phase shift to oscillate at the frequency that oscillation would otherwise occur. Other solutions exist, such as lag-lead compensation (notch filters) and feedback compensation.

Relative Stability

A system whose response grows without bound or oscillates without damping is defined as unstable and unacceptable. If the loop gain to this system is reduced to the level that the system barely satisfies the criteria of stability, namely, the system response does not grow without bound or oscillate without damping, then the system response will be called stable, but the prolonged damped oscillation will undoubtedly remain unsatisfactory. This system does not meet the requirements of good relative stability. "Good" relative stability is a subjective criteria.

One measure of relative stability is the damping coefficient of the system. A system that has a damping coefficient of under 0.5 will probably be considered too oscillatory and not have good relative stability. On the other hand, if the damping coefficient is over 0.9, the system may be very stable but the response will be sluggish, causing a large delay time and rise time, causing it to be considered unsatisfactory. As a very general rule of thumb, a damping coefficient of 0.7 may be considered ideal. This damping coefficient translates into an overshoot of about 6 percent (see Figure 8-24) and a frequency magnitude peak of 0 percent (see Figure 8-27). This example shows the usefulness of the damping ratio as a means of describing dynamic systems. There are alternate measures of relative stability for systems with higher terms that cannot be described by the damping coefficient.

The significance of examining the requirements of each application is stressed by mentioning that some systems will not tolerate overshoot. Examples of such applications are pressures in pressure vessels and nuclear reactors. In these cases, the damping coefficient must be altered to produce no less than unity damping coefficient.

9.4 System Parameters

The most basic parameters of any feedback control system are the system inertia, the system damping, and the system feedback gain. These three parameters play a similar role to the inertia, friction, and spring constant that were discussed in the previous chapter. The control system inertia is identical to the mechanical system inertia, as discussed in the previous chapter. In addition, the similarity of the control system damping and mechanical friction is straightforward, in that they both dissipate the energy of motion in the form of heat and they both affect their respective systems identically. Finally, the similarity of a spring to the system loop gain can be realized by manually moving the output shaft of a feedback control system away from its commanded position and noting that the restoring force to the output shaft is proportional to the angular displacement—in exact correspondence to a linear spring. In this section, the effect of each of these parameters on the behavior of a control system is discussed.

A feel for the effect of the parameters is provided by examining the TF:

$$G(s) = \frac{1/J}{s^2 + \dfrac{B}{J}s + \dfrac{K}{J}}$$

where J is moment of inertia, B is damping, and K is spring constant. The natural resonance frequency is given by

$$\omega_n = \sqrt{\frac{K}{J}}$$

The damping coefficient is given by

$$\zeta = \frac{B}{2} \cdot \sqrt{KJ}$$

The overall system response is given by the function

$$x(t) = A + B e^{-\zeta \omega_n t} \sin(\omega_d t + \phi)$$

where

$$\omega_d = \omega_n \sqrt{1 - \zeta^2}, \qquad \zeta < 1$$

$$\phi = \arccos(\zeta)$$

With these expressions for ω_n, ζ, and x in mind, let us consider the effect of the inertia, friction, and gain on the system response.

Inertia

If the inertia is increased, the system response becomes more oscillatory, i.e., more oscillations and larger overshoots. These oscillations occur at a lower frequency. The offset will be unaffected.

To visualize the effect of increased inertia, imagine that we load an automobile to the limits of its permissible weight and then observe the suspension response when an input is supplied, possibly in the form of a road irregularity such as a railroad crossing. In the fully loaded vehicle, the ride will have larger oscillations, both in magnitude and in period, and the oscillations will continue longer than in an unloaded vehicle.

In a feedback control system, the step response is similarly affected. An increase in inertia causes the system to overshoot more and to oscillate longer with a larger number of oscillations before the response is dampened.

Thus it can be seen that systems with large inertia values have a highly oscillatory response that can be a serious problem.

Friction

If the friction is increased, the system response becomes more damped, i.e., the overshoot and the number of oscillations are decreased. The oscillations occur at a slightly lower frequency and the offset is increased.

To return to our automobile suspension example, an illustration of the effect of increasing the friction would be to place very stiff shock absorbers on the car. Stiff shock absorbers would have the same effect as increasing the friction coefficient. Alternatively, if the shock absorbers were to fail and cease to dampen the suspension response, then the ride would be highly oscillatory in that the overshoot and the number of oscillations would increase.

In the quest for improving control system performance, increased friction may or may not be a useful quantity. In some cases, dampers are added to the system to diminish the amount of oscillation. On the other hand, if the damping is increased excessively, then the system becomes too sluggish and the offset may become unduly large. The control system designer must find a solution by providing an amount of damping that sets the response between these two extremes.

Gain

If the gain is increased, the system response becomes more oscillatory, as is the case when the inertia is increased; however, the oscillations will occur at a higher frequency. The offset is decreased.

Compared to the automotive suspension example given above, increasing the gain would be comparable to increasing the stiffness of the springs of the suspension. As a case in point, a system with large gain is said to be "stiff," or alternatively, it is said to have low compliance to disturbances.

As is the case with damping, the control system designer must find a compromise between too much gain, which will cause poor relative stability, and too little gain, which will cause the system to be too sluggish and have too much offset.

In feedback control design, the setting of the system gain is the most common method of adjusting system response. Many control systems have an amplifier with a variable gain control. Adjusting the gain control is the quickest and easiest method of feedback control compensation.

Example 9-3   Parameter Selection

It is desired to improve the system response by decreasing the transient time (i.e., decreasing the settling time) without increasing the number of oscillations (i.e., decreasing the damping ratio).

Solution. The only method of decreasing the transient time is to increase the gain; however, this measure alone will also increase the number of oscillations. Thus, to maintain the number of oscillations, the damping must also be increased.

It might appear that another solution is to decrease the inertia; however, the inertia is usually a property of the load that is to be controlled, not something that the control designer has the ready option of changing. Nonetheless, the effect of the inertia can be controlled by the use of a gear train that effectively reduces the inertia as seen by the prime mover. By causing the output shaft to operate at a reduced speed relative to the input (motor) shaft, the available torque is increased in proportion to the decrease in speed. Thus, the effective inertia seen at the motor shaft is decreased by both the increase in torque and the decrease in speed available at the output, or the gear ratio squared. The gear train is covered in Chapter 12.

9.5   Nonlinear Effects

The above discussion involves linear control. In a linear control system a doubling of the error signal results in a doubling of the torque applied to the load. No control system is totally free of nonlinear effects; these nonlinearities distort the error signal and alter the system response. Four of the most significant nonlinearities are *saturation, hysteresis, backlash,* and *transport lag.*

Saturation

Saturation occurs in several kinds of equipment: two of the most common are amplifiers and motors. Saturation is described as follows: at larger values of input the output saturates; that is, the output does not increase in proportion to the increase in input. This effect is illustrated in Figure 9-6.

The effect of saturation—regardless of whether it is the saturation of the torque output of a motor or the power output of an amplifier—is to limit the output, which in turn causes the system

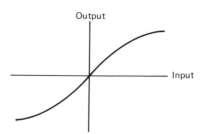

FIGURE 9-6. Illustration of saturation

response to be more sluggish and increases the transient time as compared to a linear component. On the other hand, if the controller is operating only with small changes in the command signal, the nonlinear element (i.e., motor or amplifier) will not be operating in its nonlinear range and saturation will not be experienced.

Hysteresis

Hysteresis and saturation are closely related in magnetic materials, such as motors that are made of magnetic material; it also occurs in other equipment such as amplifiers and transducers. Hysteresis is the condition where the output follows a different path when it increases than it does when it decreases, such that it has the characteristic "s" curve as shown in Figure 9-7. Thus, a device with hysteresis has an output/input relation that is based on its past history.

The effect of hysteresis on the operation of a control system is that the controlled object achieves different values depending on the direction that it came from. For example, if an instrument servo is used to record the value of the temperature of a furnace, the recorded value will have a different relationship to the actual furnace temperature when the furnace temperature is increased than when the furnace temperature is decreased. This same principle of hysteresis accounts for various kinds of memory, but it especially corresponds to magnetic core memory where the bit of memory is stored in the residual magnetism of the hysteresis loop.

Backlash

Backlash is present in almost all servomechanisms, since it is not possible to remove all "looseness" in a mechanical drive. The easiest visualization of this phenomenon is a gear mesh with two loosely fitting gears, the drive gear, and the driven gear. As long as the drive gear is forcing the driven gear forward, a linear relationship exists between input and output, but when forward motion ceases and the

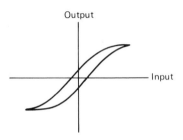

FIGURE 9-7. Illustration of hysteresis

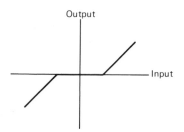

FIGURE 9-8. Illustration of backlash

drive gear is reversed, no corresponding change in the driven gear occurs, owing to the looseness in the fitting of the gears. Backlash is illustrated in Figure 9-8. The effect of backlash is that for each occurrence of a reversal in the direction of the motion of the output, the output and input lose their correspondence and there is an offset error.

It is of interest that the deadspace that characterizes backlash is in some cases purposely built into the operational characteristics of a controller. In this case, it is called a *deadband amplifier,* and its purpose is to prevent unnecessary use of control effort when the output is sufficiently close to the commanded value. An example is the use of reaction jets for attitudinal control on an orbiting space vehicle. If the attitude is within an approximate range of the desired value, then the deadband amplifier will not provide an output, thus saving energy. Once the vehicle rotates beyond the limits of the deadband, reaction jets will be activated. Thus for small deviations around the desired control value, no correcting action is taken in order to save fuel.

Transport Lag

Another nonlinear feature that occurs in control systems is transport lag, also called the *delay function*. A simple example of transport lag

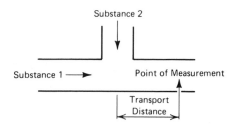

FIGURE 9-9. Illustration of transport lag

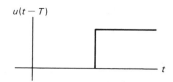

FIGURE 9-10. Illustration of transport lag response

is shown in Figure 9-9, where two substances are being mixed to yield the desired acidity. The hot-cold water shower example found in this chapter is another example of transport lag. The relationship between the transport lag time *(T)* and the transport distance *(d)* is determined by the velocity *(v)* of the solution of the two substances:

$$T = \frac{d}{v}$$

An illustration of transport lag is shown in Figure 9-10 for the case of a step input occurring at $t = 0$. The output is a step output at $t = T$ seconds.

Transport lag time is often called *delay time,* but this name causes confusion with the delayed response due to an exponential term, such as due to an RC circuit, $1/(\tau s + 1)$, where the τ is the time constant of the circuit.

The effect of transport lag is to cause a lag in the control loop, which can cause oscillation due to the lag in information passing around the loop and, in extreme cases, can cause the entire system to be unstable.

9.6 Kinds of Feedback Control

An important aspect of feedback control design is the kind of feedback that is used. The four main categories of feedback are

1. on-off feedback
2. proportional feedback
3. rate feedback
4. integral feedback.

In practice, it is common to use more than one kind of feedback, such as proportional and integral feedback. Before discussing combinations of feedback, we describe these four main categories.

On-Off Feedback

On-off feedback consists of feeding back a full-on signal or a full-off signal that indicates whether the output condition is satisfied or not satisfied. For example, a home heating system typically operates on the basis that when the thermostat setting is not satisfied, a full-on signal is transmitted to the heating plant, which in turn operates at full capacity. When the heat is supplied to the thermostat in sufficient quantity to satisfy the thermostat, then the feedback signal reverts to the full-off condition and the heating plant is turned fully off. Figure 9-11 illustrates this control system in block diagram form.

On-off feedback is the simplest kind of feedback to implement. The feedback element can be a simple switch such as a limit switch, pressure switch, or other on-off device. The on-off action causes the feedback signal to alternate between its zero value and its full value.

One difficulty with on-off feedback is that the control system output tends to oscillate from full-on to full-off as in the case of the heating system. With a feedback position control system, the output would tend to oscillate from full-on in one direction to full-on in the opposite direction. To prevent this oscillation, a deadband or deadspace amplifier is incorporated in the loop. The principle of the deadspace is similar to the characteristic of backlash. Over a range of operation of the feedback signal, the amplifier's output is zero. Thus, the output will not immediately reverse once the full-on condition has been satisfied. Similarly, in the case of the on-off feedback for the furnace control, the furnace will not oscillate rapidly between on and off due to the deadband characteristic of the thermostat; that is, the thermostat error signal will have to deviate outside of the two- or three-degree Fahrenheit deadband space before there will be an output signal from the thermostat. An illustration of on-off control response following a step input is shown in Figure 9-12. The response oscillates between the upper and lower limit.

A common example of on-off control with deadband is a television antenna controller, as may be found in many residences (at

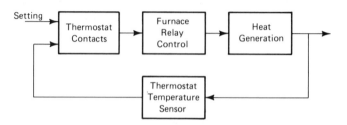

FIGURE 9-11. **Block diagram representation of a temperature control system using on-off feedback**

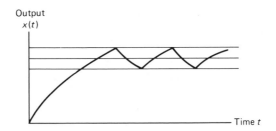

FIGURE 9-12. **Typical step response for an on-off control system**

least prior to cable TV). In this control unit, there is a set of two limit switches in the sending unit and a small bidirectional motor to drive the antenna in the receiving unit as well as to provide an on-off signal to the sending unit. When the control dial in the sending unit is manually rotated, one of the switches is activated, which, through electrical cables, drives the motor in the receiving unit as well as feeding back the signal and driving the motor in the sending unit. When the antenna reaches the desired position of rotation—within the allowance of tolerance in the spacing of the switches—the motor in the sending unit also rotates until the activating switch is returned to its open position and the feedback sequence is completed.

On-off feedback was also dealt with earlier in this text in the discussion of relay control, but there is a significant difference in its use here. The difference is in the tightness of the control loop. In the relay control systems discussed in Chapter 2, the coverage was limited to static cases where the large deadband that was between the on and off condition prevented unstable oscillations of the systems; thus, the dynamics of the system were not in effect. An example is the relay control system for the water tank-level control problem included in the Chapter 2 problems. In that example, the ON and OFF limit switches were widely spaced from each other and the time lag between the motor turning on and the motor turning off and vice versa was sufficiently long that it was not possible for unwanted oscillations to occur. The tolerance on the water level was so large that no special demands were placed on the control equipment. A more challenging design problem is posed by the requirement that the water level be controlled by on-off action of the pump motor accurately to within a fraction of an inch. A more sophisticated design approach would be necessary to solve this dynamic problem.

The advantage of on-off control is that it is simple and economical to implement the sensor, the amplifier, and the actuator. These advantages are the rationale for the use of "idiot" lights in automobile instrumentation panels. For example, transmitting the on-off representation of oil pressure is simpler than transmitting a continuous signal of values ranging from zero to the maximum.

A major disadvantage of on-off control is the deadband. The deadband is needed to prevent undesirable frequent shifts between on and off. However, deadband causes a lack of sensitivity as well as a lag in system response. On-off control can also limit component life, owing to too-frequent switching.

In summary, on-off control is an expedient and simple approach, but its limited capability precludes it from being used in active feedback control applications where we need tight loop control over the process.

Proportional Feedback

The phrase "proportional feedback" is defined as a feedback signal that is proportional to the output. Since the feedback signal will be provided by a transducer that senses the system output, the feedback transducer must be linear. An example of a proportional feedback control transducer is a linear potentiometer. The voltage output of the potentiometer is proportional to the angular displacement of the shaft, thus providing the proportional output.

The value of using proportional feedback over on-off feedback is that the feedback can take on a continuous range of values and the strength of the correction is proportional to the error in the output. For this reason the error can be reduced to a much smaller value. The need for using deadband is eliminated. Although proportional feedback does improve the system compared to on-off feedback, some offset could still exist, and the effect of nonlinearities, such as backlash, could cause error in the feedback loop.

An example application of proportional feedback control is a temperature controller of a metallurgical heat-treat oven. A servo-controlled valve controls the flow of gas fuel to the combustion chamber. A temperature transducer provides an electrical signal that is proportional to the oven temperature. The prime mover is a motor and gear train combination that provides proportional position control of a gas valve. The nature of the operation is as follows: when new parts are brought into the oven, the oven temperature is subjected to a large disturbance; i.e., the oven temperature decreases greatly. This temperature decrease is sensed by the temperature transducer, which provides a proportionally decreased electrical signal back to the amplifier/comparator. Since the feedback signal is now below the reference signal or setpoint, an error signal is generated that is amplified and fed to the motor. The motor in turn causes the gas valve to open, which increases the temperature in the oven. A block diagram of this control system is shown in Figure 9-13.

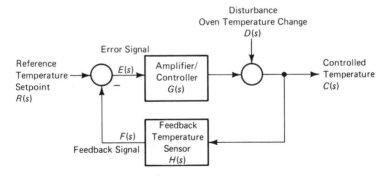

FIGURE 9-13. **Block diagram representation of a temperature control system using proportional feedback**

Proportional Band Control

In practice, it is not practicable to provide a temperature controller that controls temperature over an unlimited range; in fact, the more limited the range of temperature control, the better the sensitivity of the system to the setpoint temperature. An example is as follows: a wide temperature-range system is one that ranges from 200 to 2,000 degrees F. The feedback from the thermocouple ranges from 2 mV to 20 mV. Thus the control system is calibrated such that a change of 100 degrees F is mechanized for a 1-mV feedback change, as shown in Figure 9-14. But if the desired temperature was between 1,750 and 1,850 degrees F, then most of the range of operation would be wasted and the mechanization of the referencing device, the amplifier, the motor, and the gas valve would be such that precise settings in the 100-degree desired range would be very difficult, owing to the lack of sensitivity in this small part of the overall range.

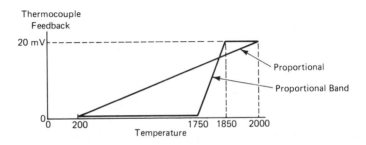

FIGURE 9-14. **Proportional bandwidth feedback**

In response to the problem posed above, instead of using proportional control over all values of the response variable, proportional-band control is used. In this mechanization, the equipment is set up so that the feedback will only be proportional over a designated band of temperatures; outside of that band it will be maximum or minimum, depending on the adjustment needed. By setting up band control, the temperature-reference setting is limited to the band—say 1,750 to 1,850 degrees in this example—but within this band the sensitivity of the setting is much greater and temperatures can be controlled much more precisely for the same gain level. Thus we see that as the band of temperature control is decreased, the gain required for the system can be simultaneously reduced, and yet we can maintain the same precision of control. As a matter of system setup, the actual band limits can be set at the desired values and they can be later adjusted to new values in coordination with adjustments to the amplifier gain and the variable valve limits.

Rate Feedback

Several words to describe rate feedback are used interchangeably; these are rate, derivative, velocity, and tach or tachometric feedback. In the case of proportional or position feedback, the relationship between the controlled variable $c(t)$ and the feedback signal $f(t)$ is

$$f(t) = K_1 \cdot c(t)$$

or in the frequency domain,

$$F(s) = K_1 \cdot C(s)$$

where K_1 is a constant determined in the setup of the feedback loop. In the case where rate feedback is added, the feedback now becomes

$$f(t) = K_1 \cdot c(t) + K_2 \cdot \frac{d}{dt} c(t)$$

or in terms of the frequency-domain variable,

$$F(s) = K_1 \cdot C(s) + K_2 \cdot s \cdot C(s)$$

The need for rate control arises whenever the system information available from position feedback alone does not suffice to provide the desired output response. An example is a motor-driven load where the load has a large moment of inertia. Position feedback will serve to provide an output with relatively small error only if the input does not change rapidly and if there are no rapidly changing disturbances. However, if sudden and large inputs occur or if the output is disturbed dramatically by some external force, then in the recovery process the load will accelerate to a large velocity, and, owing to its inertia, it will coast past its setpoint and reach an extreme considerably beyond the setpoint before it stops; then it will also overshoot in going in the opposite direction, etc. The extent of these overshoots depends on the amount of system gain, load inertia, and system damping. In the case of no system damping, the system oscillations will continue forever without reduction. In the case of limited system damping, the response will be too oscillatory.

A possible solution to this problem is to change the system parameters. In section 9.4, it was stated that an increase in friction caused the system response to become more damped, i.e., the overshoot and number of oscillations would decrease. Thus increasing the viscous friction and thereby the damping would improve the relative stability of the system.

The drawback to increasing damping to improve the relative stability of the system is that the response is greatly slowed and the offset is increased in proportion to the increase of friction. Thus the need for another method of feedback arises. The effect of rate feedback has a very similar effect to using a larger damping coefficient, but it does not alter the speed of the response as greatly and the offset is not affected. These considerations are of great merit alone where rate damping is needed, but one more example provides additional insight into the value of rate feedback.

Consider the case of a Saturn V with its enormous amount of thrust preparing for launch. At the instance of takeoff, all engines are firing and the vertical stabilization provided by the launching tower has been removed—an obvious need exists for a control system that will provide the required relative stability in both the pitch and yaw orientation. With attitudinal position feedback alone, it is clear that the problem given above is present, namely, that the lack of any damping in the orientation will not limit oscillations in angular position and these oscillations may grow with time. It will be boom-boom time. Also, the NASA engineer who suggests that damping should be provided in the form of friction will not win any points, since it is not apparent how to add the damping. The answer to control of this problem is to add rate feedback; with this additional feedback information, not only will the controller be able to reduce the angular position error to near zero, but also the dynamic information of rate-of-change-of-variable will provide the equivalent of damping, which will prevent wild oscillations but without introducing additional offset error. For this reason, rocket controls incorporate both gyro-rate and gyro-position feedback to sense the angular velocity and angular position of rocket ships.

In the case that the value of rate feedback may have been oversold, one should not think of it as being a replacement for position feedback for position control systems. The position feedback is needed for the system to track the position input reference. In the absence of this feedback (consider the above equation with the K_1 term set to zero), the feedback system would become a velocity-control system where the input reference would command rate and not position.

Integral Feedback

In the control of processes and applications where offset is a major consideration, the use of the proportional plus derivative (PPD) controller discussed above is not adequate. The rate feedback is no help in reducing offset, and the proportional feedback can only be used to reduce the offset by increasing the loop gain; however, this has to be traded off against stability problem considerations. A more satisfactory solution to the offset problem is the use of integral feedback. In this case, the integral of the error signal is fed back to the feedback summer. In the case where integral feedback is added to proportional feedback to produce proportional plus integral (PI) feedback, the feedback equation is

$$f(t) = K_1 \bullet c(t) + K_3 \bullet \int c(t) \, dt$$

or in terms of the frequency-domain variable,

$$F(s) = K_1 \bullet C(s) + K_3 \bullet \frac{C(s)}{s}$$

Example 9-4

For the given PI feedback control system shown in Figure 9-15, determine the final value of the error $e(t)$.

Solution.   The error signal $E(s)$ is found from the expression

$$E(s) = \frac{R(s)}{1 + G(s)H(s)} = \frac{\dfrac{1}{s}}{1 + \dfrac{1}{s + 4} \bullet (1 + \dfrac{6}{s})} = \frac{s + 4}{s^2 + 5s + 6}$$

and the time-domain response is found to be

$$e(t) = 2e^{-2t} - 3e^{-3t}$$

(See Appendix.)

The value of the error converges to zero as the time increases. Thus the use of PI feedback reduces the offset error to zero. In the case where the integral feedback is removed (by setting the constant 6 to zero), the offset does not converge to zero. The expression for $e(t)$ in the case of no integral feedback is

$$e(t) = 0.8 - 0.2e^{-4t}$$

Thus the offset is 0.8 when integral feedback is not present.

Integrators cannot be inserted in a circuit without paying a price, namely, the integrator causes a special problem with respect to drift. If even a small dc bias is unavoidably present in the circuit, then there will be a drift away from the desired setpoint as this value is integrated and its effect is increased over time. For this reason, practical PI controllers do not use pure integrators; rather, they use fading memory filters that look like integrators but lose information that has become dated. Such a seemingly sophisticated device is not all that complicated to mechanize; in fact, it can be designed as our old (and well-worn) friend, the RC voltage-divider network. The time constant of this network will be a measure of how long the initial information is stored, since with time the charge on the capacitor will be discharged through the resistor. The length of this memory time for integrating feedback signals is called the *reset rate*, which is inversely related to the time constant. Thus, when the reset rate is high, the integral response will be quickly effected in the loop, and when the reset rate is low, the proportional response will dominate longer in the system response.

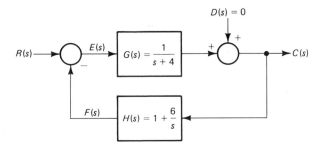

FIGURE 9-15. Block diagram representation of a PI feedback control system

It possibly appears from the previous example that integral feedback could be used solely without proportional feedback without affecting the form of the response. However, the removal of the proportional feedback term decreases the damping in the loop and causes the response to degrade in relative stability. Thus there is a need for position in addition to integral feedback control.

PID Feedback Control

The buzz words of this decade seem to be PID control. Certainly there are people using the expression and possibly selling PID controllers that do not have the familiarity that the student has with the concepts in this title. PID feedback means that the feedback is proportional plus derivative plus integral. It has the form

$$f(t) = K_1 \cdot c(t) + K_2 \cdot \frac{d}{dt} c(t) + K_3 \cdot \int c(t)\, dt$$

or in terms of the frequency-domain variable,

$$F(s) = K_1 \cdot C(s) + K_2 \cdot s \cdot C(s) + K_3 \cdot \frac{C(s)}{s}$$

Hopefully, the justification for going to PID feedback is not just to solve the problem by throwing more terms at it. In comparison to PI control, the addition of rate control would be called for where the disturbances and inputs are large enough that large error signals could be generated, and where the output is not responsive (e.g., large moment of inertia) to changes in the input such that large signal oscillations would be generated. The addition of rate feedback will mitigate the oscillatory nature of the circuit. By the fact that the rate feedback is looking at the rate of change of the variable, it will anticipate the level of the variable in the future and this will reduce the delay or lag that is present and causing the oscillation.

9.7 A Final Example

Now if we go back to our example of the shower, we can relate the kind of control that is being used to set the hot and cold water faucets.

1. If the shower is turned on but no effort is made to set the temperature until the transients have died out, and then the faucets are set to the exact value desired, then the kind of feedback is integral feedback and the controlling motion is to bring the final offset to exact zero.

2. If the shower temperature is monitored as it changes from the ambient value to the desired set value, and the valves are continuously monitored to maintain the water temperature in spite of the changing mixture levels that are needed, then the kind of feedback is proportional feedback to keep the loop error small, but not necessarily zero.

3. If the water temperature and the rate of change of the water temperature is used to continuously adjust the faucet setting, then the kind of feedback is proportional plus derivative feedback. If this effort is successful, then the temperature will be more quickly brought in line.

Needless to say, humans and their sensory and motor systems are far too complex to fit under neat titles of proportional, rate, and integral; nonetheless, there is a close correspondence between these reactions and the human response. Of course we are continuously monitoring the variables around us, such as shower water temperature, and using a range of combinations of control.

The shower example shows the complexity of everyday situations by exhibiting other characteristics that we have discussed.

1. The action of checking the water temperature manifests transport lag. It is an interesting experiment during the time of changing the faucet setting to detect the water temperature close to floor level; by using such a large transport lag, the setting can easily become 180 degrees out of synchronism with the sensing, and the water temperature can oscillate from hot to cold. By sensing the temperature close to the spray head, the transport lag is shortened and the temperature is more easily set.

2. The action of the faucet is such that backlash can be present, especially with worn faucets such that turning the faucet backward has no effect on the water flow until the rotation exceeds the deadspace of the faucet. Certainly saturation is reached when either faucet is turned to its extreme.

3. Loop gain is a little tougher concept to work into this example, but it has to do with the sensitivity of the skin to the water temperature, the human reaction, and the sensitivity of the faucet.

4. Other concepts, such as damping and inertia, also are less transparent in this example since they are principally manifested in the cognitive processes of the human nervous system.

Problems

9.1 Which of the following systems (a–e) are appropriately described by the following system types (1–5)?

  1. discrete-time system
  2. static system
  3. dynamic system
  4. no feedback loop
  5. feedback loop

    a) automobile driver and automobile steering
    b) furnace control for residential heating
    c) classroom lighting
    d) water reservoir control of problem 2.13
    e) programmable controller of fast-changing process

9.2 a) Name two systems that are not feedback systems unless a human is included in the loop.

  b) Name two systems that have feedback as an integral part of the feedback control system.

  c) Identify whether the above four examples are continuous or discrete.

9.3 Name the three necessary functional elements of dynamic control systems.

9.4 For the diagram shown in Figure P9.4, the following parameters are given:

$$G(s) = \frac{15}{s^2 + 4s + 6}, \qquad H(s) = 2, \qquad L(s) = \frac{1}{s(2s + 3)}$$

  a) Determine the transfer function $C(s)/R(s)$ for $D(s) = 0$.

  b) Determine the transfer function $C(s)/D(s)$ for $R(s) = 0$. (*Hint:* The block or blocks between D and C in the forward path are the forward loop gain and the blocks between C and D in the feedback path are the feedback loop gain.)

9.5 Based on the equation that $f = Ma$, or in angular terms $T = Ja$, where T is torque, J is moment of inertia, and a is angular acceleration, it is determined that the velocity of a motor rotor with rotor moment of inertia J is

$$v = \frac{1}{J} \int T \, dt$$

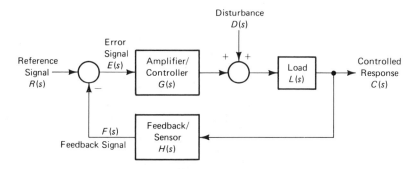

FIGURE P9.4. General block diagram representation of a control system

Assume that $J = 1$. Given that the above integral can be evaluated as the area under the curve for the torque expression, find the imparted motor rotor velocity for the following torque pulses by drawing a sketch of the torque curve (*Hint:* Rectangle) and computing the area under the curve.

a) $T = 1$ Nm for $t = 0$ to 100 sec, $T = 0$ elsewhere.

b) $T = 10$ Nm for $t = 0$ to 10 sec, $T = 0$ elsewhere.

c) $T = 100$ Nm for $t = 0$ to 1 sec, $T = 0$ elsewhere.

d) $T = 1/x$ Nm for $t = 0$ to x sec as x approaches zero, $T = 0$ elsewhere.

9.6 The feedback control system has the transfer functions given below:

$$G(s) = \frac{10}{s^2 + 5s + 6} , \quad H(s) = 3$$

a) Considering the forward loop TF only without feedback, determine if the system response without feedback is oscillatory, and determine the value of ζ and ω_n.

b) Considering the overall transfer function with feedback, determine if the system response with feedback is oscillatory, and determine the value of ζ and ω_n.

9.7 Assume that the transfer functions $G(s)$ and $H(s)$ are expressed as ratios of constants to terms of s:

$$G(s) = \frac{M}{P(s)} , \quad H(s) = \frac{N}{Q(s)}$$

and that the closed-loop system TF $G'(s)$ is given by the expression

$$G'(s) = \frac{G(s)}{1 + G(s)H(s)}$$

a) For the above $G(s)$ and $H(s)$, find $G'(s)$ in terms of M, N, $P(s)$, and $Q(s)$.

b) For the expression found in a, determine the value of $G'(s)$ given that

$$G(s) = \frac{10}{s^2 + 4s + 36}, \quad H(s) = \frac{2}{s}$$

c) Repeat b above for the following expressions:

$$G(s) = \frac{K}{s^2 + 2\zeta\omega_n s + \omega_n^2}, \quad H(s) = 1$$

9.8 For the values of $G(s)$ and $H(s)$ as given here:

$$G(s) = \frac{10}{s^2 + 4s + 36}, \quad H(s) = 2$$

determine the expressions

$$|G'(j\omega)| = \frac{|C(j\omega)|}{|R(j\omega)|}$$

$$\angle G'(j\omega) = \angle C(j\omega) - \angle R(j\omega)$$

9.9 For a feedback control system, the forward-loop TF and feedback TF are

$$G(s) = \frac{K}{s^2 + 12s + 24}, \quad H(s) = 1$$

determine the value of K such that the overall feedback control system will have a damping coefficient of $\zeta = 0.7$.

9.10 Given the overall transfer function

$$G'(s) = \frac{C(s)}{R(s)} = \frac{1}{s + 1}$$

find the output *C(s)* for
a) *r(t)* = unit step input.
b) *r(t)* = unit ramp input.
c) *r(t)* = unit impulse input.
d) *r(t)* = unit sinusoid input.

9.11 A system has the transfer functions

$$G(s) = \frac{20}{s^2 + 5s + 10}, \quad H(s) = 1$$

Determine the damping factor and the damped resonant frequency.
9.12 Repeat 9.11 with *H(s)* = 2.
9.13 Determine which of the following characterizations represent a stable system. Explain your answer.

a) $v(t) = 12e^{2t} \sin 3t$

b) $G(s) = \frac{12}{s^2 - 5s + 6}, \quad H(s) = 1$

c) $\zeta = -0.6$

d) oscillator

e) $\zeta = 0.707$

9.14 a) Name four nonlinear effects and describe when (if at all) they may be desirable.
   b) Name six kinds and/or combinations of kinds of feedback control. Write the time-domain and frequency-domain representation of each.

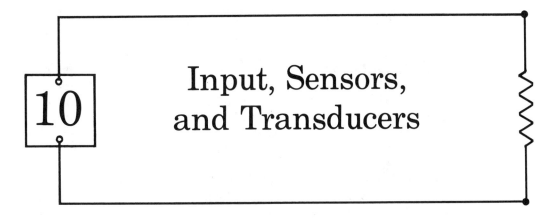

Input, Sensors, and Transducers

10

10.0 Introduction

The next three chapters are concerned with the implementation of the control systems that were discussed in Chapter 9. Figure 10-1 illustrates this implementation by showing the relationship of the three major aspects of a control system.

As pointed out in the introductory chapter of this text, the first component of the system is the sensor. The word *sensor* is used synonymously with the words *transducer, measuring device,* and *input device.* An example in the automobile literature is a temperature sensor called a *temperature transmitter unit*; this sensor is essentially a resistor whose resistance is temperature-dependent. A sensor provides a measure of the physical quantity of interest in a usable form in that it produces an analog of the quantity. For example, a thermostat provides an electrical signal that is a measure of the controlled temperature. This chapter presents sensor principles and examines particular sensor types.

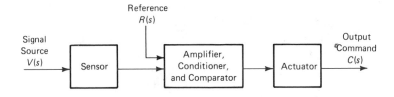

FIGURE 10-1. Symbolic representation of control system components

Following the sensor in Figure 10-1 is the amplifier. The signal from the sensor must be amplified, conditioned, and compared with the desired setting *R(s)*. The amplifier, conditioner, and comparator are the subject of Chapter 11. Finally, the actuator—also called the prime mover, the final correcting device, and the final controller element—converts the amplified signal from the amplifier to an output to provide the desired outcome; actuators are the subject of Chapter 12.

The control components for Figure 10-1 can be arranged in a feedback control configuration by feeding the output *C(s)* back to the input *V(s)*. In the case where the input to the sensor is identically the same as the output, namely,

$$V(s) = C(s)$$

then the feedback is called *proportional feedback*. Other feedback types such as on-off, integral, and/or derivative feedback may be used. Another necessary element for an operational feedback system is the reference or setpoint *R(s)*. The reference is provided to the comparator to provide an error signal that is dependent upon the difference between the feedback signal *V(s)* and the setpoint signal *R(s)*.

10.1 Properties of Transducers

A transducer (sensor, input device, etc.) is defined as a device that converts energy from one form to another. Electrical signals are often advantageous when compared to other forms, such as pneumatic or fluidic signals; thus, electrical transducers are common. An example of an electrical transducer is a potentiometer where the shaft position input determines the signal voltage output.

A thermostat is a sensor example where the temperature input determines the electrical signal transmitted to the furnace. This transducer may be on-off as in the case of a residential furnace control, or it may be proportional as in the case of the automotive temperature transmitter unit (assuming that a temperature gauge [meter] is used as the output device as opposed to using an "idiot" light).

The selection of a transducer (sensor, input device, etc.) is based on several criteria including sensitivity, linearity, repeatability, speed, resolution, range, offset, signal form, durability, and cost. These are defined on the following pages.

Sensitivity. Sensitivity is the ratio of the change in the output to the change in the input. High sensitivity in a transducer is desirable in that it provides amplification. For example, if the output of a sensor varies from 0 to 10 V over its operating range, then less amplification is required than is necessary for a similar sensor that provides a 0 to 10 mV output.

Linearity. Linearity is the proportionality of the output to the input. For example, if doubling the input causes the output also to be doubled, then the sensor is linear. Obviously, saturation will set in as input is increased and the point will be reached where the system is no longer linear, but if the transducer is linear over the operating range of input, then it is considered to be linear. Linearity is generally a desirable feature with the exception that special designs may call for designing a certain nonlinearity into a transducer.

Repeatability. Repeatability is a measure of the ability of the sensor to have the same output for each operation, a desirable feature. For example, if the oven temperature is increased a set amount, then it is desirable that the temperature transducer provide a repeatable measure of this increase. The reason for needing repeatability is so that accuracy in control will not be lost from one operation to the next.

Speed. The speed of a transducer is a measure of the ability of the output to respond instantly to the input. It is inversely related to the delay or time constant of the transducer. Some transducers may have a response that has a large time constant, or the implementation of the transducer may cause the transducer response to have a large time constant. For example, if a temperature sensor is mounted to a large framework member of an oven, then the reaction time would be slower than if it were placed inside the oven environment. For implementing an effective control system, a fast reaction time is generally desirable, since long delays cause the system to be less stable and less responsive.

Resolution. Resolution is a measure of the precision of the output's correspondence to the input; that is, it is the amount of input required to produce a change in output. If the output does not track small but significant changes in the input, then the resolution is described as being poor. Another example of resolution is a potentiometer where the input is the movement of the wiper across the turns of wire and the output is the electrical voltage change as the wiper moves from wire to wire. The resolution is less than perfect because small movements of the wiper do not change the output, since no new turn of wire is contacted. The effect of potentiometer resolution error in a feedback control system is that the discrete steps in the output of the potentiometer will cause the controller to constantly seek the null point where the feedback error signal goes to zero, but due to the resolution error in the potentiometer, the system will constantly "hunt" for the proper output value. The word "hunt" means that the output of the control system will be constantly changing over a small part of its range in an effort to provide the exact feedback through the brush wiper.

Range. The range of the transducer is the measure of the extent to which the transducer can convert input variations to an electrical signal. Most transducers show saturation when they are used outside of their normal range of operation. An example is that a Bourdon tube may be used to measure pressures from 0 to 15 psi. If used outside of this range, say at 20 psi, its mechanical limits will be exceeded. Thus, it is important to match the measurement range to the sensor range and to select a transducer that has a range that is adequate for the application.

Offset. The offset of a transducer is the nonzero output of the transducer for zero input. Offset causes the output to be nonlinear. One example of a phenomenon that causes offset is *hysteresis*. The output curve for hysteresis is shown in Chapter 9. Offset is undesirable in that usually it is desired that the output be zero when the input is zero. Zero adjustment for transmitters are provided to correct for offset.

Signal Form. The signal form designates the waveform of the input and output of the transducer. For example a control transformer cannot operate on dc signals. On the other hand, a d'Arsonval meter cannot operate on ac signals. Other waveforms are chopped dc signals and modulated carrier signals for amplification, squarewave frequency for speed pickup, and pulse-duration for density measurement.

Durability. Durability is a measure of the lifetime of a component. The useful life may be less than the physical life in that it may become less repeatable or degrade in some other performance parameter even though it continues to operate. Another consideration is the ruggedness of the component. For example, transistors are more durable than vacuum tubes to mechanical vibrations (but possibly less durable to nuclear radiation).

Cost. All of the above criteria have to be measured against the cost of the transducer. For large-volume or low-budget designs, the cost may turn out to be the most stringent criteria of all.

Other Criteria. Obviously, the most difficult job in selecting a transducer is foreseeing the unknown and performing a careful analysis of the particular application. The selection may depend on some criteria that is not apparent early in the design of the control system. Additional criteria that may turn out to be important are weight, size, reliability, appearance, noise susceptibility, heat generation, noise generation, etc. The list is limited only by the number of requirements for satisfying the application.

Transducers can be classified by the kind of phenomena that they are measuring. Some of the most prominent are listed in Table 10-1.

TABLE 10-1. Classes of Transducers

PHYSICAL PHENOMENA	EXAMPLE OF TRANSDUCER
Position	Potentiometer, LVDT, microsyn, gyroscope
Velocity	Tachometer
Acceleration	Accelerometer
Temperature	Thermocouple, thermistor, RTD
Pressure	Bourdon tube, bellows, piezoresistive ICs
Force	Strain gauge, load cell
Flow rate	Pitot tube
Humidity	Hygrometer
Proximity	Capacitance probe, Hall effect device
Light intensity	Photocells
pH	pH probe
Density	Gravitometer
Thickness	Ultrasound

10.2 Transmitters

Transducers are rarely directly coupled to control circuitry, due to the weakness of the signal generated by most transducers and the need for a controlled output that corresponds to a small segment of the transducer's total range. In addition, a standard voltage or current is not always possible from various devices, thus requiring extensive variation in control circuit interface design. In addition, electrical and magnetic radiation may interfere with the signal. The signal transmitter such as is used in industry and other harsh environments combats these problems. It incorporates a dc-coupled, low-noise amplifier with adjustable operating point (zero) and gain (span) controls. By adjusting this amplifier circuit to provide a given output signal for the minimum value physical input and a predefined maximum value for the largest physical input value of interest, a wide variety of transducers can be interfaced to the same control circuits and connected at a distance far from the controls themselves.

The standard values for minimum and maximum signal levels vary with the industry involved, but the following values are common:

4-20 Milliamperes

1-5 Volts

10-50 Milliamperes

0-10 Volts

2.5-15 Volts

To aid in detection of a failed transducer, defective amplifier, or cable, the low values are generally not zero values of current and voltage. The 1- to 5-volt standard grew out of the common practice of using a series resistor in a current loop to develop a signal for the input to a voltage-operated control circuit. The resistor had to be a small value to reduce the effect of electrical noise in the environment, and therefore a 250-ohm 1 percent device is used, producing 1-5 volts for a 4-20 mA current loop.

The transmitter is calibrated in the field, both at installation and during preventive maintenance. This is most often accomplished by manufacturing the amplifier and transducer together in a single package with multi-turn potentiometers as a part of the assembly. To calibrate the transmitter, a minimum physical value is applied to the transmitter and the "zero" potentiometer is adjusted to give the zero output reading out of the transmitter; then the maximum physical value of interest is applied to the transmitter and the "span" is adjusted. Since this is really a gain adjustment, the zero is also affected and the procedure must be repeated until both maximum and minimum values are correct. Special algorithms have been developed to reduce the number of iterations required.

FIGURE 10-2. An assortment of potentiometers

10.3 Potentiometers

One of the most common and easiest to use transducers is the potentiometer. An assortment of potentiometers is shown in Figure 10-2. A potentiometer is a three-terminal, variable resistor that is commonly used as a voltage divider, as shown in Figure 10-3. The output of the potentiometer is the voltage V. When the potentiometer is used as a position feedback device, the input is mechanical position θ, which can vary from 0 to 1, i.e., 0 percent to 100 percent. In the case of a one-turn potentiometer, this would correspond to its full range of rotation, roughly from 0 to 350 degrees. Similar comparisons can be made for ten-turn and rectilinear potentiometers. The supply voltage V_s may look like an input, but for this purpose it is not the input of interest; it is a bias supply that provides the power to this transducer, and the level of bias will determine the sensitivity of the output voltage to the input angular change.

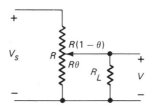

FIGURE 10-3. A potentiometer with a load

Potentiometer Transfer Function and Loading

First the relationship between the voltage V and the supply voltage V_s is considered. In the case that the potentiometer is not loaded, the TF is $V/V_s = \theta$, where θ is the angular shaft position, normalized to the range from zero to one. With respect to the transfer function V/θ, the relationship is

$$\frac{V}{\theta} = V_s \tag{10-1}$$

Thus the relationship is a proportionality between the output V and the input θ, namely, the constant V_s.

In the case that the potentiometer is loaded by the equivalent load resistor R_L, then the TF becomes the voltage division between the parallel combination of R_L and $R\theta$ and the rest of the potentiometer resistor $R(1 - \theta)$:

$$\frac{V}{V_s} = \frac{R \cdot \theta \cdot R_L / (R \cdot \theta + R_L)}{R \cdot \theta \cdot L / (R \cdot \theta + R_L) + R(1 - \theta)} =$$

$$\frac{R \cdot \theta \cdot R_L}{R \cdot \theta \cdot L + (R \cdot \theta + R_L)R(1 - \theta)} =$$

$$\frac{\theta}{\theta + (1 + R \cdot \theta / R_L)(1 - \theta)} \quad (10\text{-}2)$$

Let the R/R_L ratio be called b, and (10-2) can be reduced to

$$\frac{V}{V_s} = \frac{\theta}{1 + b \cdot \theta(1 - \theta)} \quad (10\text{-}3)$$

Now the relationship between the output V and the input θ can be found as

$$\frac{V}{\theta} = \frac{V_s}{1 + b(1 - \theta)} \quad (10\text{-}4)$$

Analysis of (10-4) shows the following:

1. The sensitivity of the TF is proportional to the bias supply value V_s.

2. If the loading is reduced to zero, i.e., decrease b to zero by increasing R_L to infinity, then the relationship for the loaded potentiometer becomes the same as that for the unloaded potentiometer, namely, $V/\theta = V_s$.

3. In the case that b is large, then the relationship between V and θ becomes nonlinear, and the V versus θ curve is parabolic, as shown in Figure 10-4.

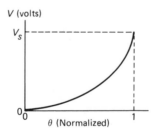

FIGURE 10-4. Transfer function curve of potentiometer output

The difference between the unloaded output V_u and the loaded output V_L is a measure of the loading error.

$$E = V_u - V_L = V_s \bullet \theta - \frac{V_s \bullet \theta}{1 + b \bullet \theta(1 - \theta)} =$$
$$\frac{V_s \bullet \theta \bullet b \bullet \theta(1 - \theta)}{1 + b \bullet \theta(1 - \theta)} \qquad (10\text{-}5)$$

Although the error voltage can be derived from (10-5) for any given value of loading, a rule of thumb is that the ratio of the load resistance to the pot resistance should not be less than 10, i.e., $b < 1/10$. Another consideration is that the pot resistance R cannot necessarily be decreased to meet this criteria, since it in turn may overload the source supplying it with voltage. If source loading is a problem, then it may be necessary to install a buffer in the form of an operational amplifier to provide the proper impedance matching.

Potentiometer Linearity

Another consideration in potentiometer analysis and evaluation is the question of how well the unloaded potentiometer transfer function fits within a set of linearity limits over the range of its operation, as shown in Figure 10.5. Linearity specifications range up to 5 percent at the high end. For precision wire-wound models, the linearity may be as low as 0.01 percent. When the linearity is described by the deviation from a straight line extending from the origin to the $(1, V_s)$ coordinate, the linearity specification is called *ohmic linearity*. Other kinds of linearity are used that do not specify that the end points must be identified in this manner, but instead specify the deviation around the end-point resistance of the potentiometer.

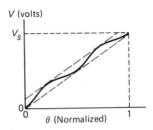

FIGURE 10-5. Transfer function curve of potentiometer output linearity

Potentiometer Resolution

Wire-wound potentiometers suffer from lack of continuity of output as a function of shaft rotation. Although it would appear that this problem could be solved by using carbon pots, it must be realized that they are not nearly as linear and cannot handle nearly the power that the wire-wound ones can; thus the resolution problem is the lesser evil. This step change in voltage ouput, called dV, is determined by the number of turns of wire N; the resolution error can be seen to be

$$R = \frac{dV}{V_s} = \frac{V_s/N}{V_s} = 1/N \tag{10-6}$$

Thus, the resolution error is inversely related to the number of turns of wire. The advantage of using a ten-turn pot (ten turns of rotation, not of wire) can be seen since the resolution error may be made as small as 0.05 percent. Another ameliorating effect is that the brush moves from one wire to another while sitting on several wire turns simultaneously; thus, the resolution is actually less than the calculated resolution from the above equation. The hunting problem that resolution error causes in control systems has already been explained under the description of resolution.

The stepless potentiometer, consisting of one length of high-resistance wire, reduces the resolution error to zero. Although this device has other inherent problems such as power limitations, impedance matching, and wear, it is a solution to the hunting problem.

Other Potentiometer Properties

Examples of additional properties that are important in potentiometer applications follow.

Compensation for loading may be realized by the use of a compensation resistor connected between a tap at the two-thirds point and the unity transfer point of the pot. Manufacturing methods can be used to introduce additional compensation for special applications.

Special potentiometer functions, such as sinusoidal generators, dividers, etc., can be realized by manufacturing nonlinear mandrels on which the windings are placed. Conformity is used to measure the tolerance of the nonlinear pot as opposed to linearity for the linear pot.

Here is a brief discussion of the mechanics of the potentiometer. The working part of the pot is the brush. The brush action wiping on the wire-wound mandrel is responsible for its operation, but it is also responsible for the drawbacks of a potentiometer. One is that a great deal of noise is generated by the operation of this brush-wiper action. Another is that to assure adequate contact between the brush and the wire turns, a spring force must be placed on the brush, such that a fair amount of torque is required to rotate the pot shaft, nominally on the order of 2 to 5 ounce-inches. Another consideration is that while resolution can be improved by the use of fine wire, this possibility must be traded off against the problem of wear of fine wire by the brush and the increased loading of the higher resistance of the fine wire.

Another consideration is that the lifetime of the pot is finite and the useful lifetime may be even more limited as the contact action deteriorates (similar to that commonly observed on the volume control of radios and TVs). The standard lifetime of a pot is one million operations. This lifetime may seem large for a hand-operated pot, but it is limited when the pot is used in a servo that is continuously driving it, so that the lifetime is reached within a few months or years.

The merit of potentiometer applications is that they are available in a wide range of sizes and costs, and are low cost and lightweight. In addition, no special supplies or circuits are required to use them, and as opposed to electromagnetic transducers, they can be used in either ac or dc circuits.

10.4 Electromagnetic Position Sensors

The previously stated problems of potentiometers—limited lifetime, limited sensitivity, and resolution error—are bypassed by the use of electromagnetic position sensors. These electromagnetic sensors include angular position sensors, such as microsyns, and linear position sensors, such as linear variable differential trasformers (LVDTs) and E-type transformers.

E-Type Transformers

The E-type transformer is the most easily understood. An electrical diagram of its features is shown in Figure 10-6.

The principle of the E-type transformer is that the strength of the magnetic coupling between the supply winding V_s and the output windings V_1 and V_2 is proportional to the displacement of the magnetic bar that carries the magnetic flux between the wings of the "E." When the bar is moved in the upward direction, the V_2 voltage is decreased in proportion to the displacement; correspondingly, when the bar is moved downward, the V_1 voltage is decreased in strength. The net effect is shown in Figure 10-7.

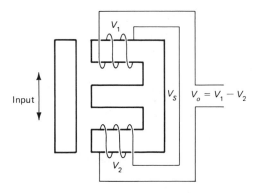

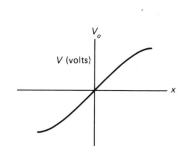

FIGURE 10-6. A diagram of an E-type   FIGURE 10-7. Transfer function
           transformer   curve of E-type trans-
                                                    former output

      The significance of the negative-going voltage (in the third
quadrant) in Figure 10-7 is that when the shunting bar is lower than
the mid position, V_2 exceeds V_1, in which case the output voltage V_0 is
reversed in polarity. Keeping in mind that the working voltage with
this transformer is ac, then the various output levels as represented by
the figure correspond to ac voltages and negative voltages signify
voltages with 180 degrees of phase shift.
      The LVDT is essentially if not synonymously the same, al-
though various manufacturers provide various designs and styles.
An example is shown in Figure 10-8.

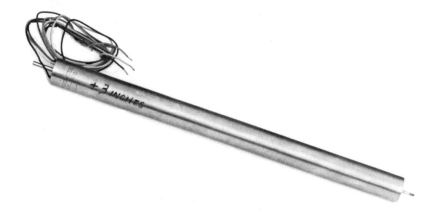

FIGURE 10-8. Illustration of an LVDT

FIGURE 10-9. Illustration of microsyn

Microsyns

The E-type transformer and the LVDT denote transducers to transform from rectilinear displacement to ac voltage, although in some instances the same terms are used for conversion from angular displacement to ac voltage.

On the other hand, the microsyn provides a translation from rotational displacement to electrical voltage. The microsyn employs a dumbell-shaped rotor and a stator consisting of two pairs of poles with primary and secondary windings located symmetrically around its circumference, as shown in Figure 10-9.

The output can be varied from the maximum negative coupling through zero to the maximum positive coupling. At the zero-coupling point, the flux in the secondary winding due to one winding is exactly cancelled by the flux component due to the other winding. Deviations from this neutral coupling point cause a change in voltage, either negative or positive, on the order of one-half volt per degree.

Properties of Electromagnetic Transducers

Two features are mentioned here. One is that the implementation of electromagnetic transducers into the system requires that the signal be ac. The use of ac is generally favorable with regard to the power amplifier section of the system, since ac signals are free from both drift and the difficult coupling problems associated with direct coupling. On the other hand, the use of ac can present a serious problem in the final correcting element due to the limited power output of ac prime movers such as two-phase motors. Alternative approaches, such as the use of modulators and demodulators, can circumvent this problem, but at the expense of increasing the system complexity. Thus the trade-off between ac and dc components in servo systems is important in determining the transducer, the amplifier, and the actuator.

When properly qualified by the above observation regarding ac versus dc operation, it can be said that the electromagnetic transducer is superior to the potentiometer, since it provides a much higher voltage/displacement gradient. For example, if 35 volts is imposed across a potentiometer that has 350 degrees of rotation, then the voltage gradient would be about 0.1 volts per degree of rotation. Using higher voltages would be impracticable and would impose excessive voltage and power requirements on the potentiometer. On the other hand, voltage gradients of 0.5 to 1.0 volts per degree can be expected from electromagnetic transducers over their range of operation.

The transfer function of the potentiometer and the electromagnetic transducer is frequently idealized in that it is treated as a constant, e.g., 0.5 volt per degree. If the transducer has such significant mechanical friction or inertia that these quantities must be considered, then they may be lumped in with the friction and inertia of the load, e.g., radar antenna, hydraulic valve, etc. In other cases, the transducer loading may be negligible.

10.5 Temperature Measurements

The three most common instrumentation transducers to measure temperature are the thermocouple, the thermistor, and the resistive temperature detector (RTD). As opposed to a thermometer, these devices have an electrical output that can be amplified and used in a control system.

Thermocouple Transducers

The thermocouple temperature measurement is based on the principle that a junction consisting of two dissimilar metals will generate an electromotive force (emf) that is approximately proportional to the temperature of the junction. The generation of this millivolt-level voltage is called the *Seebeck effect*. A more useful form than the junction only is to join the respective ends of two dissimilar metal wires to form a loop, and then the net emf in the loop can be found from the expression

$$V_{net} = V_{junction\ 1} - V_{junction\ 2} \qquad\qquad (10\text{-}7)$$

Since thermocouples are frequently used to measure high temperatures such as ovens and furnaces, it is common to speak of one junction as being the subject temperature junction and the other as being the reference temperature junction or cold junction. In this terminology, the (10-7) becomes

$$V_{net} = V_{hot\ junction} - V_{cold\ junction} \tag{10-8}$$

In other words, the net emf is proportional to the difference in the temperatures of the two junctions.

As an example, consider a thermocouple junction that produces 55 mV emf at 2000 degrees F and 11 mV at 32 degrees F. The voltage produced by such a thermocouple using the 32 degrees F junction as the reference junction in (10-8) is

$$V_{net} = 55\ mV - 11\ mV = 44\ mV$$

The table of thermocouple emfs would thus show that this thermocouple produces 44 mV at 2000 degrees F, given that the reference junction temperature is 32 degrees F.

An example of the use of a thermocouple measurement system used to measure furnace temperature is shown in Figure 10-10. By placing one junction, called the *hot junction*, in contact with the object to be measured (such as the wall of a furnace) and the other junction, called the *cold junction*, at a known and probably less-high temperature, then placing a voltmeter in the loop, the voltmeter reading should be proportional to the difference between the hot and cold temperatures. The above system would provide a monitoring system for the furnace temperature.

The next step in implementing a control system is to replace the d'Arsonval voltmeter with an instrumentation voltmeter that could provide an assortment of signal-processing features (including

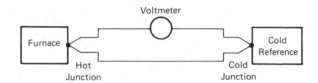

FIGURE 10-10. Example of thermocouple measurement of furnace temperature

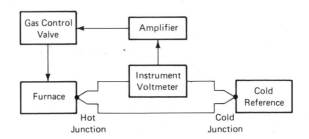

**FIGURE 10-11. Example of thermocouple control of
furnace temperature**

analog-to-digital conversion for computer monitoring and processing
if so desired), so that the output could be used to control the power flow
to an electric heater or to control the position to a gas valve. The final
outcome would be the control of the furnace temperature. A combination circuit diagram and block diagram of such a temperature control
system is shown in Figure 10-11. The block diagram of the temperature control system is shown in Figure 10-12.

The temperature control of the cold junction is important in
measuring temperatures. For approximate measurements, it may
suffice to assume that room temperature is 75 degrees F and the
reference will be set accordingly. However, if the ambient (room) temperature changes, then the furnace temperature will be affected. For
example, let us assume that the furnace control is operating so that
the furnace temperature is at the point set by the reference with zero
error. If the ambient temperature is increased, then the generated emf
is decreased, as shown by the thermocouple equation above. Then the
error signal, which is the difference between the setpoint and the net
emf from the thermocouple transducer, will increase, since

$$Error = Reference - Thermocouple\ emf \tag{10-9}$$

or

$$E(s) = R(s) - T(s) \tag{10-10}$$

With the increase in error signal, the furnace temperature will
increase correspondingly to the ambient temperature increase. Thus,
cold-junction temperature control is important to temperature control.

Several methods are available to account for the cold-junction
temperature. One is to use room temperature as the reference, as

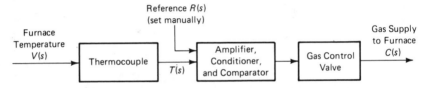

FIGURE 10-12. Block diagram of furnace temperature control

mentioned above. The advantage of this method is that it is simple; the corresponding disadvantage is that it is only as accurate as the room temperature is close to the originally set temperature.

Another method of cold-junction reference is to use 32 degrees F (0 degrees C), by using an ice-water reference, which is more accurate but also more cumbersome. This method is used often in scientific laboratory work where ice is readily available and precision is required.

Another method of cold-junction reference is to measure the ambient temperature and consult with a table to look up the subject temperature based on the thermocouple potentiometer measurement. This method is time consuming when done manually, but it can be used in microprocessor work if the table is stored in semiconductor memory. It is often used in scientific work.

The method that is most usable and is reasonably precise is to design a temperature-compensating resistor into the thermocouple circuit, such as a thermistor. The principle of this self-compensating circuit is that the compensating resistor changes in resistance value as the temperature increases in a manner that offsets the effect of the cold-junction emf change. An example of such a circuit is shown in Figure 10-13.

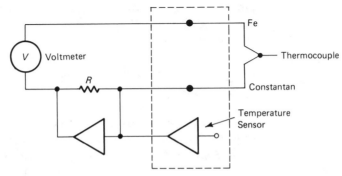

FIGURE 10-13. A self-compensating thermocouple circuit

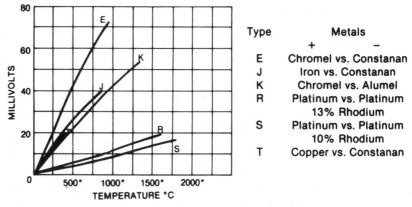

Type	Metals	
	+	–
E	Chromel vs. Constanan	
J	Iron vs. Constanan	
K	Chromel vs. Alumel	
R	Platinum vs. Platinum	
	13% Rhodium	
S	Platinum vs. Platinum	
	10% Rhodium	
T	Copper vs. Constanan	

Courtesy Omega Engineering

FIGURE 10-14. Transfer function curve of thermocouple output

Thermocouples come in a variety of materials and characteristics. Some of the common ones are the E type (chromel-constantan), the J type (iron constantan), the K type (chromel alumel), and the R type (platinum-rhodium). These and other commonly used thermocouples have been calibrated for voltage versus temperature characteristics. Tables of characteristics for each of these thermocouples are published as industrial standards. The voltage versus temperature curves are essentially proportional curves, as represented in Figure 10-14.

Although the voltage-to-temperature relation is not linear enough for exact measurement without extensive linearization, the transfer function of the thermocouple as represented by the above curves can be approximated as a simple constant, e.g., 30 mV/1000 degrees F. The transfer function of the overall temperature sensing system typically has an exponential delay function due to the thermal inertia in the measured element and the thermocouple. An example of the transfer function is

$$G(s) = \frac{K}{Ts + 1} \tag{10-11}$$

where K is the constant mentioned above and T is the time constant consisting of the ratio of the thermal inertia per thermal resistance. The thermal delay also depends on the method of attaching the thermocouple to the measured element and the quality of the attachment.

An illustration of the variety of thermocouple transducers is provided in Figure 10-15.

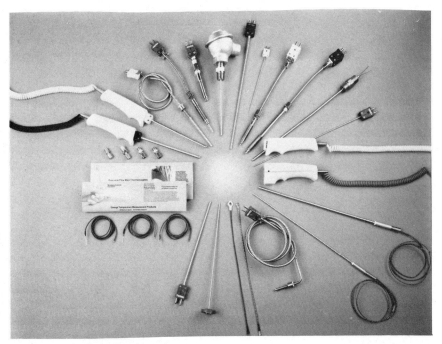

Courtesy Omega Engineering

FIGURE 10-15. Variety of thermocouple transducers

Thermistor Transducers

Thermistors are made from metal oxides and are typically manufactured as small discs or small beads, called *bead thermistors,* as illustrated in Figure 10-16.

The principle of operation of the thermistor is that its resistance changes as the temperature changes. Both positive and negative temperature-coefficient thermistors are available. The term negative temperature-coefficient means that the resistance of the thermistor decreases as the temperature increases; conversely, positive temperature-coefficient means the resistance increases as the temperature increases. The negative temperature-coefficient thermistor is the most common. A typical temperature range is from −0 to 800 degrees F, with a typical sensitivity of negative 80 percent resistance change for a 100-degree temperature change.

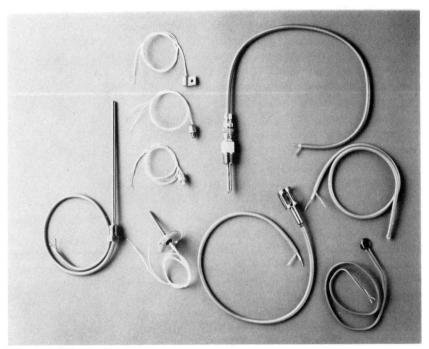

Courtesy Omega Engineering

FIGURE 10-16. Variety of thermistor transducers

The use of a thermistor in a control circuit would typically require that the circuit be designed so that the output would increase proportionally to the increase in temperature, although the thermistor would be decreasing in resistance value. One circuit that provides such a characteristic is a *bridge circuit* with the subject thermistor forming one leg of the balanced bridge, as shown in Figure 10-17. With a change in temperature, the bridge output changes correspondingly.

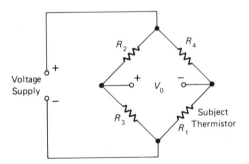

FIGURE 10-17. Thermistor temperature control circuit

RTD Transducers

A resistive temperature detector (RTD) is composed of metals, such as nickel, copper, and platinum. Since the resistance of metals increases with temperature, RTDs have a positive temperature coefficient. RTDs are used similarly to thermistors, but they have the advantage of having a wider temperature range of up to 2,000 degrees F; however they have the disadvantage of being less sensitive to a temperature change, with a typical sensitivity of positive 40 percent resistance change for a 100-degree temperature change. Figure 10-18 shows a variety of RTD transducers.

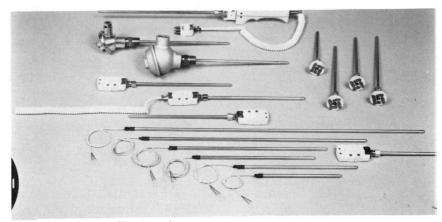

Courtesy Omega Engineering

FIGURE 10-18. Variety of RTD transducers

10.6 Strain Gage Transducers

The strain gage transducer (SGT) is used to measure force. The operating principle is that the strain gage changes in resistance as it changes its physical dimensions. This dimension change is caused by the dimension change of the parent or subject material to which the SGT is bonded. The cause of the dimension change is an applied force and/or torque, resulting in stress being applied to the subject material with consequential strain, for which this transducer is named. Applications for strain gage transducers include strain measurements on pressure vessels, torque shafts, and load cells. The advantages of SGTs are that they are small, lightweight, and often uniquely applicable to the application. An illustration of several SGTs is shown in Figure 10-19.

SGTs are made of a conductor (such as a copper-nickel alloy) bonded to mounting paper and laid in a zigzag pattern. The mounting

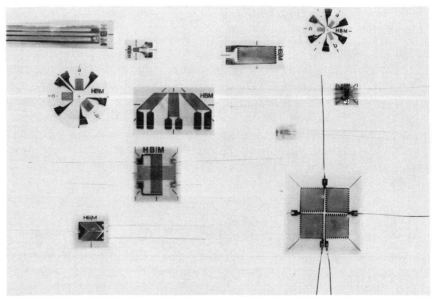

Courtesy Omega Engineering

FIGURE 10-19. Illustration of strain gages

paper is bonded to the subject material by means of cement so that any change in the dimension of the material will be reflected in the zigzag conductor strip. By virtue of the material being subject to tension, it will stretch, in accordance with Hooke's Law, at least over a range of force. Thus, the material will elongate in proportion to this tension, with the proportionality constant being the product of Young's modulus of elasticity of the material and the cross-sectional area of the material. The layout of the zigzag of the conductor is such that the conductor will be subjected to the greatest length change when the elongation due to the applied force is along the same axis as that designated for the conductor, as illustrated in Figure 10-20. Since the resistance R of the conductor depends on its cross-sectional area A, the length l, and the resistivity constant ρ, the relationship is

$$R = \frac{\rho \bullet l}{A} \tag{10-12}$$

Under the force of tension, l is increased and A is decreased, which produces an increase in resistance. Under the force of compression, l is decreased and A is increased, which produces a decrease in resistance. Typical changes are on the order of a few percent. The sensitivity of the SGT is referred to as the *gage factor G,* which is the ratio of the per-unit resistance change to the strain. Since strain is the

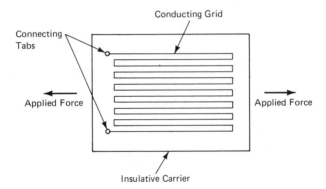

FIGURE 10-20. Schematic of a strain gage transducer

per-unit length change, the gage factor is given by the expression

$$G = \frac{dR/R}{dL/L} \tag{10-13}$$

where L is the overall length of the subject material and dL and dR are the incremental changes in length and resistance, respectively. Thus, gage factor is the ratio of the per-unit resistance change to the per-unit length change of the subject material. A typical value of gage factor is 2.

The transfer function (TF) of the SGT is defined as the ratio of the per-unit resistance change to the applied force F:

$$TF = \frac{dR}{R} F \tag{10-14}$$

In terms of gage factor, this means that the above TF can be written

$$TF = G \frac{dL}{L} F \tag{10-15}$$

The ratio of dL/L is of special significance in mechanics of materials: it is called the *strain*. The relationship between the strain on the material and the applied force-per-unit cross-sectional area is given as

$$F/A = Y \frac{dL}{L} \tag{10-16}$$

The proportionality constant Y is Young's modulus of elasticity of the subject material. Substituting the above into the expression for the strain gage yields

$$TF = G \cdot Y \cdot A \tag{10-17}$$

Thus, the strain gage transfer function of per-unit resistance change

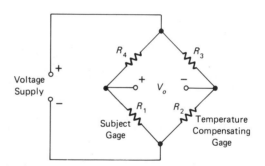

FIGURE 10-21. Strain gage bridge circuit

to force applied is the product of gage factor G, Young's modulus for the subject material Y, and the subject material cross-sectional area A.

Usually the strain gage is wired as a leg of a bridge network with another temperature-compensating gage, called the *dummy gage,* used in the adjacent leg of the bridge, as shown in Figure 10-21.

For a balanced bridge, the opposite leg products are equal:

$$R1 \cdot R3 = R2 \cdot R4 \tag{10-18}$$

and the output $V_0 = 0$. Any temperature change of the strain gage $R1$ does not affect the output, since the bridge remains balanced due to $R2$ changing correspondingly.

Another bridge configuration uses strain gages in electrically opposing legs that are mounted physically opposite each other on the subject material so that the electrical effect of a physical change is multiplied. This configuration also requires that two dummy gages be placed in the other legs for temperature compensation.

The bridge output can be shown to be proportional to the change in the subject resistor, assuming that once the bridge is balanced, no other resistances change. The transfer function of the overall strain gage circuit is the ratio of the voltage V_0 to the force applied and is given as

$$TF = V_0/F = K \cdot G \cdot Y \cdot A \tag{10-19}$$

where K is the proportionality constant of the bridge.

10.7 Pressure Transducers

Pressure transducers generally provide an electrical output. This output is related to the pressure applied to the pressure-sensitive element: the output may be proportional to the pressure or it may be some special function of the pressure, such as an on-off function. In the case of the pressure switch, the electrical output is simply an on or off condition of a set of contacts determined by whether the pressure is above or below the threshold level setting of the pressure switch. In continuous control systems, it is desired that the output be proportional to the pressure. Figure 10-22 shows an assortment of pressure transducers. Pressure transducers include the *Bourdon tube,* the *bellow type,* the *piezoresistive type,* and the *capacitive cell.*

The Bourdon Tube

The most commonly used pressure-sensing device is the Bourdon tube. It works on the principle that pressure applied to the oval cross section of the tube causes the tube to change to a more nearly circular cross section. This change causes the tube to straighten along its length. By connecting the tip to a mechanism that magnifies and controls the amount of movement of the output linkage, the desired level of mechanical output motion is achieved.

The output of a Bourdon tube can be a dial for purposes of manually monitoring pressures, or it can be another transducer, such

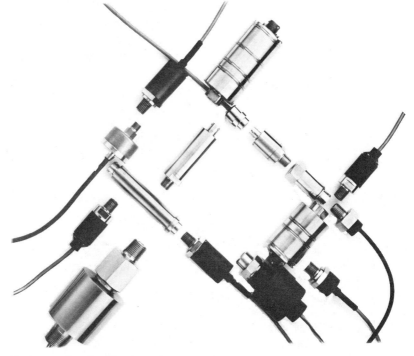

Courtesy Omega Engineering

FIGURE 10-22. An assortment of pressure transducers

as an LVDT to convert the energy to an electrical output so the electrical signal can be used ultimately to control the pressure.

The Bellows

Bellows have a better sensitivity to low pressures than Bourdon tubes. Whereas Bourdon tubes are only sensitive as low as 15 psi, bellows can be used to 3 psi or lower. Bellows consist of a series of diaphragms that are connected together and then connected in turn to an output device. When the pressure is altered, it causes the bellows to change shape and provide a mechanical output. This mechanical output can be used to provide a metered output for manual operation or an instrumentation output for automatic operation.

The Piezoresistive Sensor

Pressure can be measured by the principle of piezoresistive changes. The principle of operation of the piezoresistive sensor is based on the fact that the monolithic silicon chip is etched out to form a diaphragm. The pressure on this silicon diaphragm causes the electrical output. By using this chip in a bridge configuration and by providing the amplification possible in an integrated circuit, it is possible to provide an output voltage that is proportional to the applied pressure. The signal-out has to be conditioned and buffered. Piezoresistive pressure sensors come in miniature sizes, such as those contained in a TO-5 package. Figure 10-23 shows a piezoresistive sensor.

10.8   Tachometers

The purpose of a tachometer is to provide an output that is proportional to the speed of the sensed element, typically the final correction element. The starting point is Faraday's law of induction, which relates the voltage per turn of wire in a winding v' to the flux ϕ by the expression

$$v' = \frac{d\phi}{dt} \tag{10-20}$$

For a dc generator, (10-20) can be used to find the relationship

$$v = K \bullet \phi \bullet \omega \tag{10-21}$$

where v is the output voltage, K is a constant, ϕ is the flux, and ω is the shaft speed.

Courtesy Omega Engineering

FIGURE 10-23. A silicon diaphragm transducer enclosed in a stainless steel housing with a thermoplastic cover

Since the *s* transform relationship between speed and position θ (see Chapter 8) is

$$w(s) = s \bullet \theta(s) \tag{10-22}$$

the above equation can be written in terms of *s* as

$$V(s) = K \bullet \phi \bullet s \bullet \theta(s) \tag{10-23}$$

and the transfer function from shaft position to voltage is

$$\frac{V(s)}{\theta(s)} = K \bullet \phi \bullet s \tag{10-24}$$

Observing that the *s* in the TF signifies differentiation, it is clear that the tachometer is an ideal device to provide derivative feedback.

The form of the tachometer is typically a very small electric generator driven by the rotating shaft of the prime mover. Examples of the effect of tachometer feedback are found in Chapter 9. An example of a servo system using rate feedback is shown in block-diagram form in Figure 10-24.

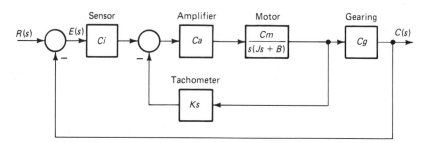

FIGURE 10-24. Symbolic representation of control components

There are various kinds of tachometers. An ac tachometer provides an output suitable for use with ac components, e.g., if the sensor in Figure 10-23 is an electromagnetic device such as a microsyn, then the ac tachometer feedback could be directly summed with the microsyn output. Alternatively, a modulating/demodulating device could be used to provide a suitable combination of outputs. The construction of ac tachometers is similar to that of two-phase servomotors, as discussed in Chapter 12. A typical value for the sensitivity of the ac tachometer is about 2 to 5 V per 1000 rpm. A dc tachometer provides an output suitable for direct use in a dc servo system. The generated emf must be commutated by the use of brushes, which does present some friction—possibly one ounce-inch—that may represent significant drag for a small prime mover. The sensitivity of the dc tachometer is about 5 to 10 V per 1000 rpm.

Another classification of tachometers is frequency-output tachometers, as opposed to the magnitude-output models that have been discussed so far. Examples of these are magnetic pickup tachometers and photocell pickup tachometers. The output is roughly a square-wave whose frequency is proportional to the shaft or linear displacement rate. In the case of the magnetic pickup, the output is triggered by the magnetic proximity of the pickup coil to the moving element (possibly similar to the magnetic pickup in the ignition system of newer spark-ignition engine automobiles). In the case of the photocell pickup tachometers, the photocell output is triggered by the interruption of a light beam by the moving element, possibly a sectored disc, where part of it is transparent and part of it is not.

Frequency output tachometers are useful in digital systems (e.g., to drive a digital output), since with some signal buffering and conditioning the signal can be used to drive the output without conversion. However, for use in a continuous feedback control system, the magnitude output tachometers are better in that their output can be used without digital-to-analog conversion.

10.9 **Other Transducers**

In addition to the position and velocity sensors discussed earlier, two other related transducers are the accelerometer and the gyroscope.

Accelerometer operation is based on the principle that the force of acceleration of a mass is

$$f = M \cdot a \qquad (10\text{-}25)$$

where f = force, M = mass, and a = acceleration. By constraining a mass to move along an axis with a spring used to limit its motion along that axis, it is possible to measure the amount of the force by measuring the displacement of the mass:

$$F = Kx \qquad (10\text{-}26)$$

where K is the spring constant and x is the displacement. Thus the relationship between the accelerometer mass displacement and the accelerometer acceleration from (10-25) and (10-26) is given as

$$x = (M/K)a \qquad (10\text{-}27)$$

and the transfer function of the accelerometer is

$$TF = X(s)/A(s) = M/K. \qquad (10\text{-}28)$$

Since M and K are constants of the accelerometer, the TF is a constant. In a more detailed analysis, the dynamics of the accelerometer would be included to refine the above derivation, but the above is a good starting point.

Accelerometers are used in many industrial applications, but traditionally the most prominent application of transducers is in navigation systems for aircraft, space vehicles, and ships. For inertial navigation, three accelerometers are mounted such that they are oriented orthogonally, for example, the first pointed so that its sensitive axis is along the local vertical line, the second pointed east, and the third pointed north. To maintain this orientation while the vehicle is in motion, the accelerometers are placed on a stable platform that is positioned by gyroscopic torquers. This assembly, called an *inertial measuring unit*, can be used along with the appropriate hardware and computer control to provide an inertial navigation system for dead-reckoning navigation. Such inertial navigation systems are found on most military and commercial aircraft and ships. The ring laser gyro is winning popularity compared with the gyroscopic type, since it operates on the laser displacement due to vehicle motion, whereas the gyro-based navigation system uses high-speed motor operation to detect vehicle motion using synchros.

Capacitance sensing bases its sensing on the capacitance between a fixed reference surface and a movable surface. This method has become increasingly popular due to the increased availability of stable, inexpensive sensing amplifiers. Capacitor sensors are used for measurement of displacement, proximity, pressure, strain, and moisture. Common examples of capacitance sensing are the touch keyboards of many popular calculators and computer terminals that use a diaphragm-covered keyboard. The principal advantage of capacitance systems is the high isolation of the sensor from the environment.

Transducers that will not be discussed here but can be found in other texts and in manufacturers' literature include pressure sensors, photoelectric devices, humidity transducers, and others mentioned in Table 10-1.

10.10 Summary

The treatment of transducers is voluminous in the technical literature in the form of books, journals, and manufacturers' product information. The hope here is that with this brief treatment of transducers, the most prominent transducers have been described and the philosophy of analysis can be carried over to other transducers. The potential user has to consider parameters such as sensitivity, linearity, repeatability, speed, resolution, range, offset, signal form, durability, and cost in selecting and applying a transducer. In particular, the user has to consider the application of the transducer to determine if the output of the transducer should be discrete or continuous and, if continuous, ac or dc.

The sensing methods discussed thus far are based upon characteristics inherent to each type of sensor. The accuracy and range of the measurement is determined by these characteristics. When measuring temperature, for example, the linearity, range, repeatability, speed, etc., is different for thermocouple sensing than for thermistors. Each of the techniques also affects the system whose characteristics it measures. An ideal sensor is a noncontact device with minimal influence on its environment; it is in this direction that measurement technology is moving.

Problems

10.1 A temperature transducer is to be selected; two are available: one with a transfer function of $5/(0.3s + 1)$ V/degree, the other with a transfer function of $12/(0.2s + 1)$ V/degree. Which would be desirable with regard to: (a) sensitivity, (b) speed, and (c) linearity?

10.2 Name transducers to measure each of the following: position, force, light intensity, and temperature.

10.3 A 10 K servo potentiometer is used to control the voltage to a differential amplifier, which represents a 20 K load to the potentiometer. The supply voltage to the potentiometer is 30 V.

   a) Determine the voltage to the amplifier if the potentiometer setting is at the two-thirds level so that two-thirds of the potentiometer resistance is in parallel with the load.

   b) Determine the difference between the answer above and the voltage to the amplifier if the amplifier input resistance was infinite instead of 20 K.

10.4 A 200-turn, 10-K potentiometer is specified as having a linearity of 5 percent. If a supply voltage of 50 V is applied to it, what is the maximum voltage error due to (a) linearity and (b) resolution?

10.5 In comparison to the potentiometer setup suggested in problem 10.4, an LVDT is to be used to measure angular position changes. The LVDT is operated with 120 V ac.

   a) Compare the voltage gradient in V/degree for each.

   b) Compute the power requirement of the potentiometer.

   c) Which device would have better resolution?

   d) Which device would use less power?

   e) Which device would have better sensitivity?

   f) Which device would be better used in a dc circuit?

10.6 An E-type thermocouple is specified as having a sensitivity of 40 mV/1,000 degrees.

   a) What is the largest temperature change that could be shown in the full range of a 100 m V temperature recorder?

   b) Would this temperature change be increased or decreased if a K-type thermocouple were used?

10.7 Determine the transfer function of a strain gage if the output changes 25 mV for a change of stress in 100 lbs.

10.8 Determine the transfer function of a tachometer if the output changes 50 V for a change of speed of 1,000 rpm.

10.9 An accelerometer has a sensitivity of 2 V/ft/sec squared. Determine its output if it is turned on its edge such that its input axis is oriented along the vertical direction.

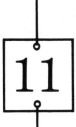

11 Interfacing Continuous Controls

11.0 Introduction

Electronics, notwithstanding its power, and complexity, has a fragility which must be protected from the harsher influences of the industrial world. In addition, signals used internally by control circuitry are often at a level that is not directly compatible with the needs of industrial sensors and final control elements. In this chapter, the problems of input and output interfacing are examined and some common solutions are presented. The common thread of the solutions is that each interfacing device amplifies either as a power booster or as an attenuator. These amplifiers provide signal conversion in level, power, or signal form. The operational amplifier is presented as the principal input device, while the junction transistor, SCR, and triac are examined as output devices.

11.1 Input Interfacing

Input interfacing in the continuous control area provides the following functions:

- Electrical isolation using nonelectrical coupling
- Signal-level shifting
- Noise filtering
- Amplification
- Signal characterization, such as linearization.

These input functions are generally accomplished by circuits based upon the operational amplifier. This device is an integrated circuit form of a much older vacuum-tube device developed during World War II. The characteristics of a modern operational amplifier (op amp) include:

- Differential input
- High gain
- High input impedance
- Low output impedance
- Wide bandwidth
- Frequency compensation
- Internal short-circuit protection.

Special varieties of the operational amplifier exist that include full electrical isolation, special chopper stabilization, and low-power or FET input stages. For the most part, however, application circuits for controls are not device-dependent and include the following:

- Noninverting amplifier
- Inverting amplifier
- Difference amplifier
- Instrumentation amplifier
- Comparator
- Integrator
- Differentiator
- Filter.

The Noninverting Amplifier

The noninverting amplifier provides an amplified version of its input at its output. The circuit diagram is shown in Figure 11-1. This circuit exhibits a very high input impedance but suffers from a lower stability than the inverting amplifier. The circuit in the figure is shown operating from a single power supply, as is often the case in many field situations. Resistor R4 is removed if the circuit is operated from dual polarity supplies. The zener diodes Z1 and Z2 protect the input from excessive voltage swings, while a bypass capacitor between the power supply lines improves stability and noise rejection.

The Inverting Amplifier

The inverting amplifier is similar to the noninverting amplifier except for the entry point of the input signal. The inverting amplifier

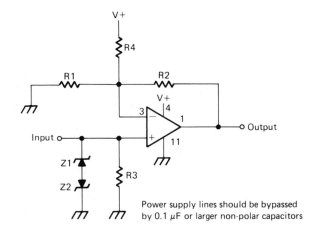

$$\text{T.F.} = G(s) = \text{Gain} = \frac{R1 + R2}{R1} \text{ for } R4 = R1 \text{ and } R2 \gg R1$$

Input impedance = R3
Zero is adjusted by R4
Gain is most often adjusted by R2

FIGURE 11-1. Noninverting amplifier

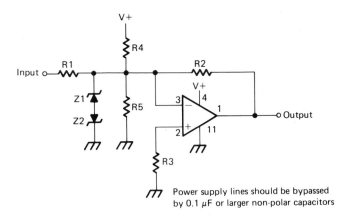

$$\text{T.F.} = G(s) = \text{Gain} = -\frac{R2}{R1} \text{ for } R4 = R5 \text{ and } R4 \gg R1.$$

Input impedance = R1
Zero is adjusted by R4
Gain is most often adjusted by R2

FIGURE 11-2. Inverting amplifier

configuration is generally more stable than the noninverting type, and it also has a simpler gain equation. This circuit is shown in Figure 11-2.

Both the inverting and noninverting amplifier provide gain with the band of frequencies from dc to a frequency limited by the slew rate of the device. The upper frequency of interest in most control applications is limited by the mechanics of the process under control, and rarely by the limits of the slew rate of the amplifiers involved.

The Difference Amplifier

As its name portends, the differential amplifier provides an amplification of the difference between the signal present at the inverting (−) and noninverting inputs (+) of the amplifier. This circuit is presented in Figure 11-3.

The advantage of the differential amplifier is in the noise-rejection capability provided by the difference between the common mode and differential mode gains. The low common-mode gain allows very low-level signals to be extracted from a high electrical noise environment by applying the low-level signal differentially to the amplifier, while the induced noise in the pickup leads is being

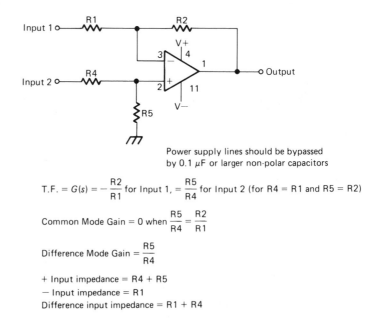

Power supply lines should be bypassed by 0.1 μF or larger non-polar capacitors

$$\text{T.F.} = G(s) = -\frac{R2}{R1} \text{ for Input 1}, = \frac{R5}{R4} \text{ for Input 2 (for R4 = R1 and R5 = R2)}$$

$$\text{Common Mode Gain} = 0 \text{ when } \frac{R5}{R4} = \frac{R2}{R1}$$

$$\text{Difference Mode Gain} = \frac{R5}{R4}$$

+ Input impedance = R4 + R5
− Input impedance = R1
Difference input impedance = R1 + R4

FIGURE 11-3. Difference amplifier

generated in common mode. So powerful is this technique that a special combination of operational amplifiers in a single package, called the *instrumentation amplifier*, is manufactured for low-level sensing.

The Instrumentation Amplifier

The instrumentation amplifier is the backbone of most data acquisition and control systems. It is essentially a differential operational amplifier with buffer amplifiers connected to the differential inputs. These buffer amplifiers provide more balanced input impedance and additional gain and stability. Such a circuit is pictured in Figure 11-4.

The extreme popularity of the instrumentation amplifier circuit has fostered the development of prepackaged instrumentation amplifiers. This prepackaging has permitted common use of the instrument amplifier with advanced features such as isolation and variable gain. Widespread use has reduced prices and encouraged compact packaging.

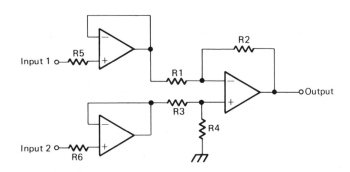

$$\text{T.F.} = G(s) = -\frac{R2}{R1} \text{ for Input 1}, = \frac{R4}{R3} \text{ for Input 2 (for R4 = R2 and R3 = R1)}$$

Common Mode Gain = 0 when $\dfrac{R4}{R3} = \dfrac{R2}{R1}$

Common mode rejection ratio (CMRR) is determined by the matching of
R1 — R3 and R2 — R4

Difference Mode Gain = $\dfrac{R4}{R3}$

Gain is not adjustable without upset of CMRR
+ Input impedance = R6
— Input impedance = R5
Gain is not adjustable without upset of CMRR

FIGURE 11-4. Instrumentation amplifier

Comparator

A special application of the differential amplifier is illustrated in Figure 11-5. In this circuit no feedback resistor is used to regulate the gain of the differential amplifier. In this mode the amplifier swings from positive saturation to negative saturation with virtually no intermediate values possible. The swing of the output is determined by the polarity of the difference between the two input lines. In effect, the amplifier is comparing the two inputs and outputting a signal that indicates which is the larger. Such an application is termed a *comparator*. The amplifier used for a comparator circuit requires a latching action and a fast slew rate. (Latching causes the amplifier to go into saturation and remain there regardless of the input value.) If one of the inputs to the differential amplifier is a reference voltage, then this circuit may be used as an alarm circuit or as an element of an analog-to-digital convertor.

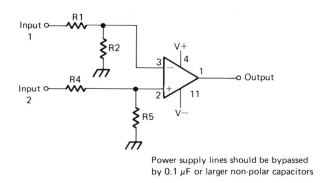

Power supply lines should be bypassed
by 0.1 μF or larger non-polar capacitors

FIGURE 11-5. Comparator

Integrator

An integrator performs an electronic approximation of a repetitive time integration of an input signal over an adjustable time period. One circuit that accomplishes this is shown in Figure 11-6. Resistor R3 in conjunction with C1 determines the integration time of the integrator, while R5 in combination with C1 determines the reset time-constant between integration periods. R5 should be 50 to 100 times the value of R3 for minimum interaction between R5 and the integration period. Resistors R1, R2, and R7 provide a zero adjustment.

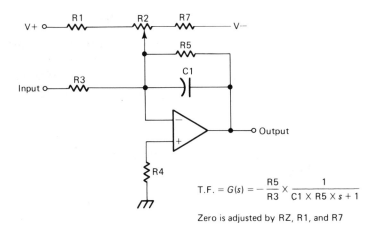

$$\text{T.F.} = G(s) = -\frac{R5}{R3} \times \frac{1}{C1 \times R5 \times s + 1}$$

Zero is adjusted by RZ, R1, and R7

FIGURE 11-6. Operational amplifier integrator

Differentiator

A differentiator performs an electronic approximation of a differentiation of the input signal with respect to an adjustable time period. A practical differentiator is illustrated in Figure 11-7. The resistors R1 and R2 in conjunction with C1 determine the time period of differentiation, while R3 reduces offset. C2 increases the stability of the circuit by reducing, through filter action, the response of the differentiator to rapidly changing signals.

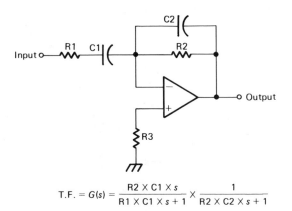

$$\text{T.F.} = G(s) = \frac{R2 \times C1 \times s}{R1 \times C1 \times s + 1} \times \frac{1}{R2 \times C2 \times s + 1}$$

R1 × C1 × 6.28 × (highest frequency expected) ≪ 1 stable operation

FIGURE 11-7. Practical operational amplifier differentiator

The Operational Amplifier Filter

Often the signal used for control contains a strong noise component. One such noise component is the 60-hertz power signal that is present at virtually every industrial site. The noise component may be greater than the amplitude of the control signal and may appear differentially at the input to the control system. In such cases the integrated-circuit filter provides a method of extracting information from a noisy line if the signal is identifiably different in frequency than the noise component. Four types of filters perform this function: low-pass, high-pass, band-pass, and band-stop. One common circuit that performs three of these functions simultaneously is called a *state variable filter,* shown in Figure 11-8. The advantage of this circuit is that it provides low pass, high pass, and band pass as needed, with the same design. Resistor R7 sets the gain of the filter as a whole, while resistors R3, R4, and R2 set the shape of the response, called *filter quality* (*Q*). Resistors R8 and R9 in conjunction with capacitors C1 and C2 set the frequency of the center of the band pass, thereby determining the low- and high-pass cutoff frequencies.

Example of an Operational Amplifier PID Control Application

Chapter 9 introduced a controller that produces an output based on the difference between a desired measurement value (setpoint) and

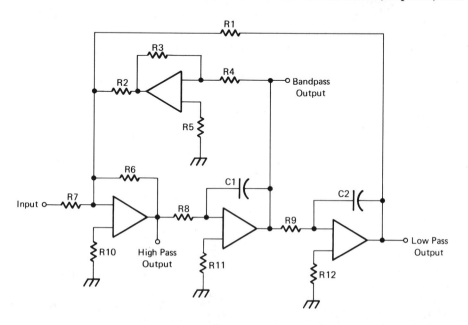

FIGURE 11-8. State variable operational amplifier filter

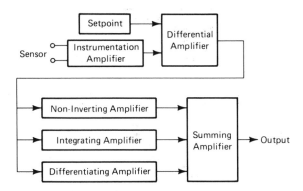

FIGURE 11-9. Block diagram of three-mode controller

an actual value. One such controller uses the magnitude of the error (P), the accumulated sum of the error over time (I), and the time rate-of-change of the error (D) to compute a control output. A block diagram for such a PID controller appears in Figure 11-9.

The controller in Figure 11-10 operates by the equations of Chapter 9. The operation of the controller is based upon the error signal, which is the difference between a manual setpoint control setting (R9) and an instrumentation input from the process under control. The error signal is processed by a noninverting amplifier, an integrator, and a differentiator. The sum of the outputs of three signal-processing circuits is the output of the controller. The gain of the noninverting amplifier is set by R14. The period of integration is set by the RESET potentiometer R20 and the period of the differentiator is set by the RATE control R26.

11.2 Output Interfacing

Junction Transistor

The junction transistor is the oldest of the solid-state amplification devices. It was first introduced in the late 1940s but was not popular as a control device until the early 1960s, when price, power handling, and life expectancy reached practical levels.

The transistor amplifier can be operated in more than one configuration of components and ground references. The transistor amplifier load, such as a solenoid or torque-motor coil, can be placed in the emitter-to-collector circuit on either the collector side or the emitter side, and the signal ground of the amplifier can be referenced at the base, emitter, or collector of the amplifier. These combinations are illustrated in Figure 11-11. The common-emitter npn transistor amplifier will be used exclusively throughout this chapter in the interest of simplicity.

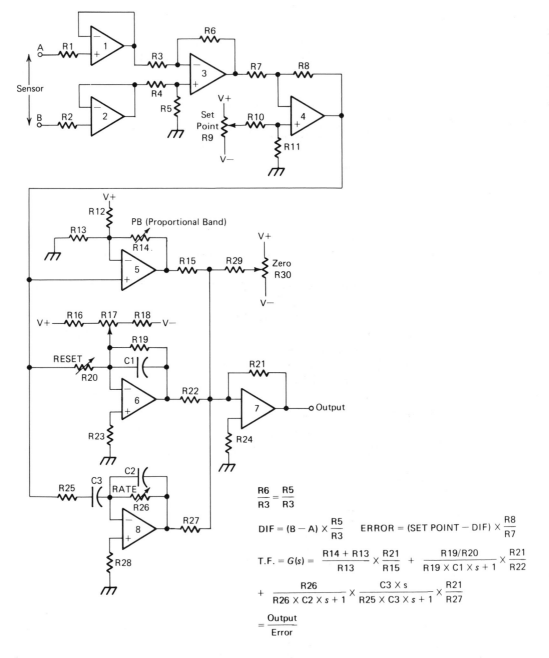

$$\frac{R6}{R3} = \frac{R5}{R3}$$

$$DIF = (B - A) \times \frac{R5}{R3} \qquad ERROR = (SET\ POINT - DIF) \times \frac{R8}{R7}$$

$$T.F. = G(s) = \frac{R14 + R13}{R13} \times \frac{R21}{R15} + \frac{R19/R20}{R19 \times C1 \times s + 1} \times \frac{R21}{R22}$$

$$+ \frac{R26}{R26 \times C2 \times s + 1} \times \frac{C3 \times s}{R25 \times C3 \times s + 1} \times \frac{R21}{R27}$$

$$= \frac{Output}{Error}$$

FIGURE 11-10. Three-mode (PID) controller using operational amplifiers

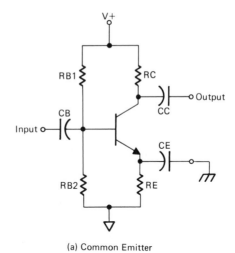

(a) Common Emitter

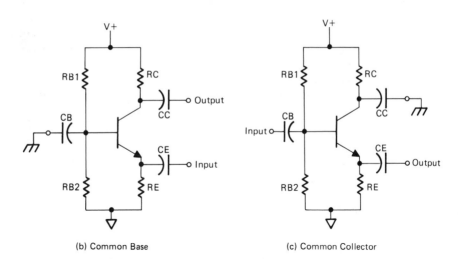

(b) Common Base   (c) Common Collector

FIGURE 11-11. Transistor amplifier configurations

The transistor amplifier can be used to amplify both ac and dc signals. The type of signals is determined by what components are used to couple the input and output signals to the amplifier. Direct coupling ties both dc and ac signals to the amplifier, while capacitor or transformer coupling allows ac signal amplification only. Control circuits are concerned primarily with dc signals, and this discussion will be limited to the direct-coupled amplifier.

Continuous Control Transistor Applications

Three-mode controllers, such as those introduced in Chapter 9, use their output signal to position valves, supply power to induction heaters, or align machine tools. It is the transistor Class A amplifier that is often used to perform the interface of low-power control signals to high-power final control elements. Such a circuit is shown in Figure 11-12.

In addition to the single-transistor amplifier, many servo-amplifiers use a pair of transistors working together in a configuration called a *Darlington pair*. The advantage of this amplifier type is that high gain is achieved while maintaining the simplicity of three terminals. This configuration is illustrated in Figure 11-13. So popular is this method of cascading transistors that this configuration is often manufactured preconnected in a single transistor package.

The energy efficiency of the Class A amplifier is approximately 25 percent. Therefore, more efficient methods of servo-amplification have been developed. One of the most common of these methods is the Class B complementary symmetry power amplifier. Such an amplifier is shown in Figure 11-14. The negative and positive output driving demands are divided between the output transistors, so that the energy efficiency of the circuit increases to a possible maximum of 78 percent, depending upon circuit characteristics.

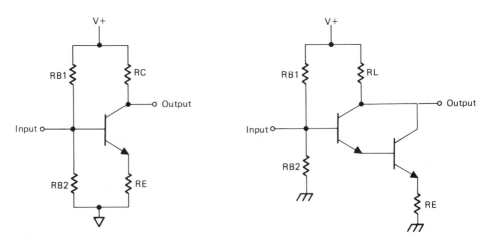

FIGURE 11-12. Direct coupled, Class A, npn, common emitter amplifier

FIGURE 11-13. Darlington pair amplifier connection

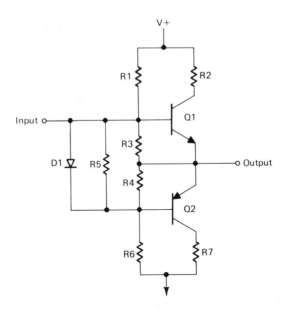

FIGURE 11-14. Class B complementary symmetry power amplifier

Principles of SCR Operation

Like the transistor, the SCR is a three-terminal device. The terminals are designated *anode, cathode,* and *gate.* As its name implies, it is constructed of semiconductor silicon and operates as a rectifier.

Two conditions are necessary for anode-to-cathode conduction:

- The anode must be biased positively with respect to the cathode.
- The gate must be biased above its "firing potential" (about 1.2 V).

One condition is necessary for maintaining conduction:

- The anode must be biased positively; the gate bias can be removed.

One condition is necessary for stopping conduction:

- The current through the device must be sufficiently low such that conduction is lost.

The SCR is packaged in a variety of cases, often of the same type as used for power transistors, since heat dissipation is a problem and

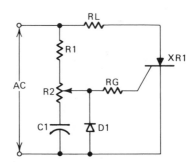

FIGURE 11-15. SCR phase control circuitry

heat-sinks are often required to prevent device destruction by thermal runaway.

SCR Applications in Continuous Control

The SCR is a switching device and may seem unsuited for continuous control applications. In ac power applications, the SCR can be used for a special form of continuous control. This is possible because the SCR has the ability to switch in microseconds. This high switching speed allows the control of each ac half-cycle by triggering the SCR at a controlled time after the start of the half cycle, and allowing the SCR to continue conducting until the zero crossing turns off the device. If the response time of the load is long when compared to the period of the ac power supplied, then the average power over the period of the ac waveform can be controlled continuously from 0 to 100 percent. An example of SCR continuous control is incandescent lighting control, where the thermal lag of a lamp is sufficiently long that the light appears to be constant in its incandescence, even though the energy to it is changing rapidly within the 60 Hz waveform.

One method of controlling the SCR conduction interval is by the use of phase control. An SCR phase-control circuit, as illustrated in Figure 11-15, can be used for half-wave control. The resistors R1 and R2 and the capacitor C1 form a phase-shifting network that provides the delay before firing the SCR. The delay occurs because the gate current, and therefore the gate voltage, must reach a critical value before the device fires. This voltage is reached at a time—with respect to the power sinewave—that is determined by the RC network phase shift and, therefore, by the value of the variable resistor R2. This action is illustrated in Figure 11-16.

As shown in the phase-control waveforms, the action of a single SCR applies only to half of the ac sinewave. In order to control both halves of the sinewave, circuits using two SCRs back to back and

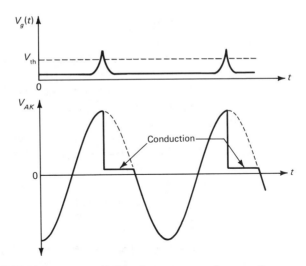

FIGURE 11-16. SCR phase control waveforms

circuits using full-wave rectifiers have been developed to provide control on both halves of the ac sinewave.

Continuous applications of an SCR also require special circuit additions to eliminate electromagnetic interference, to improve triggering stability, and to provide zero-crossing load switching. Such a circuit is shown in Figure 11-17. Choke L1 in conjunction with capacitor C1 acts as an electromagnetic interference filter. The PI filter in the gate circuit reduces the potential for false triggering, while the full-wave rectifier bridge of D1–D4 provides modulation of both halves of the sinewave.

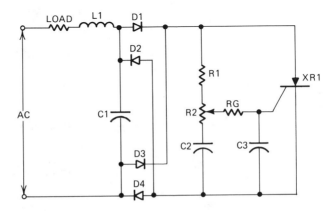

FIGURE 11-17. SCR full-wave practical heater control

Triac Principles

Full-wave control may be accomplished with two SCRs by connecting them, in parallel anode-to-cathode, and coupling the trigger circuits together. The problems with this circuit lie in the requirement for two power devices, the need for matching of device characteristics, and the gating circuit complications. The twin SCR problem was resolved with the advent of the triac.

The triac is a three-terminal device which, like the SCR, conducts when gated by a small gate-current and remains gated until the main terminal (MT1, MT2) difference voltage drops to zero; however, unlike the SCR, the triac can conduct current in either direction when gated with the proper signal. The triac is packaged in the same case styles as is the SCR.

Triac Applications for Continuous Control

The triac is used in phase control of ac loads. The triac is switched on at a specific point during each half-wave of load voltage and switches itself off when the MT1 to MT2 voltage goes through zero. The power to the load is then proportional to the time of conduction. If the triac is gated on 12.5 milliseconds after the ac current waveform passes through zero, then the power applied to the load will be one-fourth of the full-wave value. The difference between triac and SCR continuous control is that the triac can control both positive and negative half-cycles within a single device. A common example of triac application is the household lamp dimmer and motor speed controls. Such a circuit is shown in Figure 11-18.

As in previous examples, dv/dt turn-on is prevented by a snubber circuit consisting of R3 and C4. A choke and capacitor combination, L1 and C1, reduces electromagnetic interference and

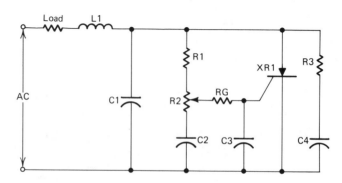

FIGURE 11-18. Triac lamp dimmer

the delay before turn-on is provided by the resistor-capacitor network of the gate circuit.

11.3 Thyristor Triggering Devices

The SCR and triac require that specific gate signal requirements be met for turn-on of the thyristor. These requirements include precise timing with respect to the ac waveform (in the case of phase control), as well as narrow minimum and maximum current and voltage requirements. The rise-time of the gate signal can also affect the predictability of thyristor turn-on. To meet these stringent requirements, special trigger circuits have been designed around three principal devices. These devices are the neon lamp, the diac, and the unijunction transistor (UJT). These devices are all breakover devices in that they have a high resistance until a threshold voltage is reached, after which time they conduct heavily.

Neon Lamp Triggering

The neon lamp is an envelope filled with neon gas. A voltage potential of approximately 60 V is required for the gas to ionize, which causes a relatively large current to flow between the electrodes. This action is useful in the triggering of thyristors. Such a circuit is illustrated in Figure 11-19. The phase-shifted voltage across the capacitor is applied to the neon lamp; however, until the difference across the lamp reaches 60 V, only leakage current flows. When the voltage across the lamp exceeds the ionization voltage, the lamp fires and causes a rapidly rising signal to be applied to the gate of the triac limited by the series resistor. This action gives increased trigger predictability, but at a price of a more limited range of control. In addition, the neon lamp is both light- and temperature-sensitive.

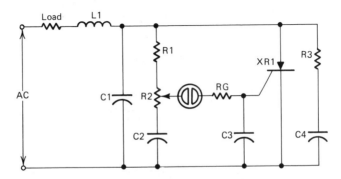

FIGURE 11-19. Neon triggering circuit for a triac

Diac Triggering

The diac is a two-terminal, solid-state device with breakover current versus voltage characteristics. It is more costly than the neon lamp, but has greater predictability and a wider range of operation. The diac replaces the neon lamp in the circuit in Figure 11-19. The diac is not photo-sensitive and has less variation from one device to the next. The diac, however, has a temperature sensitivity that shifts its breakover voltage to a lower threshold as temperature increases. An improved device that is similar in principle is the *silicon bilateral switch* (SBS). The SBS has a lower breakover voltage than a diac and a greater temperature stability. This device also prevents hysteresis in the turn-on characteristics of triac phase control.

Triggering Using the Unijunction Transistor

The unijunction transistor (UJT) is a three-terminal device unlike the breakover devices discussed so far. As can be seen from the voltage versus current curves for the UJT (Figure 11-20), this device is a controllable breakover device. When the voltage between the emitter and base 1 is below the threshold voltage, virtually no current flows from base 1 to base 2. When the threshold voltage is exceeded, then the resistance from base 1 to base 2 drops to nearly 0 ohms.

A UJT trigger-circuit is shown in Figure 11-21. The UJT has very stable temperature characteristics and, due to the extremely low emitter current requirements, has excellent repeatability. The zener diode used in this circuit gives isolation from voltage variations in the supply line.

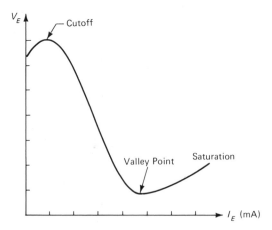

FIGURE 11-20. Unijunction transistor current versus voltage characteristics

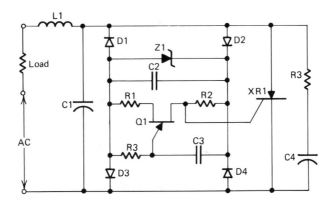

FIGURE 11-21. UJT trigger circuit for triac phase control

Thyristor Application Cautions

Although thyristors have many strengths to recommend their use, some special limitations must be considered. The thyristor is a heat-producing device and, in addition, is heat-sensitive. Adequate heat-sinking for both the intended load and the maximum ambient conditions must be provided to prevent failure of the thyristor. If a thyristor fails, it usually fails shorted, i.e., it fails in the ON state. Therefore, safety devices must be provided to compensate for this characteristic. Thyristors may be destroyed by faults of overvoltage and overcurrent faster than many fusing devices can react, and therefore they require special fuse-speed coordination.

Thyristor phase controls produce large amounts of radio frequency interference that can easily induce false triggers in integrated circuit controllers and instrumentation. Careful attention to low-ohm earth grounding of shields can help reduce radio frequency interference problems.

Finally, SCRs and triacs require that the current and voltage across the thyristor be in phase when the thyristor turns on and off. This limits the use of triacs and SCRs in control of induction motors, large coils, and fluorescent lighting.

Problems

11.1 What are three functions of continuous control interfacing?

11.2 The operational amplifier provides input interfacing and signal processing. What are four desirable characteristics of a modern op amp?

11.3 What are the functions most commonly performed by the op amp in continuous control circuitry?

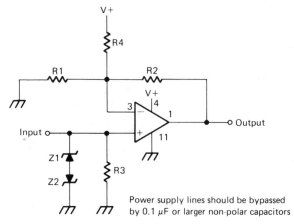

$$\text{T.F.} = G(s) = \text{Gain} = \frac{R1 + R2}{R1} \text{ for } R4 = R1 \text{ and } R2 \gg R1$$

Input impedance = R3
Zero is adjusted by R4
Gain is most often adjusted by R2

FIGURE P11.4.

11.4 The circuit in Figure P11.4 provides what function?

11.5 What is the gain and input impedance of the circuit in Figure P11.4?

11.6 Figure P11.6 is an inverting amplifier circuit. What is the gain equation of this circuit and what are the differences between this circuit and the noninverting amplifier?

11.7 What is the purpose of diodes Z1 and Z2 in Figure P11.6?

11.8 What is the single largest advantage of the differential amplifier circuit over the inverting amplifier for low-level sensor control schemes?

11.9 Describe the function of each of the operational amplifiers in Figure P11.9.

11.10 What are the advantages of the instrumentation amplifier for control applications?

11.11 Is the gain of the comparator circuit operational amplifier higher or lower than that of the noninverting amplifier?

11.12 Sketch a circuit that uses four comparators to convert analog voltages to binary numbers.

11.13 Sketch an alarm circuit that uses a comparator as the principal device.

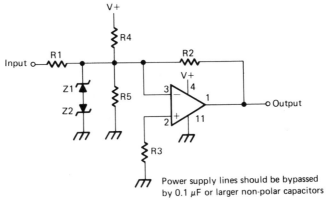

T.F. $= G(s) =$ Gain $= -\dfrac{R2}{R1}$ for R4 = R5 and R4 $\gg$ R1.

Input impedance = R1
Zero is adjusted by R4
Gain is most often adjusted by R2

FIGURE P11.6. Inverting amplifier circuit

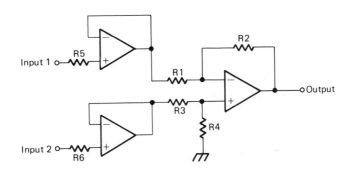

T.F. $= G(s) = -\dfrac{R2}{R1}$ for Input 1, $= \dfrac{R4}{R3}$ for Input 2 (for R4 = R2 and R3 = R1)

Common Mode Gain = 0 when $\dfrac{R4}{R3} = \dfrac{R2}{R1}$

Common mode rejection ratio (CMRR) is determined by the matching of
R1 − R3 and R2 − R4

Difference Mode Gain $= \dfrac{R4}{R3}$

Gain is not adjustable without upset of CMRR
+ Input impedance = R6
− Input impedance = R5
Gain is not adjustable without upset of CMRR

FIGURE P11.9. Instrumentation amplifier

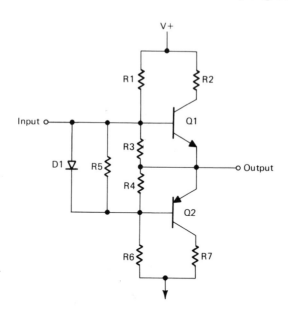

FIGURE P11.6. Buffer circuit

11.14 Using an integrator and differentiator circuits, make a sketch of a three-mode controller as described in Chapter 9.

11.15 Describe how a filter circuit may improve stability of a three-mode controller.

11.16 What is the purpose of the circuit in Figure P11.16?

11.17 Assume a sinewave is applied to the circuit in Figure P11.16.

    a) Which components are active during each half cycle?

    b) What are the advantages and disadvantages to the circuit in comparison to the Class A power amplifier?

11.18 What is purpose of each component in Figure P11.18?

11.19 What would be the effect of moving the load RL in Figure P11.18 to the line side of the triggering network?

11.20 What are some possible means of coupling the circuit in Figure P11.18 to the output of an operational amplifier?

11.21 What is the advantage of the circuit in Figure P11.21 in comparison with the circuit of Figure P11.18?

11.22 What is the purpose of the components L1 and C1 in Figure P11.21?

11.23 What is the purpose of components C4 and R3 in the circuit in Figure P11.21?

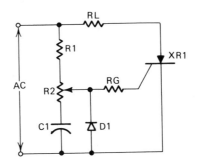

FIGURE P11.18. SCR phase control circuit

11.24 What is the effect of capacitor C3 in Figure P11.21 on the range of operation of the lamp dimmer?

11.25 The circuit in Figure P11.21 produces a nonsinusoidal waveform across the load. What application limitations does this imply?

11.26 The gate circuit in Figure P11.21 may be replaced by a digital pulse generating circuit which is synchronized to the ac line voltage. What are some possible applications of this triggering method?

11.27 What are some of the advantages of the UJT triac-triggering method over that of an RC phase-shift network?

11.28 What applications are best suited to an SCR or triac as compared to a transistor amplifier?

11.29 How could a digital circuit be interfaced to a triac phase-control system?

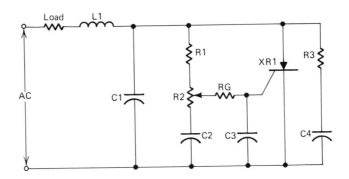

FIGURE P11.21. Triac lamp dimmer

12 Actuators, Prime Movers, and Final Correcting Elements

12.0 Introduction

Referring again to a diagram that shows the relationship of sensor, amplifier, and actuator (see Figure 12-1), it can be seen that the topic of this chapter is the last block: the *actuator*. The actuator is also called the final correction element, the prime mover, and the positioner.

The most common actuator is a motor. This chapter treats both dc and ac motors. Servomotors constitute a special class of motors that are built precisely to be used in control systems. The name servomotor is derived from the terms servomechanism and motor. The output power of ac servomotors is limited to from 1 to 100 watts; dc servomotors are appropriate for larger applications where the output would range from small fractional horsepower to multiple horsepower. In addition, synchros, step motors, brushless dc motors, and linear forcers are discussed.

12.1 Properties of dc Motors

Two major classes of dc motors are *integral horsepower* and *fractional horsepower* (fHp). Most servo control applications utilize the

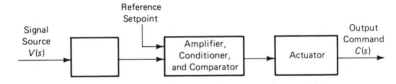

FIGURE 12-1. Symbolic representation of control components

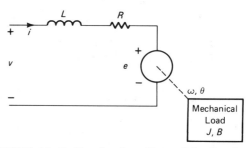

FIGURE 12-2. Basic circuit model of a dc motor

fHp motors. Another classification of dc motors is based on the means of field excitation. The kinds are permanent magnet field and wound field. In the case of the wound field, there are various kinds of windings: straight series, split series, shunt, and compound. Before these types of motors are discussed, the basic equations that describe the operation of these motors are presented.

Figure 12-2 shows the basic circuit model of a dc motor. The electrical equation of this motor model is

$$v = L \frac{di}{dt} + Ri + e \tag{12-1}$$

The e term represents the counter emf due to the generator effect:

$$e = C\omega \tag{12-2}$$

where C is the emf constant and ω is the speed.

The torque available at the motor shaft, ignoring internal torque losses and assuming constant magnetic flux, is

$$T = Ki \tag{12-3}$$

where K is the torque-current constant. The mechanical equation of this motor load is

$$T = J \frac{d\omega}{dt} + B\omega \tag{12-4}$$

where J represents the combined moment of inertia of the load and the motor, and B represents the combined friction losses of the load and the motor.

The above equations can be used to determine the transfer function of the motor speed ω with respect to the applied voltage v (see Chapter 8 for a description of transfer functions). Transforming (12-4) to the complex frequency domain and solving for ω as a function of s produces

$$T(s) = Js\omega(s) + B\omega(s) \tag{12-5}$$

and

$$\omega(s) = \frac{1}{Js + B} T(s) \tag{12-6}$$

Solving for $\omega(s)$ in terms of armature current, based on the torque equation (12-3) produces

$$\omega(s) = \frac{K}{Js + B} I(s) \tag{12-7}$$

Solving the electrical equations (12-1) and (12-2) for $I(s)$ provides

$$I(s) = \frac{V(s) - E(s)}{Ls + R} = \frac{V(s) - C\omega(s)}{Ls + R} \tag{12-8}$$

and substituting this into (12-7) gives

$$\omega(s) = \frac{K[V(s) - C\omega(s)]}{(Js + B)(Ls + R)} \tag{12-9}$$

Solving for $\omega(s)$ produces

$$\omega(s) = \frac{KV(s)}{(Js + B)(Ls + R) + KC} =$$
$$\frac{KV(s)}{JLs^2 + (JR + BL)s + BR + KC} \tag{12-10}$$

Thus, the motor transfer function for angular velocity (shaft speed) out versus voltage in is

$$\frac{\omega(s)}{V(s)} = \frac{K}{(Js + B)(Ls + R) + KC} =$$
$$\frac{K}{JLs^2 + (JR + BL)s + (BR + KC)} \tag{12-11}$$

If position is the output variable, then the above becomes

$$\frac{\theta(s)}{V(s)} = \frac{K}{s(Js + B)(Ls + R) + KC} =$$

$$\frac{K}{s[JLs^2 + (JR + BL)s + (BR + KC)]} \qquad (12\text{-}12)$$

since the relationship between position $\theta(s)$ and velocity $\omega(s)$ is

$$\theta(s) = \omega(s)/s \qquad (12\text{-}13)$$

This transfer function is the starting point for using a dc motor as a part of a control system. The control designer would have to determine the effect of the roots given by the denominator to determine the motor response. The motor transfer function is probably the most significant part of the system response in terms of system dynamics.

One particularly significant example of using the motor transfer function is the case of inertia load and "small" armature inductance, where the damping term B is negligible or nonexistent and the inductance L is small. Then the transfer function between the velocity ω and voltage V (12-11) becomes

$$\frac{\omega(s)}{V(s)} = \frac{K}{Js(Ls + R) + KC} = \frac{K}{JLs^2 + JRs + KC}$$

$$= \frac{K/JL}{s^2 + \dfrac{R}{L}s + \dfrac{KC}{JL}} \qquad (12\text{-}14)$$

The roots of the denominator are found to be

$$s_1 = -\frac{R}{2L} + \sqrt{\left(\frac{R}{2L}\right)^2 - \frac{KC}{JL}}$$

$$s_2 = -\frac{R}{2L} - \sqrt{\left(\frac{R}{2L}\right)^2 - \frac{KC}{JL}}$$

or

$$s_1 = -\frac{R}{2L} + \frac{R}{2L}\cdot\sqrt{1 - \frac{4LKC}{JR^2}}$$

$$s_2 = -\frac{R}{2L} - \frac{R}{2L}\cdot\sqrt{1 - \frac{4LKC}{JR^2}} \qquad (12\text{-}15)$$

If the inductance is small, the approximation that

$$\sqrt{1 - x^2} = 1 - \frac{x}{2} \tag{12-16}$$

can be made where $x = 2/R \sqrt{LKC/J}$. Thus, the roots become

$$s_1 = -\frac{R}{2L} + \frac{R}{2L} \cdot \left(1 - \frac{1}{R} \sqrt{\frac{LKC}{J}} \right)$$

$$s_2 = -\frac{R}{2L} - \frac{R}{2L} \cdot \left(1 - \frac{1}{R} \sqrt{\frac{LKC}{J}} \right) \tag{12-17}$$

The above can be simplified to the expressions

$$s_1 = -\frac{1}{2}\sqrt{\frac{KC}{LJ}}, \quad s_2 = -\frac{R}{L} \tag{12-18}$$

where the second root is obtained by assuming that $(1/R) \cdot \sqrt{LKC/J}$ is negligible compared to 1. The significance of this result is that the speed-voltage motor transfer function can be shown to be

$$\frac{\omega(s)}{V(s)} = \frac{\dfrac{K}{JL}}{\left(s + \dfrac{1}{T_1} \right) \left(s + \dfrac{1}{T_2} \right)} = \frac{\dfrac{2}{R} \cdot \sqrt{\dfrac{LK}{JC}}}{(T_1 s + 1)(T_2 s + 1)} \tag{12-19}$$

where the time constants of the circuit are $T_1 = 2 \cdot \sqrt{LJ/KC}$ and $T_2 = L/R$. Thus, the analysis of the application of a dc servomotor in a control system can be accomplished by identifying the motor and load parameters J, R, K, C, and L. The tools of step response and frequency response can be applied.

12.2 Motor Types

A first step in describing servomotors is to review the characteristics of several motor types: the *series field*, the *shunt field*, and the *permanent magnet field* dc motor.

Series-Field dc Motors

The series-field motor has the field winding connected in series with the armature winding, as shown in Figure 12-3. The main feature of this type of motor is that the field winding must consist of a conductor

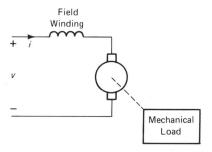

FIGURE 12-3. Series field dc motor and mechanical load

that is capable of carrying the relatively large armature current and usually has fewer turns than the shunt-field motor.

Recalling that the torque depends on the flux as well as the armature current, that the flux is proportional to the field current, and that the field current is identically the same as the armature current for the series motor, then the conclusion is reached that the torque is very large at low speeds and drops off rapidly as speed increases, as shown in Figure 12-4. Also, the current curve is shown.

The characteristics of series field motors are such that they lend themselves very well to traction applications where large starting torque is required but speed regulation is not important. An example is a starting motor for an automobile. Series motors have disadvantages in servo applications. One disadvantage is that they are difficult to reverse in direction, since this requires either a split field winding (one for forward rotation and the other for reverse rotation) or a reversing switch arrangement for the field winding. They cannot be field-controlled by electronic amplifiers in the sense that shunt-wound motors can.

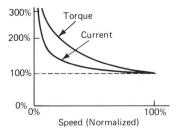

FIGURE 12-4. Torque and current versus speed for a series dc motor

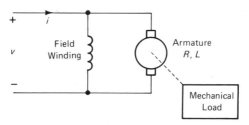

FIGURE 12-5. Shunt field dc motor and mechanical load

Shunt-Field Motors

The shunt-field motor has the field winding connected in parallel with the armature winding, as shown in Figure 12-5. The main feature of this type of motor is that the field winding is accessible separate from the armature winding and provides independent control of the flux. The winding usually consists of a large number of turns of small-size conductor.

The shunt-wound motor has better speed regulation at the expense of less starting torque as compared to the series-wound motor, but the starting torque is more than adequate for most control applications. The torque and current versus speed relations are shown in Figure 12-6.

The characteristics of shunt-field motors are such that they lend themselves to control applications better than series-field motors; they can be reversed by armature or field polarity reversal or by using a split-shunt winding. Either armature or field control of shunt-field motors can be used to control the torque and/or speed of the motor, as described in section 12.3.

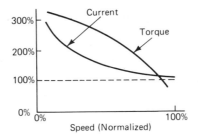

FIGURE 12-6. Torque and current versus speed for a shunt dc motor

Permanent-Magnet Motors

With the development of magnets with stronger coercive strength and smaller size, the permanent-magnet motor is becoming more common in control applications. With the use of permanent magnets, the field flux is constant and there is no need for power supplied to the field. In addition, for a given motor horsepower output, the high coercive strength of the magnets provides greater starting torque in a reduced physical size as compared to a shunt-field motor. The torque-versus-speed characteristics are otherwise very similar to a shunt-field motor. Sizes are commonly fHp, but sizes as large as 1 Hp are not uncommon.

12.3 dc Servomotor Control

Two kinds of electronic control of dc motors are common: *armature control* and *field control*.

Armature Control

An example of an armature-controlled load is shown in Figure 12-7. The main feature of this type of control is that the field winding is separately excited by a constant source to provide field flux, and the armature winding is controlled by the controller amplifier (at the terminals marked a and a' in Figure 12-7) to provide proportional control, e.g., speed control, position control, or bidirectional control. The transfer function is identical to (12-11), with the realization that the torque and counter emf constants K and C depend on the field-flux excitation level. Thus, the transfer function for velocity is

$$\frac{\omega(s)}{V(s)} = \frac{K}{(Js + B)(Ls + R) + KC} \tag{12-20}$$

with the same possible simplifications for no damping and small

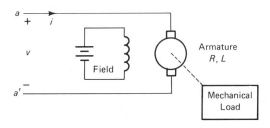

FIGURE 12-7. Armature-controlled motor and mechanical load

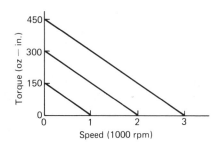

FIGURE 12-8. Torque-speed curves for a shunt dc motor

inductance that were derived in (12-19). Similarly, the TF for position (12-12) also applies.

The torque-speed curves for the dc motor for a family of excitation levels can be idealized to those shown in Figure 12-8. Examples of motor parameters for such a motor are:

$$K = 15 \text{ oz. in.}/\text{A}$$
$$C = 10 \text{ V/krpm}$$
$$R = 1.2 \text{ ohms}$$

The disadvantage of armature control is that it is difficult to provide an amplifier of sufficiently low output impedance and power output to drive even moderate-size fHp dc motors. In this consideration, field-control motors have an advantage. More comparisons are made at the end of the following section on field control.

Field Control

A figure of a field-controlled load is shown in Figure 12-9. The main feature of this type of control is that the armature winding is separately excited by a constant source to provide armature reaction flux, and the field winding is controlled by the controller amplifier (at

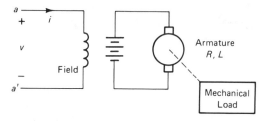

FIGURE 12-9. Field-controlled motor and mechanical load

the terminals marked a and a' in Figure 12-9) to provide proportional control. This method of control will only be feasible for small machines; in larger machines, the armature source current is difficult to generate. Also, this method of control is appropriate to control speed around a set point, especially for overspeed control, since the speed is inversely related to the field flux.

The transfer function is similar to (12-11), with the realization that the armature current is constant but the constants K and C depend on the field-flux excitation, which is determined by the field current, given as

$$I_f(s) = \frac{V_f(s)}{L_f s + R_f} = \frac{T(s)}{K_f} \tag{12-21}$$

where the torque equation has been rewritten as a function of field current, which is now the variable, and the armature current as part of the constant, namely,

$$T(s) = K_f * I_f(s) \tag{12-22}$$

Thus the transfer function for the field control motor velocity is

$$\frac{\omega(s)}{V(s)} = \frac{K_f}{(Js + B)(L_f s + R_f)} = \frac{K_f/BR_f}{(T_1 s + 1)(T_2 s + 1)} \tag{12-23}$$

where the time constants are

$$T_1 = J/B, \; T_2 = L_f/R_f \tag{12-24}$$

Although the TF may appear similar to that for the armature-controlled motor, it is different in that the T_2 time constant increases the exponential delay and degrades the performance of the control system. Thus, armature control is desirable with the qualification that a greater demand is placed on the amplifier.

12.4 ac Servomotor Control

This text has now come full circle to confront once again the problem that was discussed in Chapter 2: ac induction motors have special starting problems, and they are not linear in their relation of applied voltage to output torque. In the context of continuous control, it can be seen that the use of single- or three-phase induction motors is not satisfactory. They do not provide the proportional control output for a range of applied voltages. In fact, if a voltage is applied and then gradually increased to the common variety of small ac induction motors, the outcome is that they will overheat and fail (or cause the operation of the circuit protection device). Parenthetically, the induction motor will not be usable for continuous control by means of thyristor drive without special circuit design, such as a variable frequency synthesizer. Otherwise, the final drive element in continuous control applications must be a dc motor, a universal motor, or a two-phase ac motor.

The provision for using an ac output device is the two-phase ac motor. The ac servomotor is made with two stator windings that are groups of coils mounted in the laminated stator, and a rotor that is one of three forms: squirrel-cage, drag cup, or solid iron. The symbolic representation of the motor is shown in Figure 12-10.

The two-phase motor must be equipped with a supply that provides two voltages that are 90 degrees different in phase. The principle of operation is that the interaction of the flux due to the control voltage and the flux due to the reference voltage is 90 degrees separate in space and thus provides a resultant flux that is rotating at a synchronous speed of $N = 120f/P$, where f = frequency in Hz and P = number of poles. This resultant flux intersects the rotor conductors, which produces rotor current that interacts with the flux to provide torque to the rotor. The speed of the rotor depends on these current and flux intensities and the loading due to friction, inertia, windage, etc.

The operation of the ac servo requires that a fixed voltage be applied to the reference winding, probably 120 V at 60 Hz. The phase of this voltage can be generated 90 degrees out of phase with the control winding supply by a two-phase supply built for that purpose, or it can be provided by installing a capacitor in series with the reference winding, possibly of value 1 to 10 microfarads, depending on the size of the reference winding. The control winding may be of higher impedance and may be center-tapped to provide for operation

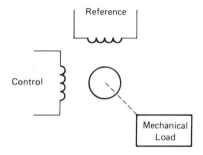

FIGURE 12-10. Representation of a two-phase ac servomotor

by a push-pull electronic amplifier to obtain bidirectional control. The magnitude of the torque response is proportional to the applied control voltage.

The transfer function of ac servomotors is derived similarly to those derived above. The resulting TF is

$$\frac{\omega(s)}{V(s)} = \frac{K}{T_1 s + 1} \qquad (12\text{-}25)$$

where the time constant T_1 is proportional to the inertia J, and K is the speed-voltage gradient. A typical time-constant value is 50 milliseconds.

Ac servos come in a range of sizes, from 1 to 100 watts. For feedback applications where stability may be a problem, ac servos are available that incorporate adjustable eddy-current dampers. By adjusting the permanent magnet position to increase the magnetic field damping, rotor drag can be increased to reduce oscillation.

Ac servos are ideal as the final output device for applications where the amplifier is ac coupled and the signal is ac. On the other hand, they are relatively heavy, inefficient in power usage, and have small power capability. Their most ideal application is for instrument servos where these drawbacks are not usually a problem.

12.5 Other Motors

Other important rotating actuators are described here: synchros, step motors, and brushless dc motors.

Synchros

Another actuator category is the family of synchros. The operation of the synchro can be explained by examination of the symbolic representation shown in Figure 12-11.

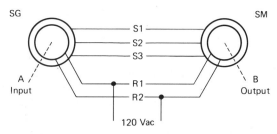

FIGURE 12-11. Symbolic representation of a synchro circuit

In terms of its electrical operation, a synchro consists of a wound rotor *(R1, R2)* whose current induces a voltage into its stator winding *(S1, S2, and S3)*. The voltages induced in the stator winding of the synchro generator SG (also called a *synchro transmitter*) are a function of the SG shaft position *A*, which is the input to the synchro system. These voltages are transmitted to the synchro motor SM (also called a *synchro receiver*). The interaction of the stator field flux and the rotor flux causes a motor action in SM that torques the output to the same position as the input *A*. Thus, a synchro generator-motor pair can be used for remote control of angular position.

Synchros also come in a variety of sizes and kinds. Two other kinds are differential generators and differential motors. With the use of a differential unit along with a synchro generator and a synchro motor, an output can be produced that is the angular sum or difference of two shaft inputs. All of these applications of synchros are without feedback. Although synchros are frequently discussed under the heading of servos, technically, they are not servos in that they do not provide error correction; they are simply position repeaters, as synchros are sometimes called.

Another kind is the synchro-control transformer: it provides an output ac signal that is the phasor sum of the voltage due to its shaft position and the voltage imposed on its stator windings. By using this control transformer output as an error signal to drive an amplifier, this kind of synchro is the error detection device in a feedback-control system.

Step Motors

Another type of actuator is the *step motor* (called a *stepper*). The principle of a step motor is that it has a large number of poles around its circumference. The transmittal of a voltage pulse to the motor rotates the shaft an angular distance equal to one pair of poles. The applied bias holds it in that position until another pulse is applied. It can be seen that the step motor is an open-loop device, but for applications that require limited torque and power (say less than 1 Hp), it satisfies the need for relatively precise position control. One disadvantage of step-motor control is the time required for the shaft to settle to its incremental stepping position, which limits its speed. Also, step angles are discrete values and the precision of the step motor is limited by the step size. Step motors have slew speed problems and are limited in their speed, in addition to having certain speeds where they lose synchronism. They also have a "jerky" output due to the cogging from one step to the next. Finally, they have limited torque and time to react to a pulse input, which restricts their ability to handle inertia loads.

dc Brushless Motors

Another type of actuator that is a more recent development is the brushless dc motor. The brushless dc motor operates by means of electronic commutation instead of electrical commutation utilizing brushes. Since the electronic circuit performs the commutation, there are no mechanical components exposed to wear, except the motor bearings. This feature enhances the lifetime of the motor and gives it exceptional efficiency by freeing it from brush losses and frictional drag. In summary, the brushless motor has advantages of excellent control of position, speed, and acceleration; it has high efficiency and low wear. Its disadvantages are that it has a more complicated electronic control circuit, and it has not been developed as extensively as brush-type dc motors and stepper motors.

12.6 Other Actuators

It seems essential to at least mention some other actuators that are in use, but the reader will need to explore other references and manufacturers' literature for specific details.

Clutches provide a means of controlling a large amount of power by virtue of applying a small amount of power. The most commonly used method in automatic control systems is the magnetically actuated friction disk clutch. When a voltage is applied to the magnetic coil in the stator, the magnetic material in the clutch faces are attracted and coupling is established. Ideally, the coupling is linear and is free from hysteresis.

Torquers and forcers place a torque or force on the load by solenoidal action. Torquers apply rotation force or torque, whereas forcers apply translational force. Since they depend on electromagnetic action, they are limited in the range of their motion. Devices are available that are fairly linear in their relationship between the driving current and the output force or torque.

When force is required over a longer distance than can reasonably be supplied by an electromagnetic device, a pneumatic or hydraulic device may be used. Examples are air cylinders and hydraulic positioners. Typically, these devices are controlled by an electromagnetic device. Another possibility is a linear or rotary actuator that uses a dc or ac motor to drive a screw jack. Loads of thousands of pounds can be controlled at rates of tenths of an inch per second.

12.7 Gear Trains

Unique from but closely related to the actuators discussed above are gear trains. Typically the very final correcting element is not a motor or other actuator—it is the gear train output shaft. The reason for this is that seldom is there a good torque-speed match between the motor and the load; the gear train provides a mechanical advantage to increase the available torque at the load. Naturally there is a price to pay for this increased torque, and that is a correspondingly decreased speed at the load. The reason that gear trains normally are step-down in speed is that it is easier to generate the power needed from the source at a high speed, whether it be from an electric motor or an internal combustion engine. Also, it is true that in many applications the load needs to have adequate torque, but the speed requirements are not as severe.

A gear train is made up of one or more meshes of gears. The gear ratio of a gear mesh N is the ratio of the speed in (w_{in}) to the speed out (w_{out}), which is also the ratio of the number of teeth *(P)* on the driven gear to the number of teeth *(M)* on the drive gear:

$$N = \frac{P}{M} = \frac{w_{in}}{w_{out}} \tag{12-26}$$

The gear-train ratio is the product of the gear ratios of the gear meshes:

$$N_T = N_1 N_2 N_3 \tag{12-27}$$

for meshes 1, 2, and 3. The final torque is stepped up by the factor N_T; the final speed is stepped down by the factor N_T. Using this result, a gear train can be selected that will provide the required torque to the load. The gear train can be considered as an impedance-matching device similar to the transformer. By matching the mechanical impedance of the load to the source by using a gear train of the proper gear ratio, it is possible to obtain the maximum torque delivered to the load.

The transfer function of the gear train is chosen as the ratio of the torque out to the torque in. Thus, the transfer function is given as

$$G(s) = \frac{T_{out}}{T_{in}} = \frac{w_{in}}{w_{out}} = N \tag{12-28}$$

or N_T for multiple gear meshes. This analysis assumes that the losses in the gear train are zero or at least negligible.

12.8 To Whence from Here?

The intent of this text is to provide the fundamentals of controls, ranging from elementary discrete to more sophisticated, dynamic controls. An appropriate continuation of this study is the examination of the merger of these parts. This synthesis requires a study of system performance, including stability, system response, and disturbance response. Analysis and design tools that are used for these purposes include Nyquist, Bode, and root-locus techniques. Beyond these classical control techniques are optimal control methods that are based on real-time, computer-based optimal control synthesizers. A blending of both the discrete and continuous areas described in the chapters of this book is the area of sample-data systems. Sample-data control uses high-speed discrete systems to provide continuous control functions. Microprocessor-based controllers are aptly suited to this control technology and present new horizons beyond control fundamentals.

Problems

12.1 Name four kinds of motors that are used in control systems.

12.2 Name four kinds of dc motors.

12.3 Referring to Figure P12.3 and following the text analysis:

   a) Write the dynamic electrical equation that describes the armature circuit of the dc motor.

   b) Write the dynamic mechanical equation that describes the motor load of the motor.

   c) Write the proportional equations that relate counter emf versus speed and torque versus current.

   d) Find the transform equation of each of the above equations.

12.4 An equivalent series RLC circuit is to be used to model a dc motor. Compare the speed-voltage transfer function, namely,

$$\frac{\omega(s)}{V(s)} = \frac{K}{(Js + B)(Ls + R) + KC} = \frac{K}{JLs^2 + (JR + BL)s + (BR + KC)}$$

   a) Find the values of R_{eq}, L_{eq}, and C_{eq} to yield an equivalent transfer function in terms of the dc motor parameters J, L, R, B, K, and C.

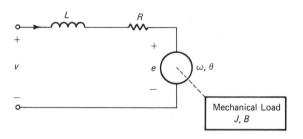

FIGURE P12.3

b) If the friction B is negligible and the other parameters are given as

$J = 0.001$ oz in sec^2

$L = 50$ mH

$K = 15$ oz. in./A

$C = 10$ V/krpm

$R = 1.2$ ohms

determine the numerical value of the above transfer function and the values of R_{eq}, L_{eq}, and C_{eq}.

12.5 For the derivation of the motor transfer function given in section 12.1:

a) Prove the derivation is accurate by retracing the steps and prove that the roots of the transfer function can be approximated as

$$s_1 = -\frac{1}{2}\sqrt{\frac{KC}{LJ}}, \; s_2 = -\frac{R}{L}$$

b) Solve for $T_1 = 1/s_1$ and $T_2 = 1/s_2$ and solve for the transfer function

$$\frac{\omega(s)}{V(s)} = \frac{1/C}{(T_1 s + 1)(T_2 s + 1)}$$

c) Determine whether the approximate TF above would produce a critical, overdamped, or underdamped system response.

12.6 Name two disadvantages of series-field motors in control-system applications.

12.7 Name the two kinds of dc motor control and explain how armature and field control is provided in each case.

12.8 Referring to ac servomotors:

a) What is the phase relationship of the field voltages for ac servomotors?

b) How is the phase shift provided to the reference winding?

c) What is the output range of ac servomotors?

12.9 Show the three stator connections and the two rotor connections for a synchro generator and for a synchro motor and show how these are wired to make a synchro pair. Show the voltage supply, the input, and the output.

12.10 State two advantages and two disadvantages of step motors.

12.11 State two advantages and two disadvantages of dc brushless motors.

12.12 What is the controlled input to a servo clutch control?

12.13 a) What is the purpose of using gear trains in servo systems?

b) What price is paid in terms of the output characteristics?

c) If the input to a five-to-one stepdown gear train is a torque of 10 ft-lb at a speed of 100 rpm, what is the output torque and the output speed? What is the power in and the power out?

d) If the load capacity of the output shaft of the motor and the gear train is given as torque divided by speed, T/ω, what is the load capacity of the motor? the gear train?

APPENDIX
Laplace Transform Analysis

A.0 Introduction

This appendix extends the treatment of dynamic continuous systems that was introduced in Chapter 8, only at a slightly more advanced level by introducing the Laplace Transform. Here, the theory of the Laplace transform is briefly covered, and examples of circuit problem solving are provided.

A.1 The Laplace Transform

In Chapter 8, the approach to system analysis is to transform the electrical or mechanical circuit parameters to the equivalent in the s-domain. Although this s-operator approach is expedient, the approach has limitations that prevent the solution of more complicated problems. It does not permit the use of non-zero initial conditions and it does not provide an easy means of handling systems that are not simply impedance functions. The Laplace transform removes these limitations.

   The Laplace transform of a function called $f(t)$ is called $L\{f(t)\}$ or simply $F(s)$. The definition of the Laplace transform of $f(t)$ is

$$F(s) = L\{f(t)\} = \int_0^\infty f(t)e^{-st}\,dt \qquad (A\text{-}1)$$

where $s = \sigma + j\omega$. The exponent σ (Greek letter sigma) in the expression $e^{\sigma t}$ is any positive number that insures absolute convergence of (A-1); however, convergence only occurs for positive values of time t. The Laplace transform is thus referred to as the one-sided transform in that it is defined as having a domain of the positive half of the real line, that is, the limits of the integral are from zero to infinity.

Example A-1   The Laplace transform of the unit step function

Find the Laplace transform of the unit step function, $u(t)$:

$$f(t) = u(t) = \begin{cases} 0, & t < 0 \\ 1, & t > 0 \end{cases}$$

The solution is found by substituting the above expression for $u(t)$ into (A-1).

$$F(s) = L\{f(t)\} = \int_0^\infty u(t)e^{-st}\,dt = \int_0^\infty 1e^{-st}\,dt$$

$$= -(1/s) \cdot e^{-st}\Big|_0^\infty = (-1/s) \cdot [e^{-\infty} - e^{-0}]$$

$$= (-1/s) \cdot [0 - 1] = 1/s$$

A question of the soundness of the mathematics of the Laplace transform arises in the determination of whether $F(s)$ will exist, i.e., whether the solution of the integral will provide a non-infinite value. It turns out that the multiplication of the $f(t)$ by the convergence factor $e^{-\sigma t}$ provides a very powerful convergence, so that for a very wide range of functions for $f(t)$ the integral of the product will be finite. For example, the Laplace transform of a ramp, i.e., $f(t) = t$, exists since the multiplication of the ramp by the convergence factor causes overall convergence. Thus, a wide range of functions can be Laplace transformed without concern over whether the mathematics will work.

Example A-2   The Laplace transform of the unit exponential function

Find the Laplace transform of the unit exponential function defined as

$$f(t) = \begin{cases} 0, & t < 0 \\ e^{-at}, & t > 0 \end{cases}$$

The solution is found by substituting the above expression for $f(t)$ into (A-1):

$$F(s) = L\{f(t)\} = \int_0^\infty e^{-at} \cdot e^{-st}\,dt = \int_0^\infty e^{-(s+a)t}\,dt$$

$$= -\frac{1}{s+a}e^{-(s+a)t}\Big|_0^\infty = \frac{1}{s+a}[e^{-\infty} - e^{-0}]$$

$$= \frac{1}{s+a}[0 - 1] = \frac{1}{s+a}$$

A.2 The Inverse Laplace Transform

The inverse Laplace transform is given by

$$L^{-1}\{F(s)\} = f(t) = 1(2\pi j)\int_{c-j\infty}^{c+j\infty} F(s) \bullet e^{st}\, ds \qquad (A-2)$$

where c is a real constant that is larger than the real part of $F(s)$. Equation (A-2) is difficult to evaluate and seldom used in practice as a means of finding inverse Laplace transforms.

A.3 The Laplace Transform and Inverse Laplace Transform by Table

Although the methods of Laplace transform derivation, such as Examples A-1 and A-2, are instructive and edifying, the common practice of finding Laplace transformations is by table lookup. The table method is possible since the Laplace transformation of a function $f(t)$ is unique and the inverse Laplace transformation of a function $F(s)$ is unique. Table A-1 is a table of Laplace transforms that are commonly used in control system work. Much more extensive tables can be found in mathematical treatments of the Laplace transform.

Example A-3   The Laplace transform of the unit exponential function by table

Find the Laplace transform of the unit exponential function by table.

$$f(t) = \begin{cases} 0, & t < 0 \\ e^{-3t}, & t > 0 \end{cases}$$

The solution is found by finding the expression for $f(t)$ in the Laplace transform Table A-1. A scan of the functions under the heading $f(t)$ shows that T4 is an exponential e^{-at}. The exponential coefficient a must be identified as $a = 3$. Then the form for $F(s)$ for T4 is found to be $1/(s + a)$. This form is rewritten as $1/(s + 3)$. Thus, the transform is

$$L\{e^{-3t}\} = \frac{1}{s + 3}$$

Similarly, it can be seen that the inverse Laplace transform of $1/(s + 3)$ can be found from the table:

$$L^{-1}\left\{\frac{1}{s + a}\right\} = e^{-3t}$$

Table A.1 Table of Elementary Laplace Transforms

TRANSFORM NO.	$f(t)$	$F(s)$	
T1	$u(t)$	$1/s$	
T2	t	$1/s^2$	
T3	$t^n \qquad n \geq 0$	$n!/(s^{n+1})$	
T4	e^{-at}	$1/(s+a)$	
T5	te^{-at}	$1/(s+a)^2$	
T6	$t^n e^{-at}$	$n!/(s+a)^{n+1}$	
T7	$\dfrac{1}{a}(1 - e^{-at})$	$\dfrac{1}{s(s+a)}$	
T8	$(1 - at)e^{-at}$	$\dfrac{s}{s+a^2}$	
T9	$\dfrac{1}{b-a}(1 - e^{-at})$	$\dfrac{1}{(s+a)(s+b)}$	$a \neq b$
T10	$\dfrac{1}{a-b}(ae^{-at} - be^{-bt})$	$\dfrac{s}{(s+a)(s+b)}$	$a \neq b$
T11	$\dfrac{1}{ab}\left(1 - \dfrac{b}{b-a}e^{-at} + \dfrac{a}{b-a}e^{-bt}\right)$	$\dfrac{1}{s(s+a)(s+b)}$	$a \neq b$
T12	$\dfrac{1}{a^2}(at - 1 + e^{-at})$	$\dfrac{1}{s^2(s+a)}$	
T13	$\dfrac{a}{b} + \dfrac{b-a}{b}e^{-at}$	$\dfrac{s+a}{s(s+b)}$	
T14	$\dfrac{c-a}{b-a}e^{-at} - \dfrac{c-b}{b-a}e^{-bt}$	$\dfrac{s+c}{(s+a)(s+b)}$	$a \neq b \neq c$
T15	$\dfrac{1}{a^2}(1 - e^{-at} - ate^{-at})$	$\dfrac{1}{s(s+a)(s+a)}$	
T16	$\sin(\omega t)$	$\dfrac{\omega}{s^2 + \omega^2}$	
T17	$\cos(\omega t)$	$\dfrac{s}{s^2 + \omega^2}$	
T18	$e^{-at}\sin(\omega t)$	$\dfrac{\omega}{(s+a)^2 + \omega^2}$	
T19	$e^{-at}\cos(\omega t)$	$\dfrac{s}{(s+a)^2 + \omega^2}$	

T20	$\dfrac{1}{\omega_d}e^{-\zeta\omega_n t}\sin(\omega_d t)$	$\dfrac{1}{s^2 + 2\zeta\omega_n s + \omega_n^2}$
	$\omega_d = \omega_n\sqrt{(1 - \zeta^2)}$	
T21	$\dfrac{1}{\omega_n^2} - \dfrac{1}{\omega_n\omega_d}e^{-\zeta\omega_n t}\sin(\omega_d t + \phi)$	$\dfrac{1}{s(s^2 + 2\zeta\omega_n s + \omega_n^2)}$
	$\phi = \arccos(\zeta),\ \omega_d$ given above	
T22	$\sinh(\omega t)$	$\dfrac{\omega}{s^2 - \omega^2}$
T23	$\cosh(\omega t)$	$\dfrac{s}{s^2 - \omega^2}$

Example A-4 The Laplace transform of the unit exponential sinusoid function by table

Find the Laplace transform of the unit exponential sinusoid function by table.

$$f(t) = \begin{cases} 0, & t < 0 \\ 0.25e^{-3t}\sin(4t), & t \geq 0 \end{cases}$$

Examination of the table shows that T20 has the same form as the above expression. Matching the expressions

$$\frac{1}{\omega_d}e^{-\zeta\omega_n t}\sin\omega_d t = 0.25e^{-3t}\sin 4t$$

yields

$$\sin(\omega_d t) = \sin(4t) \Rightarrow \omega_d = 4 \text{ rps},$$

$$\varepsilon^{-\zeta\omega_n t} = \varepsilon^{-3t} \Rightarrow \zeta\omega_n = 3.$$

Solving $\omega_d = \omega_n\sqrt{(1 - \zeta^2)}$ for $\omega_d = 4$ and $\zeta\omega_n = 3$ yields $\omega_n = 5$ rps and $\zeta = 0.6$. Thus, the expression for $F(s)$ is given as

$$F(s) = \frac{1}{s^2 + 6s + 25}$$

It is left as an exercise to start with this expression for $F(s)$ and arrive at the above value of $f(t)$.

A.4 Properties of the Laplace Transform

The usefulness of the Table A-1 is dependent upon using the following properties to extend the functions to general functions.

1. Multiplication by a constant. The Laplace transform of the product of a constant K and a function of time $f(t)$ is the product of the constant and the transformed time function:

$$L\{K \cdot f(t)\} = K \cdot F(s) \qquad\qquad \text{(A-3)}$$

The proof can be shown by substitution into (A-1) and is left as an exercise.

Example A-5 Constant multiplier of a Laplace transformed function

a. The Laplace transform of $12e^{-3t}$ is $12/(s + 3)$, based on the fact that the transform of e^{-3t} is $1/(s + 3)$ and that 12 is a constant multiplier.

b. The inverse Laplace transform of $25/s$ is $25u(t)$, based on the fact that the inverse transform of $1/s$ is $1u(t)$ and that 25 is a constant multiplier.

2. Sums of functions. The Laplace transform of the sum of time functions is the sum of the transforms:

$$L\{f_1(t) + f_2(t)\} = F_1(s) + F_2(s) \qquad\qquad \text{(A-4)}$$

This proof can also be shown by substitution into (A-1).

Example A-6 Sum of Laplace-transformed functions

a. The Laplace transform of $12e^{-3t} - 6e^{2t}$ is $12/(s + 3) - 6/(s - 2)$, based on the fact that each transform can be taken individually.

b. The inverse Laplace transform of $12/s + 6s/(s^2 + 25)$ is $12u(t) + 6\cos(5t)$, based on the fact that each inverse transform can be taken individually.

3. The Laplace transform of the derivative of a function. The Laplace transform of the derivative of a function is given as follows:

$$L\{d/dt(\,f(t))\} = s \cdot F(s) - f(0 +) \qquad\qquad \text{(A-5)}$$

where $f(0 +)$ is the value of the time function at $t = 0 +$, $(\lim t \to 0)$.

The above can be shown by integrating by parts after letting

$$u = e^{-st}, \qquad dv = df(t)$$

in the equation

$$\int_a^b u \bullet dv = u \bullet v\big|_a^b - \int_a^b v \bullet du.$$

Example A-7   Laplace transform of a derivative of a function

The Laplace transform of $d/dt[e^{-3t}]$ is $s/(s+3) - 1$, based on (A-5) where the $s/(s+3)$ is arrived at by multiplying the transform of e^{-3t} by s and the 1 is arrived at by evaluating e^{-3t} at $t = 0$.

4. The Laplace transform of the *n*th derivative of a function. The Laplace transforms of higher-order derivatives are given as

$$L\left\{\frac{d^n[f(t)]}{dt^n}\right\} = s^n \bullet F(s) - s^{n-1} \bullet f(0+) - s^{n-2} \bullet df(0+)/dt$$

$$- \cdots - \frac{d^{(n-1)}[f(0+)]}{dt^{(n-1)}} \qquad (A\text{-}6)$$

Example A-8   The Laplace transform of the third derivative of a function

The Laplace transform of the third derivative of e^{-3t} is

$$\frac{s}{s+3} - s^2 + 3s - 9$$

5. The Laplace transform of an integral of a function. The expression for the Laplace transform of an integral of a function is

$$L\left\{\int_{0+}^t f(t)\, dt\right\} = F(s)/s + f^{(-1)}(0+)/s \qquad (A\text{-}7)$$

where

$$f^{(-1)}(0+) = \lim_{t\to 0+} \int_{0+}^t f(t)\, dt$$

Equation (A-7) is found by letting $u = e^{-st}$, $dv = f(t)\, dt$ and integrating by parts.

Example A-9   The Laplace transform of the integral of a function

The Laplace transform of the integral of e^{-3t} is $1/[s(s+3)] - 1/(3s)$ based on (A-7).

6. The Laplace transform of the nth integral of a function. The Laplace transform of the nth integral is given by the expression,

$$L\left\{ \int\int\int \ldots f(t)\,dt^n \right\} = \frac{F(s)}{s^n} + \frac{f^{(-1)}(0+)}{s^n} + \frac{f^{(-2)}(0+)}{s^{n-1}}$$

$$+ \cdots + \frac{f^{(-n)}(0+)}{s} \tag{A-8}$$

Equation (A-8) is found similarly as given above for (A-7).

A.5   Solution of Integro-differential Equations by Laplace Transform

Differential equations that are linear and have constant coefficients are solved by taking the transform, solving for the unknowns algebraically, and taking the inverse transform. In order to find the inverse transform, it is convenient to use partial fraction expansion to reduce the expression so that a practical transform table can be used. Three important cases of partial fraction expansion follow.

1. Roots that are simple and real:

$$\frac{P(s)}{(s+a)(s+b)(s+c)} = \frac{A}{s+a} + \frac{B}{s+b} + \frac{C}{s+c} \tag{A-9}$$

2. Roots that are repeated r times:

$$\frac{P(s)}{(s+a)^r} = \frac{K}{s+a} + \frac{K}{(s+a)^2} + \cdots + \frac{K}{(s+a)^r} \tag{A-10}$$

3. Roots that are complex conjugates:

$$\frac{P(s)}{(s^2 + as + b)(s^2 + cs + d)} = \frac{As + B}{s^2 + as + b} + \frac{Cs + d}{s^2 + cs + d} \tag{A-11}$$

With the use of the above partial fraction expansion forms, the need for extensive tables is obviated.

Integro-differential equations can be solved in six steps:

1. Write the integro-differential equations.
2. Transform the equations from the time domain to the frequency domain.
3. Insert the initial conditions.
4. Solve for the unknowns.
5. Expand the solutions into acceptable forms.
6. Solve for the inverse transforms.

Example A-10   Laplace transform solution of a simple series circuit

Find the current $i(t)$ for the simple series RL circuit in Figure A-1.

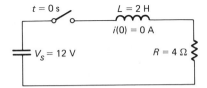

FIGURE A-1. A resistor-inductor circuit with a voltage forcing function

1. $12u(t) = 2\dfrac{di}{dt} + 4i$
2. $12/s = 2[sI(s) - i(0 +)] + 4I(s)$
3. Initial conditions: $i(0 +) = 0\ A$ given
4. $12/s = (2s + 4)I(s)$

$$I(s) = \frac{12/s}{2s + 4} = \frac{6}{s(s + 2)}$$

5. The coefficients A and B are solved for as

$$A = \frac{6}{s + 2}\bigg|_{s=0} = \frac{6}{2} = 3, \quad B = \frac{6}{s}\bigg|_{s=-2} = \frac{6}{-2} = -3$$

Therefore,

$$I(s) = \frac{6}{s(s + 2)} = \frac{A}{s} + \frac{B}{s + 2} \quad \text{(partial fraction expansion 1)}$$

$$= \frac{3}{s} + \frac{-3}{s + 2}$$

6. $i(t) = 3 - 3e^{-2t} = 3[1 - e^{-2t}]u(t)$

The response is shown in Figure A-2.

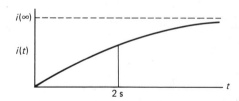

FIGURE A-2. Response for RL circuit of Example A-10

Example A-11   Laplace transform solution of a simple series circuit with non-zero initial conditions

Find the current $i(t)$ for the simple series RL circuit in Figure A-1 as in Example A-10, only with the initial condition $i(0) = 2A$. Starting the same as before in Steps 1 and 2, we have

3. Initial conditions: $i(0 +) = 2A$ given.

4. $12/s + 4 = (2s + 4)I(s)$

$$I(s) = \frac{4 + 12/s}{2s + 4} = \frac{2s + 6}{s(s + 2)} = \frac{A}{s} + \frac{B}{s + 2}$$

5. The coefficients A and B are solved for as

$$A = \frac{2s + 6}{s + 2}\bigg|_{s=0} = \frac{6}{2} = 3, \quad B = \frac{2s + 6}{s}\bigg|_{s=-2} = \frac{2}{-2} = -1$$

6. $i(t) = [3 - 1e^{-2t}]u(t)$

In this example, the response is similar to the response of Example A-10 except that the initial condition and thus the transient is different.

As an exercise, the above two examples can be solved using the equation

$$x(t) = x(\infty) - [x(\infty) - x(0)]e^{-t/\tau}, \quad t > 0 \tag{A-12}$$

where

$$x(\infty) = x \quad \text{as} \quad t \to \infty$$
$$x(0) = x \quad \text{as} \quad t \to 0 +$$
$$\tau = \text{time constant} = L/R$$

The Laplace transform has uses beyond solving equations that can be solved by (A-12). It can be used to solve multivariable problems involving multiple meshes and/or nodes. It can be used to solve mechanical and other physical problems as well as electrical problems. And of course it can be used to solve control system problems. But first, as an example of the use of Laplace transform to solve higher-order system problems, the following example shows the kinds of response that are possible with a second-order electrical system.

Example A-12   RLC series circuit response

For a forced resistor-inductor-capacitor series circuit as shown in Figure A-3, determine the capacitor voltage and current for $t > 0$.

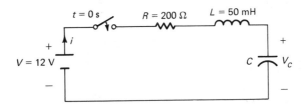

FIGURE A-3. A forced R-L-C circuit

1. The voltages around the loop are summed:

$$Vu(t) = L\,di/dt + Ri + (1/C)\int i\,dt$$

2. The transform is taken:

$$V/s = L[sI(s) - i(0)] + RI(s) + 1/(Cs)[I(s) + q(0)]$$

3. Initial conditions are inserted. Assume initial inductor current is zero and initial capacitor charge is zero. Group terms:

$$V/s = [Ls + R + 1/(Cs)]I(s)$$

4. Solving for the current yields

$$I(s) = \frac{V/s}{Ls + R + 1/(Cs)} = \frac{V/L}{s^2 + (R/L)s + 1/LC} \qquad \text{(A-13)}$$

The voltage across the capacitor can be taken as

$$v_C(t) = \frac{1}{C}\int i\,dt$$

or in terms of the Laplace transformed equations

$$V_C(s) = \frac{1}{Cs}[I(s) + q(0)] \tag{A-14}$$

Three possible cases exist: a) the overdamped case, b) the critically damped case, and c) the underdamped case. Each one requires different treatment.

Case a)   The overdamped case $C = 6.67 \ \mu\text{F}$

a-5.   Substituting numerical values for V, R, L, and C, (A-14) is rewritten as

$$V_C(s) = \frac{600(10)^6}{s\left[s^2 + 4000s + 3(10)^6\right]} = \frac{600(10)^6}{s(s + 3000)(s + 1000)}$$

Based on (A-9), the above expression can be expanded as

$$V_C(s) = \frac{A}{s} + \frac{B}{s + 3000} + \frac{C}{s + 1000}$$

The coefficients A, B, and C are solved for from multiplying through by the common denominator and canceling like terms such that one has

$$600(10)^6 = A(s + 3000)(s + 1000) + Bs(s + 1000) + Cs(s + 3000)$$

In this case, the solutions for A, B, and C are readily written as

$$A = \frac{600(10)^6}{(s + 3000)(s + 1000)}\bigg|_{s=0} \qquad B = \frac{600(10)^6}{s(s + 1000)}\bigg|_{s=-3000}$$

$$C = \frac{600(10)^6}{s(s + 3000)}\bigg|_{s=-1000}$$

and

$$A = 200, \qquad B = 100, \qquad C = -300$$

a-6.   Taking the inverse Laplace Transform by table lookup from the book, the answer is obtained

$$v_C(t) = 200 + 100e^{-3000t} - 300e^{-1000t} \qquad t > 0$$

Case b) The critically damped case $C = 5.00\ \mu F$

Again substituting the values for V, R, L, and C, one obtains

$$V_C(s) = \frac{800(10)^6}{s\left[s^2 + 4000s + 4(10)^6\right]} = \frac{600(10)^6}{s(s + 2000)^2}$$

b-5. This equation fits the form of (A-10). Thus the expansion is

$$V_C(s) = \frac{A}{(s + 2000)^2} + \frac{B}{s + 2000} + \frac{C}{s}$$

The A term can be solved for directly by multiplying through by the common denominator and setting $s = -2000$ to obtain

$$A = \frac{800(10)^6}{s(s + 2000)^2}\bigg|_{s = -2000} = -0.4(10)^6$$

By subtracting the highest order term

$$\frac{A}{(s + 2000)^2}$$

off from each side, we obtain

$$\frac{800(10)^6}{s(s + 2000)^2} - \frac{-0.4(10)^6}{(s + 2000)^2} = \frac{B}{s + 2000} + \frac{C}{s}$$

Thus B and C can be found as before to be

$$B = -200, \qquad C = 200$$

b-6. Thus the time-domain solution for capacitor voltage is

$$v_C(t) = 200 - 0.4(10)^6 t e^{-2000t} - 200 e^{-2000t} \qquad t > 0$$

Case c) The underdamped case $C = 4.00\ \mu F$

Again substituting the values for V, R, L, and C, one obtains

$$V_C(s) = \frac{1000(10)^6}{s\left[s^2 + 4000s + 5(10)^6\right]} = \frac{1000(10)^6}{s\left[s^2 + 4000s + 4(10)^6 + 1(10)^6\right]}$$

c-5. This equation is similar to the form of (A-11). Thus the expansion is

$$V_C(s) = \frac{A}{s} + \frac{Bs + C}{s^2 + 4000s + 5(10)^6}$$

The A term can be solved for directly by multiplying through by the common denominator and setting $s = 0$ to obtain

$$A = \left. \frac{1000(10)^6}{s^2 + 4000s + 5(10)^6} \right|_{s = -2000} = 200$$

By subtracting the $200/s$ term from the left-hand side of the above equation, one obtains

$$V_C(s) = \frac{-200(s + 4000)}{s^2 + 4000s + 5(10)^6} = \frac{-200(s + 4000)}{s^2 + 4000s + 4(10)^6 s + 1(10)^6}$$

which can be manipulated to have the form

$$\frac{-200(s + 2000)}{(s + 2000)^2 + (1000)^2} + \frac{-400(1000)}{(s + 2000)^2 + (1000)^2}$$

which in turn matches the general form (A-11):

$$\frac{K_1(s + a)}{(s + a)^2 + \omega^2} + \frac{K_2 \omega}{(s + a)^2 + \omega^2}$$

c-6. Using the Laplace transform table to find the inverse transform yields

$$v_C(t) = 200 - e^{-2000t}(200 \cos 1000t + 400 \sin 1000t), \qquad t > 0$$

These three cases can be plotted similarly to Figure 8-24 to show the range of possible system responses for a second-order system.

Index

421